Together in One World

Together in One World

Ninety-nine stories for the primary school assembly

Jeanne L. Jackson

RMEP

Religious and Moral Education Press
A wholly owned subsidiary of Hymns Ancient & Modern Ltd
13a Hellesdon Park Road
Norwich, Norfolk NR6 5DR

First published 2007

Second impression 2011

Third impression 2013

ISBN 978-1-85175-353-6

Typeset by Regent Typesetting, London

Printed in Great Britain by
MPG Books Ltd, Bodmin, Cornwall

Contents

for Val

Acknowledgements

With many thanks to:

Anne Montefiore, Christian Aid Schools and Youth Publishing Manager, for all her help and advice.

Christian Aid, for permission to use *Guns into Art, Pachchai Mutthu's dances, Tsunami; after the wave* and *Send my friend to school.*

Irene Peace (retired Headteacher) and YAMSEN, for their ongoing and outstanding work with the Yorkshire Association for Music and Special Educational Needs, and their inspiration for *Sammy and the Town Hall concert.*

Julie Wilding (Primary Phase Adviser) for her help and advice, and Mr George Pyle for allowing me to retell, albeit briefly, his story as *Julie's dad.*

Mary Mears, at RMEP, for her support and encouragement in asking me to write another assembly book.

Val Pennington, for friendship, encouragement, support, and masses of help with researching material for this collection.

Introduction

Together in One World is a new collection of stories for the primary school assembly.

Together in One World is arranged thematically, in three sections, which encourage children to extend their thoughts from themselves to others and to the world around them, and can therefore be used systematically throughout the year, or as a dip-in resource.

The themes chosen are those of interest and concern to children and teachers today. The stories are from a wide variety of sources including myths, legends, fables and folk tales; people and events from history; true stories from recent news items; and original, specially written fiction. Many of the stories echo topics that will already be ongoing in the classroom. The aim of the collection, as with previous ones, is to present stories that are thought-provoking, stimulating and above all enjoyable, and whose themes and ideas can be carried from the assembly into the classroom and be combined with work already planned. In this way the ideas and thoughts raised in assembly become part of the thinking of the school, and the assembly becomes a meaningful, integrated, purposeful and enjoyable part of the school day.

In line with current legislation, the stories are '*wholly or mainly of a broadly Christian character*' in that they reflect the '*broad traditions of Christian belief without being distinctive of any particular Christian denomination*' (Section 7, Education Reform Act 1988). However, since many of these broad traditions – tolerance, respect, honesty, thoughtfulness, sincerity, generosity, caring for others, caring for the world, etc. – are also found in other major world religions, many of the stories will appeal to children of different backgrounds and beliefs, and none presupposes a level of religious belief or commitment. The stories retell equally well to small groups of children or large whole-school assemblies, although for obvious reasons it is easier to elicit discussion, response and opinion from smaller numbers of children. Most of the stories in this collection can be told to a wide age and ability range, although purists may want to differentiate them. I believe that a good story transcends age barriers – each listener will take from the story what they are capable of understanding, from the simple superficial level to deeper hidden meanings.

Story telling is said to be the oldest art form, predating both music and drama. People learned through story, and in the days before the written word, it was the only means of handing down the accumulated knowledge, wisdom, fears and thoughts of a people. Today we are bombarded with visual and audio messages. Our children are surrounded by sound and images. No other children in history have received as much information on a daily, if not hourly, basis as our children receive today. Yet, there is a place for the best traditions of story telling. Story telling, especially in the context of school assembly, provides a period of quiet calm, with opportunity for reflection and meditative thought. It is in this spirit that this collection of stories is presented.

But, in today's very visual and technological world, our children are used to having something to look at; many children are unpractised in the art of *listening*. I find it useful to have an object to help children focus on the subject. Sometimes I hide whatever it is under a cover or inside a box to encourage thought about what the assembly might be about. I have resisted the temptation to list 'props', as each assembly leader will be able to find something appropriate suggested by the story itself. However, certain stories would have greater impact if an enlarged photograph, or a projected image could be shown during the assembly. For example, the Tree of Life in 'Guns into art' (p. 124), or Bill Anders' Earthrise at Christmas in 'Earthrise' (p. 320), will add a sense of awe to the stories. Websites where appropriate photographs can be found are given at the end of the relevant stories. I have also added websites teachers may wish to use for further information on certain stories or themes.

Together in One World is intended to be as user-friendly as possible. The principal themes are all clearly listed in the contents, but each story is also cross-referenced in a thematic index at the back of the book, making it as straightforward as possible for the busy teacher to find a story to fit a particular theme. A story source index is also included for those teachers looking for a particular type of story as opposed to a theme. In common with my other collections of assembly stories, each story in *Together in One World* begins and ends in a conversational style which is easily adapted by the narrator. Each story ends with an optional prayer or reflection.

As ever, I hope this collection will meet a need in primary schools, and that the stories will be *enjoyed* by both children and staff.

Ourselves

Theme 1

Rights

Mrs Rosa Parks

We are fortunate now that we live in a country where everyone has rights. All you children have a right to be treated fairly and to be cared for, looked after and protected. You all have a right to be educated. You all have a right to be here in school. Everyone has a right to be treated equally and fairly, wherever they're from, or whatever their background is. Everyone has a right to have their voice heard.

But these rights haven't always existed. In the past people have had to struggle to gain the rights that we often take for granted today. Today's true story is about a woman who lived in Alabama in the southern states of America, just over 60 years ago.

Mrs Rosa Parks* stood at the bus stop and waited for the next bus. She shifted her weight from one leg to the other and hoped the bus would soon be here so she could sit down at last. She was tired and her feet ached. She'd been standing up all day in the clothing department of a big store where she worked in the centre of Montgomery in Alabama. Now her work for the day was finished and she was looking forward to getting home.

Home, for Rosa Parks, was on the outskirts of the town in an area reserved just for black people, for Montgomery was a segregated city. White and black people both lived there, but they lived almost completely separate lives. In fact there were rules and laws which prevented black people and white people from meeting together and from mixing together. Children were not allowed to go to school together; adults were not allowed to go out together, and they were not allowed to sit together in cafés or cinemas or

* Further information can be found at www.e-portals.org/Parks.

theatres. Black people and white people were not even allowed to sit next to each other on a bus.

Rosa Parks waited for her bus. She hoped it wouldn't be the same driver as the day before. He was white, like all the bus drivers in Montgomery, and when she'd paid her fare at the front of the bus, he told her she couldn't use that door and she'd have to get on at the back. As she stepped off to make her way round to the door at the rear, he'd revved up the engine and driven off, leaving her standing in the middle of the road with no bus fare for the next bus that came along. She'd had to walk the five miles home. Earlier that same week another white driver had shouted abuse at her as she got on his bus.

At last Mrs Parks' bus came. She got on and paid her fare. This driver didn't make her get off again. She hurried down the middle of the bus to the seats at the back where black people were allowed to sit. All the seats at the front of the bus were reserved for white people and the blacks were not allowed to sit there. She sank into her seat, glad to take the weight off her aching feet and legs.

The bus rumbled on and stopped at every stop, taking on board more and more passengers. In this part of town they were all white. The bus stopped again. Another passenger got on. A white man. There was no seat for him anywhere on the bus.

'Hey, you!' called the driver to Mrs Parks. 'You were the last black on the bus. Stand up and give this white man your seat!'

Everyone looked at Mrs Parks. They all expected her to give up her seat. That's what black people had to do if a white person wanted to sit down.

Rosa Parks sat up straight and looked the bus driver in the eye. 'I paid for my seat,' she said. 'I'm gonna sit in it!' And she sat squarely facing the front.

'You give up that seat like I'm telling you,' shouted the driver.

The white man waited for her to move.

Everyone on the bus fell silent.

Everyone could feel the tension.

'I paid for my seat,' said Rosa again. 'I'm not gonna move.' And she stayed where she was.

'You get up now, lady, or I call the police,' yelled the driver.

Everyone watched and listened. No one moved. Including Rosa. She stayed in her seat.

'That's it!' shouted the driver, and he turned off the engine, called the police and waited for them to arrive.

They came. Rosa Parks was arrested for breaking the segregation laws, and taken to a police cell.

Rosa was, in fact, the third black person to be arrested during that year of 1955 for refusing to give up their seat on a bus, and the black leaders in Montgomery decided it was time for the community to pull together and challenge the situation on the buses.

One of the leaders, Martin Luther King, called a meeting that same evening. More than 40 people turned up.

'It's time the laws were changed,' they all said. 'It's not right that black people should have to give way all the time to white people. Mrs Parks had every right to sit on that bus. She'd paid for her seat just like the rest of the passengers, and her money's as good as the white man's!'

'We should boycott the buses,' they said. 'We'll get everyone to refuse to use them. We'll simply walk wherever we want to go. If we all stop using the buses we won't be paying our fares, and the managers will soon take notice if their profits go down!'

So they planned a boycott of all the city's buses. They printed out notices to give to everyone they knew so that all the black people would know of the boycott. The notices said:

Don't ride the bus to work or town or school from Monday 5th December. Another woman has been arrested for refusing to give up her seat. Support this boycott. Don't ride the buses.

They waited to see what would happen.

On Monday morning at six o'clock, Martin Luther King looked at the bus stop outside his house. Normally there would be a queue of people there by now. There was no one. At two minutes past six, a bus came past. Empty. A few minutes later another bus rumbled by. It, too, was empty. At quarter past six came another. This time there were just two white people on board. Then came another – empty, and another – equally empty. And so it went on, all through the day. Bus after bus with no passengers. Yet on the streets were dozens of black people, all walking to work, or school, or to the shops, or to the town. The boycott was working. The black people had refused to co-operate with a system that was unfair to them.

Rosa Parks was released from her police cell and later, much later, the city leaders of Montgomery realised that the black citizens had to have the same rights as the white people, and the laws began to change; though it was to be many more years before there were equal rights between black people and white people.

I wonder what you think of Rosa Parks' story. She eventually lived to be 92 years old and she died in 2005. I don't suppose she ever forgot the day she refused to give up her seat to a white man on the bus, 50 years earlier, and I think she'll be remembered for her actions for many more years to come.

We need to remember to stand firm for fairness and equality and rights for everyone, like Rosa did. Maybe we could all try, today, to be fair to the people we meet, and to remember that we all have equal rights.

~

Help us, Lord, to stand firm for fairness and equality and equal rights for people. Help us to make sure we remember people's rights. Amen

Mr Gilbert and the school field

In today's story, Mr Gilbert was sure that he had a right to use the field he'd known since he was a boy. But, he didn't consider how his actions were affecting other people. He was so busy making sure he got his rights, he forgot that he also had responsibilities. Rights and responsibilities almost always go together.

Mr Gilbert had lived next to the school for as long as anyone could remember. In fact, Mr Gilbert had lived in his house since before the school was even built . . . as he was very fond of telling everyone.

'I used to live here when I was a boy, you know,' he used to say. 'I played on these fields before that school was built. We used to have a grand old time.'

And Mr Gilbert would go on to say how there used to be a footpath right across where the school playing field was now, and how everyone used to walk it.

In fact, Mr Gilbert had known the field for so long, that he considered it to be *his* even though there was now a school on it. He believed he had a *right* to use the field. But things came to a head when he made a gate in the school fence . . . and bought a dog!

The headteacher was somewhat surprised to see Mr Gilbert out in his garden one summer's day with saws and hammers and wood and nails. He sawed right through the school fence which separated his back garden from the school field, and then put in a gate. He oiled the gate's hinges and tested that it opened and closed smoothly. Then he went into his house and came out again with a small brown and white dog prancing at his heels. She was even more disconcerted to see the dog squat down on the grass and Mr Gilbert make no attempt to clean up after it!

She marched outside to speak to him.

'Mr Gilbert! What on earth are you doing? You cannot make a gate onto the school field. You must *not* come into the school grounds, and you must *certainly not* allow your dog to . . .' but she didn't have time to finish her sentence before Mr Gilbert interrupted.

'I'm sorry Mrs Jennings, but I have every right to come across here. If you look at a map you'll see a footpath across this field, and as everyone knows, people have a right to walk on a footpath that's marked on a map!'

'Mr Gilbert! That footpath was moved when the school was built,' said Mrs Jennings. 'It now runs along the road at the side of the school. Surely you must know that? Surely you know that we can't have people walking about on the school field whenever they want? And certainly not with a *dog*. We have the safety of the children to consider.'

'There's nothing you can do about Nell here,' laughed Mr Gilbert. 'You see, she's a Cavalier King Charles Spaniel, and they are royal dogs. It seems you are not aware that they, as royal dogs, have a right to go anywhere they want in the kingdom. It's the law! So you see, we both have every right to be here.' And with that, Mr Gilbert turned round and marched away across the field, leaving Mrs Jennings standing there, speechless.

She strode back into school and called an emergency governors' meeting.

'We should contact the police,' said one governor.

'Get a court injunction to stop him coming onto the premises,' said another.

'We must certainly do *something*,' said the chairman. 'It's a question of health and safety, not to mention security.'

'I know he doesn't *mean* any harm,' said Mrs Jennings. 'It's a question of somehow making him understand that even though he thinks he has rights, he also has responsibilities,' she continued. 'He has a responsibility to keep his dog away from where children play, and to help us keep the school secure by not coming into the school grounds unless we invite him. I've had an idea.' And she told them what she'd thought.

The next day Mrs Jennings spoke to the children and all the school staff and as many parents as were present in assembly about rights and responsibilities. Then a small group of them went to Mrs Jennings' office to plan the afternoon.

At two o'clock Mr Gilbert and Nell set off for their usual afternoon walk across the field. Mr Gilbert left his gate open. He and Nell walked right across the playing fields as far as the trees on the other side. They played for a while with Nell's ball then set off back again. As he walked back towards his house, Mr Gilbert was astonished to see dozens of people in his garden and on the school field next to it. He also thought he could see a goat, a horse and several dogs.

'What . . .? What's . . .? What on earth is going on in my garden?' he said, hurrying now, and almost running to get back to his house to see what the commotion was.

As he neared the gate that he'd built between his garden and the school field, he stopped and stared. Several of the teachers were sitting at his garden furniture clearly having a picnic. Lots of children were playing in his garden and others were playing football and cricket in the field, using the fence as goalposts and his gate as the wickets! Some of his neighbours, parents of children at the school, were also in the garden, as were at least half a dozen dogs. Two goats were nibbling his lawn, and a horse was tied to his apple tree. The chair of the school governors had taken off his shoes and socks and was sitting with his feet in Mr Gilbert's ornamental pond, and the headteacher was sprawled out on a sun-lounger with a cold drink in her hand.

'Oh, hello, Mr Gilbert,' she called to him cheerily. 'I'm so glad you can join us. Come on in and enjoy the garden party. We're just about to have some tea and cakes.'

Just as she said this, the school cook and her assistants came in through the gate with enormous trays of food in their hands.

'You can't . . . You can't just use my garden like this without permission,' he exploded. 'And what about all these animals? They're eating my plants! And just look at what those dogs are doing all over my flower beds,' and he went purple in the face as he pointed to some of the dogs.

'Oh dear!' said Mrs Jennings. 'But I'm afraid I can't be responsible for my guests' dogs.'

'Guests?' said Mr Gilbert.

'Guests!' said Mrs Jennings. 'You see we decided to have a whole school garden party this afternoon, and I have invited all these people to join us. It's such a nice day we thought we'd have our party outdoors, and since you've made your lovely garden part of our school field . . . you know, since you put the gate in, we presumed we had a right to use it. In fact we thought you'd be happy for us to use it.'

'Happy?' shouted Mr Gilbert. 'How can I be happy when you're in my garden without permission and you're letting all those animals do what they want on my flower beds!'

'Exactly, Mr Gilbert,' said the headteacher, sternly. 'Exactly!'

And Mr Gilbert understood what she meant.

'Now,' went on Mrs Jennings, 'suppose you put this fence back as it was, and make sure you walk Nell on the proper footpath from now on. And suppose I make everyone here understand that this is *your* garden and not part of the school. And then suppose that I invite you to come along and help with our school gardening club. How would that sound?'

'Sounds good to me,' said Mr Gilbert.

'It's all a question of rights and responsibilities, isn't it,' said Mrs Jennings.

'Rights and responsibilities,' agreed Mr Gilbert.

Mr Gilbert eventually understood that he didn't have a right to use the school field. But he, like us, has a right to go to and use all kinds of different places. We have a right to walk on public footpaths; children have a right to play in designated playgrounds. We have a right to walk on beaches and to enjoy the countryside. But we have a responsibility to look after those places, to keep them clean and safe for others.

$$\sim$$

Let's think, for a few minutes, of places we have a right to go. Let us think of how we can show responsibility to those places. Let's remember also that many places, like shops and sports grounds, have the right to refuse entry to people who don't show responsibility.

A boiled egg

Have you ever been in a situation where you felt it was your right *to do or have something, and you've then become very indignant because it's not happened the way you thought it should? Maybe someone said you could have something and then they forgot. Maybe you felt this was unfair and you felt you wanted to get your own back. Sometimes when we feel aggrieved we also feel resentful or even revengeful. But those feelings don't solve anything. We may have rights, but we need to have common sense and fairness, too. In today's story, someone had a* right *to something, but they were greedy and tried to get more than their right.*

It happened in the summer when Ted and Archie were working on their allotments. Ted had been cleaning out his hen house, and Archie had just finished pulling out weeds from between his rows of vegetables. They both stopped work and decided to have a lunch break.

'What have you got today, Archie?' asked Ted.

Archie peered into his sandwich box. 'She's not put much in,' he grumbled. 'There's only an apple and a bit of old cheese. She hasn't even given me a chocolate biscuit!'

'Ahh, you should have a wife like mine,' laughed Ted. 'Look!' and he held out the lunchbox his wife had packed him that morning. There was a huge bacon, lettuce and tomato sandwich, two hard-boiled eggs, a chunk of cheese, a packet of crisps, some savoury biscuits, four pieces of fruit, an enormous slab of home-made fruit cake, an apple pie, a chocolate bar and a big iced bun with a cherry on top.

'Wow!' said Archie.

'Yeah!' said Ted, and he began to tuck in.

Within a couple of minutes Archie had finished his lunch and was looking enviously at Ted's. Ted was steadily munching. 'Still hungry?' he asked.

'Mmm, I am a bit,' said Archie.

'Tell you what,' said Ted, with a sly look in his eye. 'I'll lend you a boiled egg if you like.'

'*Lend* me an egg,' laughed Archie, thinking Ted was joking. 'How can you *lend* me an egg?'

'Look, do you want to borrow my egg, or not! I'll lend it to you but one of these days when I want it back I shall expect you to repay me,' said Ted, craftily.

Archie was more than a little surprised to hear that Ted might want the egg back one day, but he was so hungry that he agreed to repay the loan whenever Ted wanted. Then he forgot all about it . . . Until exactly four years later, when they were sitting having a rest under the apple tree.

'About that egg I lent you,' said Ted.

'Egg?' said Archie.

'Egg!' said Ted. 'You remember, you agreed to repay me when I said I wanted it back. Well, I've decided I'd like you to repay me now. I've worked it all out and you owe me about twenty thousand pounds.'

'Twenty thousand pounds!' exclaimed Archie. 'You cannot be serious! I can't possibly owe you twenty thousand pounds for one boiled egg! Anyway, I haven't got twenty thousand pounds.'

'Well, that's what you owe me,' repeated Ted. 'I have rights, you know, and you agreed to repay me.'

Archie realised that Ted was not joking. He was taking the matter perfectly seriously. 'But how can I possibly owe you all that?' he asked.

'I lent you an egg four years ago, remember? If you hadn't eaten it, that egg could have grown into a hen that summer. The next year that hen would have had 20 chickens, and the following year those 20 chickens would each have had 20 more. By now I would have had 8000 chickens from that one egg. Chickens cost about £2.50 each, so you owe me £20,000.' And he held out his hand for the payment.

Archie didn't know what to do. After all, he had agreed to pay back the loan of the egg, but he never thought he would be asked to do so, and certainly never ever thought he would be asked to pay back £20,000. He didn't have £20,000.

'I can't pay you all that,' said Archie, worriedly.

'You'll have to. It was an agreement. I have a right to be paid back. If you don't repay me I shall take you to court and then it'll cost you even more,' and Ted marched away, shouting back over his shoulder, 'You can have until tomorrow!'

Archie turned to go home, and just as he did so he noticed old Heskel leaning on his spade by the allotment gate. Heskel had been working on the land for as long as anyone could remember. He was a wise old countryman and people often turned to him for advice.

'You don't look any too happy,' he said to Archie. 'Anything I can help with?'

And Archie told him the whole sorry story and how concerned he was about what to do.

'Listen,' said Heskel, and he whispered something in Archie's ear. Archie's face suddenly brightened, he said thank you to Heskel and hurried away.

A short time later Archie was back in the allotment, this time with a can of baked beans. He set to work and dug over a strip of earth. He raked it and hoed it, then built a small fire at one end. He tipped the baked beans into a pan, put them on the fire and heated them. When they were nice and hot, he lifted the pan off the fire, spooned out the beans and started to plant them, one by one, into the prepared earth.

By now a small crowd had gathered to watch Archie do these strange things. Ted joined the crowd.

'What's going on?' he asked.

'This stupid man is planting baked beans,' said one of the crowd. 'He must be mad if he thinks baked beans are going to grow.'

'Hey, Archie, what are you doing?' shouted Ted.

'I'm planting beans,' Archie called back. 'I'm doing it for you. All the money I get from these beans when they grow, is for you, to pay off what I owe you.'

'You idiot!' shouted Ted. 'Those beans will never grow. You can't grow plants from baked beans!'

'Oh yes I can,' said Archie. 'If your boiled egg could have grown into a live chicken, then my baked beans can grow into plants,' and he carried on working in the soil.

Ted knew his trick had failed. He knew he didn't have the right to expect more than the original loan from Archie. He knew his greedy plan had been thwarted. He walked away in shame.

The following day everything was normal on the allotments, and the repayment of the egg was never mentioned again.

I wonder what you think of Ted's plan to get back more than just the egg. I know he had a right to ask for the loan back again, but maybe it would have been better if he'd just given Archie the egg in the first place.

~

Perhaps we could all think of trying to give something to someone today. We don't necessarily have to give away an object; we can give our time, or our help, or our encouragement, or our thanks.

Theme 2

Responsibilities

For want of a nail

Do you remember the other day when we were late with school dinners? It all happened because some children who were supposed to bring the registers and dinner numbers to the school office forgot to do it at the right time and as a result all the information came in late. Somehow those lost minutes were never found and the whole morning went wrong. It all happened because a small job wasn't done properly.

There's a nursery rhyme about a small job being done carelessly; you probably know it. It goes:

For want of a nail, the shoe was lost,
For want of a shoe, the horse was lost,
For want of a horse, the rider was lost,
For want of a rider, the battle was lost,
For want of a battle, the kingdom was lost.
And all for the want of a horseshoe nail!

This rhyme doesn't mention the word responsibility *yet that's what it's about. It's saying that we all have a responsibility to do the best we can with everything, even the smallest job. It's saying that it's not responsible to do slipshod work and to try to cut corners.*

Here's the story behind the rhyme.

The battle had been brewing for some time. They all knew it was coming; the only question was – when!

King Stanislav and King Vladek had been leaders of neighbouring kingdoms for years; and they had been arguing and fighting for years. You see, each believed that he had the right to the land which belonged to the other. Neither would give in and both thought they were right.

'They're at it again,' the people would say when they heard one or the other army on the move. And over the years bits of each kingdom would be won over to the other side until the people who lived near the borders didn't know whether they were coming or going or were Stanislavian or Vladekian.

Now, King Stanislav's spies were out surveilling the kingdom of Vladek. They came hurrying back with news of an imminent attack.

'The Vladek army is ready to advance,' they reported to the king. 'They could be here in less than a day.'

'Prepare for battle!' announced King Stanislav. 'King Vladek's army is on its way!'

All the king's men hurried away to do their jobs in readiness for the battle ahead.

The Royal Silversmith polished and sharpened all the silver swords, and checked the straps and handles of the silver shields.

The Royal Armourer inspected and cleaned all the soldiers' armour. He tested the helmets, the breastplates and the chain mail.

The Royal Flagbearers polished their poles and furled their flags.

The Saddlers inspected the saddles and harnesses, bridles and reins to ensure that all was safe and secure.

The Royal Blacksmith looked at the horses' hooves and shoes to see that they were clean and firm. First he checked the soldiers' horses, then he inspected the king's horse. But, unfortunately, he was not a particularly industrious worker, in fact he was rather lazy, so when he found a small nail slightly loose in one of the king's horse's shoes, he said to himself, 'Well, I've been working all day and I'm too tired to replace that horseshoe now. Anyway, it won't matter; it's only one little nail in one little shoe of one little horse. That's not going to make any difference to the army.' And he took the horse back to the stable and went to bed.

The next morning the army gathered outside the castle. The horses snorted and whinnied and stamped the ground, anxious to be off. The soldiers made last-minute adjustments to their armour which glinted and sparkled in the sunshine. The Flagbearers unfurled the flags and pennants so that they fluttered in the breeze. The king's horse was led, clipclop, clip-clop, to the front of the waiting army and the king, in full Royal battledress and shining armour, mounted his horse.

Suddenly, King Vladek's army was seen approaching on the brow of the hill.

There was a moment's total and still silence from the Stanislav army, then 'CHARGE!' shouted the king, and the army burst forward. With trumpets blaring and flags streaming the soldiers spurred their horses on. On and on, faster and faster, with the king in the lead. Towards them, making an ever diminishing gap, rode the Vladek army at top speed.

But . . . that tiny loose nail in the king's horseshoe was still loose!

As the horse galloped over the grass the nail became looser, and then it dropped out, and when that happened the horse stumbled and fell and the king flew head over heels over its ears into an undignified heap on the ground.

The first line of soldiers fell over the king, and the second tumbled over the first. The third line of soldiers tripped over the second, and the fourth plunged into the third. The fifth came a cropper as the sixth crashed down, and the seventh crumpled into the pile.

By now the entire army was in an enormous heap on the ground and whilst it was picking itself up and dusting itself down, King Vladek's army surrounded the field and the castle . . . and claimed the kingdom.

And so it was that King Stanislav lost his battle, and his kingdom: all because one lazy blacksmith thought one small nail didn't matter.

The world now knows that it did!

Everyone in our school, including all the teachers and helpers, and all the children, do jobs to help our school run smoothly. Some of those jobs are difficult or important. Other jobs are smaller and easier but they are still important. If all the small jobs are done well and efficiently, it can help the larger jobs to go well too.

Let us think for a moment of some of the jobs we are likely to do today. Let us remember that even the smallest jobs are important and let us think of how we can do them to the best of our ability, and how we can be helpful.

The ship's cook

Have you ever been asked to be responsible for two things at the same time? Maybe your mum has asked you to keep an eye on your smaller brother or sister, and you've been asked to tidy up. Suppose your brother or sister needs you for something and that means you can't get on with the tidying up; or suppose you concentrate on putting your things away and don't notice that your brother or sister has started to be naughty. It can be difficult to choose just which responsibility to concentrate on.

In today's true story, the captain of a passenger ship travelling between France and England had several responsibilities, but something happened which meant he had to decide which one he should give priority to.

The 'Normandie' was a huge ship; a passenger ferry which could carry 600 cars and more than 2000 passengers. And that day it was full. Most of the passengers were holiday-makers on their way back home after their holidays in France.

At eight o'clock in the morning, the ship was secured for sea, the captain gave the word to go, the ship's hooter sounded and the journey began.

'The weather's good, the sea is calm, we should have a good crossing,' announced the captain. 'And we should arrive in Portsmouth on time, in approximately four and three-quarter hours. We don't expect any delays.'

The passengers sat back to relax for their journeys. Some of them read, some played games, a few went to the on-board shops, several sat out on deck in the sunshine, and some went to the café and restaurant. And it was in the café, about an hour later, that the problem began.

The ship's cook began to feel ill.

'I think you'd better go to your cabin and lie down,' said the assistant cook. 'I'll take over here. Go on! And I'll send for the ship's nurse.'

But before he could get to his cabin, the cook collapsed and had to be helped to a seat. The nurse hurried to see him.

'He looks very ill,' she said. 'I think he's had a heart attack. He really needs a doctor. In fact, he really needs a hospital.'

'I'll go and tell the captain,' said the assistant cook.

The captain sent out a message to all the 2000 passengers, asking if there was a doctor on board, but, unfortunately, on this journey, there wasn't.

'It really is urgent that he sees a doctor,' said the nurse. 'We have to do something.'

The captain looked at his schedule. They were now well over one hour away from the French coast. To turn back would take almost three hours by the time he could get the ship secured at the quayside. He had a responsibility to the ferry company to make sure the ship ran on time and without delays. To turn back would mean that the passengers wouldn't set off again for about *four* hours. He had a responsibility to the passengers to ensure that they arrived at their destination on time.

The captain looked at the ill man. Maybe he would be all right until they reached England. Then they could get him to hospital. The captain considered his choices. He could turn back. It would take three hours and he would make all the passengers late. He could go on. It would take three and three-quarter hours but the passengers would be on time. He had a responsibility to them.

He looked again at the ill man. His cook. On his ship. One of his crew. And the captain knew he had a responsibility to care for *him*. He knew there was no time to lose. He had made his decision.

'Make him as comfortable as you can,' he said to the nurse. 'I'll get help as fast as I can,' and the captain strode to the control bridge. He radioed the French coastguard.

'I have an ill man on board,' he said. 'Suspected heart attack. Request immediate medical help. Over.'

The coastguard replied. 'Will scramble emergency helicopter with medical staff. Stand by at approximately 45 minutes. Over.'

'Will cut all engines to stop movement. Over and out.' And the captain went to give orders to the engine room staff to stop all engines and bring the ship to a halt. The anchors went down to secure the ship and hold it as still as was possible in the sea.

Then the captain took the microphone to speak to the passengers.

'We have an ill man on board who needs urgent medical attention,' he explained. 'We are waiting for the emergency helicopter from the French coastguards to airlift him to safety, but whilst we wait we must cut our engines to stop as much of the ship's movement as possible. As soon as the man is airlifted to safety, we shall resume our journey, but I regret we shall be delayed by possibly two hours.'

The passengers accepted the information and no one complained about the delay. Everyone realised that the captain had a responsibility to his crew member and that he was doing his best to ensure he received the care he needed.

Exactly 45 minutes later, the French coastguard helicopter arrived and hovered over the ship as a doctor was lowered to the deck, and shortly after, the cook was airlifted into the helicopter on a stretcher. He was whisked away to hospital in France, where he later recovered.

The ship eventually arrived in England just over two hours late and the captain apologised to the passengers for the ship's late arrival.

I wonder what you think the captain should have done. Did he give the right priority to his responsibilities? Do you think he should have apologised to the passengers for their late arrival? Do you think it's difficult to be responsible for something?

~

Dear God, help us to act responsibly when we have to care for someone else. Help us to think clearly and to consider the safety of children younger than us, of our younger brothers and sisters, and of our pets. Help us to take responsibility for ourselves, as well as others. Amen

Tasha at the café

As you know, all the teachers and governors here at school have a responsibility to look after you and to keep you safe. Your parents have a responsibility to look after you and keep you safe when you are at home. And if you go into a shop, or a restaurant, or a park, or a playground, the owners have a responsibility to ensure that the place is a safe environment for the people using it.

Lots of people have a responsibility to look after you. But there's someone else who has a responsibility too. I wonder if you know who that is.

It's you!

Each one of us has a responsibility to do what we can to look after ourselves, and that includes children. For example, we all have a responsibility to do as we are told about things like not fooling around near water, or not playing near busy roads. We all have a responsibility to heed notices and signs that are there for our safety. We all have a responsibility to read instructions and follow directions, for example when we are walking or cycling or driving on the roads. You all have a responsibility to remain on the school premises until you are allowed to leave.

In other words, we all have a responsibility to use our common sense to help keep ourselves safe. But, just sometimes, it's easier said than done! Take the story of Tasha, for example!

Natasha, I'm afraid, is a rather spoilt and wilful child, who is far too used to getting her own way. In Natasha's house, it's too often her mum doing what Tasha wants instead of the other way round. The result of this is that Tasha has begun to expect that she should always have her own way. And when she doesn't, then Tasha has a tantrum! She has even learned that having a tantrum is, in itself, a way of getting what she wants! As I said, she is a rather spoilt and wilful child.

One day, Tasha was invited to go shopping with her friend Laura and Laura's mum. They were going to the new supermarket at the other side of town, and Laura's mum said they could have lunch in the café there.

'I don't think there'll be anything there I like,' said Tasha. 'But I'll have some crisps and juice.'

'Well, we won't decide what to eat now,' said Laura's mum, sensibly. 'We'll wait until we get there and see what there is!'

'I won't like anything!' argued Tasha.

At the supermarket Laura and Tasha spent ages looking at all the clothes and deciding what they would buy if they had enough money. Tasha was surprised to learn that Laura didn't necessarily get everything she wanted.

'But what if you really *really* wanted something; your mum would buy it then, wouldn't she?' asked Tasha.

'Depends!' said Laura. 'Depends on whether she can afford it.'

'*My* mum gets me anything I want,' said Tasha, arrogantly.

A few minutes later they all went upstairs to the café, queued up at the counter and Laura's mum asked the two girls what they'd like. There was plenty to choose from.

'I think I'll have pasta bake,' said Laura's mum. 'Laura? Tasha?'

'Chicken and chips, please,' said Laura.

'Crisps and coke,' said Tasha.

Laura's mum said she ought to have something more substantial, but Tasha was adamant she wanted only crisps and coke. Laura told her mum that Tasha liked beans on toast, so that was ordered as well. Tasha was not pleased.

'I won't eat it!' she said.

They chose a table and went to sit down. Laura set out the knives and forks and they waited for the hot food to be brought to the table. Tasha opened her crisps. 'I'm not eating beans!' she said, so loudly that people sitting nearby turned to look at her.

The order arrived and Tasha looked at her plate. It didn't occur to her to say thank you to Laura's mum for buying the food, or for bringing her to the supermarket. She was only interested in making a fuss, and enjoying the attention of the other people sitting nearby.

She tipped the crisps onto the beans and began to pick them off again with her fingers.

'Tasha!' said Laura's mum, with a note of warning in her voice.

'I always eat them like this,' she said.

'Not when you're with us, you don't,' said Laura's mum, and Tasha sensed she was going to be told off, so she stood up suddenly and her chair fell over with a crash.

More people turned to look. 'Well I need a paper napkin,' she shouted, and flounced off to the counter to get one. On the way she passed a table with two small children sitting with their mother, quietly eating their meals. She grinned at them and twirled round so that her sparkly skirt flared out. More people turned to look. Tasha grabbed a handful of paper napkins and ran back to her table. Laura had picked up her chair. She sat down with a bang that made the table wobble and her glass of coke spill all over her skirt.

'Tasha! Sit down!' said Laura's mum, crossly, and looking embarrassed.

'How can I sit down when I'm sopping wet!' shouted Tasha and she jumped up to get yet more paper napkins.

By now the whole café was looking at them, and people were beginning to mutter. 'You'd think that woman could control the child, wouldn't you?'

Laura looked at the people on the next table and said, 'It's not my mum's fault,' and she started to cry.

Over at the counter, Tasha had reached up to the napkin dispenser again, only to find it was empty. She thumped the top of it with her fist to see if more napkins would come down, but she caught her hand on the edge of the metal holder.

'Ouch! Look, I'm bleeding,' she yelled as she waved her hand around for everyone to see.

'Natasha! Come here this minute!' called Laura's mum.

'Can I help you, Madame?' said the café manager, appearing from nowhere at the side of the table.

'I'm going to make an allegation against you!' shouted Tasha to the manager. 'This is all your fault. You should keep your customers safe! You shouldn't allow accidents to happen!' and Tasha sat down on her chair glaring at him and clutching her hand.

She expected the manager to look worried, to apologise to her and even to offer some kind of compensation. Perhaps he would give her a free voucher to spend in the store, she thought, to make up for the damage to her hand. At the very least she expected him to arrange for some first aid for her cut and to accept responsibility for the accident. Tasha sat there, smugly, and waited for an apology.

'I'm sorry . . .' he began, and Tasha smiled to herself. He *was* going to apologise.

'I'm sorry . . .' he said again, '. . . But I can accept no responsibility WHATSOEVER for your accident!'

'But it's your fault!' screamed Tasha.

'I'm sorry, but it's NOT!' said the manager, firmly. 'I have a responsibility to make this café a safe place and I have done so. You, young lady, have a responsibility to behave in a sensible manner, which, I might add, you have not done. Not only is the accident your fault, but so is the mess you've caused, and the upset to the rest of my customers. You owe me an apology for your disgraceful behaviour!'

'But . . .' began Tasha.

'Natasha!' warned Laura's mum.

'I'm sorry,' said Tasha, and for the first time ever, she realised that she meant it. She *was* sorry that she'd caused such a fuss, and she realised that in fact she *did* have a responsibility to do her part in keeping herself safe. It wasn't just up to everybody else.

I wonder what you think of Natasha's behaviour. I wonder if you've ever met anyone like her. I do hope you've never behaved like her! I'm glad she learned by the end of the incident that she had some responsibility for her own safety, and that it wasn't not all up to other people.

Other people, most of the time, will do their best to make sure we are all safe when we are in school, or out shopping, or playing, or even on holiday, but we all have a responsibility to look after ourselves, to be aware of health and safety, to be sensible and to behave well.

~

Let's think of some ways in which we can help to be responsible for our own safety. Imagine you're at the swimming baths, for example; how could you keep safe there? You can follow instructions, not run at the side of the pool, and take care to look if you jump in. Imagine you're riding your bike; how can you keep yourself safe? Imagine you're in a playground with your friends; how can you keep yourself safe there?

You might like to talk about keeping safe, further, with your teacher later today.

Theme 3

Feelings

Edward

Have you ever had something go wrong, and then felt afterwards that it's just not worth bothering to try? Sometimes we all feel like that, grown-ups as well as children. Sometimes we feel that we just can't do something, so we give up on it. The trouble is, doing that usually makes us feel even worse, because we know we haven't tried to improve things.

Feelings are funny things. We can have very strong feelings about things, and those feelings can affect how we behave. Sometimes that's a good thing because it spurs us on. But sometimes feelings can be quite negative, and they can prevent us making progress. The boy in today's story had some of those negative feelings, and they were not helping him at all.

The boy was called Edward. He was in Year 4 and he had a bit of a reputation for being naughty. He wasn't really a difficult boy, or a trouble-maker, but somehow he never seemed to work quite as hard as his parents and teachers thought he could; he often seemed to get into arguments, even with his teacher, or his mum; and he always seemed to be in the wrong place at the wrong time. In fact, if ever there was any bother of any kind, Edward always seemed to be in the middle of it.

'I don't know why you can't try a bit harder,' his teacher used to say.

'I don't know why you can't be more like your sister Emma,' his mum used to say. And Edward didn't know why, either. He'd started off trying hard. When he was in Year 1 and Year 2 he felt he'd tried really hard to do his best, but somehow he still got into trouble. Then last year, in Year 3, he'd started to fool around a bit with his friends, but that had got him into even more trouble, and although he used to make his friends laugh, it didn't make him feel any happier. In fact, once or twice, he'd felt it was really unfair because his friends hadn't stuck up for him; they'd been too busy trying to wriggle out of trouble themselves.

By now, in Year 4, Edward *knew* he was naughty. He felt he wasn't as good as all the others at his schoolwork, or at games, or at anything really. And he felt miserable.

Then, one day soon after the start of the new term, his teacher suddenly said, 'I need someone to do an important job for me. I'm looking for some-one sensible and reliable . . .' and she looked round the class.

The children stopped what they were doing and looked round as well. Some of them, who thought they might be chosen, sat up very straight and still and hoped she would choose them! Edward looked round too, wonder-ing who she would choose. Perhaps Pria, she was always sensible, or maybe Sarah, she was reliable. She might choose Bryn or Heetesh, they were always being given jobs to do, or it could be Mae, she was always well-behaved.

But Miss Taylor didn't look at any of those children. She looked straight at Edward. 'You're helpful and sensible,' she said. 'Would you like to do this job for me?'

Edward turned round to see if she meant someone else sitting behind him, but she didn't.

'Yes, you Edward,' she said.

One of the boys sitting nearby started to laugh.

'Do you have a problem, Adam?' she asked.

'No, Miss,' said Adam, and he quickly removed the smile from his face.

'Good! Now, Edward, I need you to take this message to Mrs Schofield in class 2, and then I'd like you to take these papers to the school office. It's important they get there straight away. Oh, and you'd better wait to see if there's a message to bring back. OK? Thank you!' And she handed him the papers and told the class to resume their work.

Edward could hardly believe that he had been chosen. He suddenly felt quite grown-up and responsible. He was determined to do this job properly. As he walked past Adam's desk, Adam grinned at him and stuck his foot out, but Edward ignored him and set off with the messages.

In class 2, Mrs Schofield thanked Edward for being helpful, and at the school office the headteacher said he was pleased to see Edward being so reliable and sensible. Edward began to feel good, and his confidence grew a little that day. Miss Taylor was clearly pleased with him when he delivered a return message to the classroom.

The following day, Edward had just begun to do his maths work when Miss Taylor came to sit with him.

'You're really getting the hang of this work, aren't you, Edward,' she said. 'You're quite good at maths.'

Edward stared at her. He felt he was useless at maths. It was always too difficult for him. 'I can't . . .' he began.

'But you can,' smiled Miss Taylor. 'Look!' And she put a whole row of red ticks on his book. 'Now, try this next page.'

'But I can't . . .' Edward began again.

'Success comes in *cans* not *cant's*, and you *can*, Edward Jones,' she said, and she went away to help someone else.

Instead of beginning to fool around now it was time for maths, Edward sat and concentrated. By the time Miss Taylor came to his table again, he'd finished the assignment and she gave him a smiley sticker on his page. His confidence grew a little bit more.

The next day Edward was again asked to take a message to the school office and he was determined to do the job well, with no fooling around and no silliness. He knew he'd been trusted, and he wanted to show everyone that Miss Taylor had been right to trust him. Edward's confidence grew a little more.

By the end of the week Edward had not been in trouble once, and it seemed to him that all the teachers expected him to behave well and to try hard. Well, if that's what they expected of him, that's what he had better do, Edward thought. Clearly they didn't expect him to be naughty any more. His confidence grew again. And, strangely, he found that it was in fact more fun being grown-up and trusted, than being naughty and silly.

Soon, everyone seemed to be saying, 'Isn't Edward helpful? Hasn't he turned into a sensible and reliable sort of boy? Isn't he good?'

Edward certainly felt good.

You may think that this is a made-up story: but you'd be wrong! This story is absolutely true. Of course, I've changed the names of all the people in the story so that you won't recognise the real 'Edward', but he's sitting here in this hall. It's funny how feelings can affect the way we behave; good feelings can motivate us and help us to think positively; good feelings can help build our confidence. Every one of us can have good feeling about ourselves, because, as you already know, everyone is good at something.

~

Let us reflect for a few moments on ways we can think positively, today. Think of something you do well, think of how positive that makes you feel. Think of something in which you're going to do your best today. It may be your work, it may be games, and it may be a job you're responsible for. Think of how you'll feel when you've done that task or activity to the best of your ability.

The money-box pig

Feeling positive is good. Feeling so positive that you get big-headed about it, is not so good!

I once had a neighbour who was very good at gardening. The trouble was, he thought he knew just about everything there was to know, and he didn't believe that anyone else knew nearly as much as him! If any of the other neighbours commented about their plants, or said what they'd found worked successfully, this man always overruled them, he always knew best, he was always right. Or he thought he was.

In the end he made everyone else feel as though their gardening skills were useless, that the whole neighbourhood felt dejected. Things came to a head after a really bad storm, when everyone's garden took a battering, including the know-it-all-man's garden. After the storm, all the neighbours worked together to help each other to rebuild their gardens, and the man realised that, in fact, other people did have skills, other people were knowledgeable, and that he wasn't the world's best gardener.

I never asked him how he felt about it all, but I suspect he felt a great deal happier once he learned not to be so big-headed.

Today's story has nothing to do with gardening! But listen carefully and you'll spot some similarities between the gardener and the money-box pig!

It was midnight and the toys were scattered about all over the floor. No one had tidied them away. There were dolls and cars, trains and Lego, GameBoys and spaceships and books. There were jigsaws and teddies, balls and game boards, action men, paint sets and trucks. Everything was all over the place, nothing was where it should be: nothing that is, except the money-box pig.

The pig was made of white china and painted all over with big red spots. It had a slit on its back for the coins to go in and a hole underneath it, closed with a rubber bung, to get them out again. The pig was stuffed with coins. So many coins, in fact, that he couldn't rattle any more, he was just too full.

The money-box pig sat in its own place, high up, on top of the toy cupboard. From here, it could see the whole room and most of the big wide world outside the window.

The pig was supercilious, self-important. He felt better than the rest. He was, after all, on a higher level than the rest. He knew he was worth more than any of them. He knew that what was inside him could buy all the rest of them put together. He knew he was valuable. And he was proud of it. He was the only one to have his own place, and he was never out of place!

On this particular night the toys were particularly bored. The children had been out all day and so there had been no one to play with them. Now, they all sat there, forlorn, in the moonlight.

The clock struck twelve.

Suddenly, the action man sat up. 'I know,' he said. 'Let's play humans!'

'Good idea,' said the big doll.

'It's our favourite game,' said the Lego pieces.

'Let's make up a play,' said the train.

'And then we'll have tea,' said the chess board.

'Then we'll talk,' said the teddies.

So they got out the toy theatre and put up the scenery. The dolls and the teddies and the action man went on the stage and learned their parts, whilst the rest of the toys arranged themselves in rows in front of it. There was a great deal of pushing and shoving before the toys were all settled.

The action man walked on stage and pulled back the curtains. He surveyed his audience. It was a full house. He looked all round and suddenly noticed the money-box pig, still sitting proudly on top of the cupboard. Oh dear! They'd left him out. No one had thought to include him.

'Come on down,' called the action man. 'Come and join in the fun. You can be in the play if you want.'

'Certainly not', replied the pig, disdainfully. 'It's all so childish. I am above all that sort of thing.'

'Oh well, please yourself,' said the action man, and he started acting.

The play was a huge success, although to be perfectly honest, the storyline was not fantastic, as the toys all got their words mixed up and completely lost the plot, but the acting was remarkable.

'Brilliant!' shouted the Lego bricks.

'Encore, encore,' clapped the keyboard.

'Marvellous!' applauded the books.

'Do it again,' called the cars.

And the entire audience banged and clapped and cheered and whistled and thumped on the floor and made enough noise to arouse the entire household, though, fortunately, it didn't.

Throughout it all, the money-box pig looked on from his high vantage point.

'What a nonsense,' he thought. 'What an incredible waste of time and energy. What stupidity. And he puffed himself up with pride that *he* was not foolish enough to join in. That *he* was above that sort of behaviour. That *he* was better than them.

The action man began an action replay and the play started again. The audience became more and more boisterous and unruly. The noise was deafening.

The pig puffed himself up even further. 'How glad I am that I am superior to them.' And he thrust out his chest. 'That I am so much more clever.' And he held his head higher. 'That I am much more advanced.' And he stretched out a trotter. 'That I am just top-notch!' And he breathed in and expanded to absolute capacity.

But, with each breath, each thrust, each puff, each stretch, he strutted a little nearer to the edge of his cupboard. The audience toys, with their backs to him, noticed nothing. The acting toys, engrossed in playing their parts, were unaware.

Until the crash.

The play came to an abrupt halt and the toys all turned towards the sound. The pompous pig lay smashed to smithereens on the floor. His china shards lay motionless but the coins, revelling in their new-found freedom, rolled and hopped and skipped and jumped, and slithered and spiralled, until they, too, stopped still.

The toys were horrified. 'The humans will think it was us,' they said, so they scattered themselves around the room, just as they'd been before, and lay quite still, as though nothing had happened.

The next morning, the broken bits of the money-box pig were swept up and put in the bin. The toys were tidied and a brand-new money-box pig was put on top of the cupboard. It was made of white china and painted all over with big red spots. It had a slit on its back for the coins to go in and a hole underneath it, closed with a rubber bung, to get them out again. The pig was absolutely empty. So empty in fact that it couldn't rattle, which made it just like the first pig.

Or did it?

I wonder what happened next. I wonder if the second pig was just as self-centred as the first. Maybe you think the story had the right ending for the circumstances? Do you think it was a sad ending? Maybe you could have a go at writing the next chapter of the story.

Did you spot any similarities between the pig in the story and my neighbour? My neighbour was not nearly as pompous as the money-box pig, but I think there were some similarities between them. I wonder what you think!

Dear God, help us to be positive and confident, but not to be big-headed. Help us to consider other people's feelings, as well as our own. Help us to remember that everyone has a place in our school and in our community, and that everyone is good at something. Amen

Melissa's shoes

Do you think it's important to consider the feelings of other people? Yes, I'm glad you think it is; I felt sure that's what you would say, because I know that everyone in our school tries to help everyone else, and part of helping others is considering how they feel. We would be in a pretty sorry state if we only thought of ourselves and never considered how other people feel, or if we never thought about how our actions might affect them.

Sometimes it's quite difficult to imagine how other people might feel, but it does no harm to try. It does no harm to try to put ourselves in other people's shoes! In fact there's a famous saying that goes don't judge someone else until you've travelled a mile in their shoes. *Do you think it really means you have to try on someone's shoes, and walk about in them? What do you think it means? Someone in today's story wasn't quite sure!*

Melissa was often in trouble. It wasn't that she was especially naughty, it was mostly because she didn't think ahead; she would do things without thinking of the consequences. And she would often make remarks or comments without thinking about how that would make someone else feel.

On this particular day, she'd been asked to stay behind in the classroom when everyone else went out to play.

'It was really unkind of you to tease William about his wheelchair,' said Miss James, her teacher. 'You know he has problems walking and has to use his wheelchair sometimes.'

'But I didn't tease him,' wailed Melissa. 'I just said it had funny wheels with those round handles that he has to push, and why couldn't he get an electric one like my grandma.'

'You need to think before you speak,' said Miss James. 'It's important to consider other people's feelings, you know. And what about Jenny this morning? You ran past her table, knocked everything off and broke her new pencil tin, and then said it was her fault for having them in the way! She was very upset, you really hurt her feelings, you know.'

'Sorry,' mumbled Melissa.

'You need to put yourself in other people's shoes a bit more, Melissa. I think you'd better stay inside this playtime, and just think about how you can be a bit more thoughtful to people,' said Miss James, and she went to sort out some things in the stock cupboard.

Melissa wandered around the classroom. None of it was *her* fault. *She* couldn't help it if William needed a wheelchair or if Jenny was always shy. She sauntered across to the window and looked out. Everyone seemed to be having a good time. Everyone was playing with their friends and *she* was stuck inside with no one to play with. Melissa felt cross and alone. She picked up someone's pencil and deliberately broke it in half and dropped the pieces on the floor. She kicked a table leg, then looked surprised as the movement made the computer on the table spring into life.

The screen brightened and an image formed. A pair of pink shoes walked across the screen. Melissa sat down to watch. She'd never seen this program on the computer before. The pink shoes were followed by a pair of hiking boots striding across the screen, and in turn these were followed by a pair of furry slippers, a pair of black plimsolls, some ballet shoes, some football boots, a muddy pair of trainers and some flip-flops. Melissa watched, fascinated. The images dissolved and two new shoes appeared. Melissa stared at them in astonishment. They were hers! They were the black patent leather shoes she had on right now. She looked down at her feet, then back at the screen. Her shoes! What were they doing on the computer?

Suddenly a cartoon girl jumped into the shoes on the screen and started dancing around. Melissa laughed. The cartoon girl kicked off the shoes and another pair came dancing onto the screen. They were white leather sandals with pink flowers printed on them. They were *Jenny's* shoes. The cartoon girl put them on and straightaway Melissa could see Jenny's home on the screen, and all Jenny's family. Melissa recognised Jenny's older sister who sometimes brought her to school, but she didn't know that Jenny had so many other brothers and sisters as well. She watched as the cartoon girl tried to look after her toys and her belongings, but it was difficult with all those other noisy, boisterous, untidy children in the family, who always seemed to be borrowing each other's things. No wonder Jenny had been so upset that morning when Melissa had broken her new pencil tin!

The cartoon girl on the computer turned a cartwheel and the white shoes flew from her feet and off the edge of the screen. A new pair of shoes came striding into view and the cartoon girl jumped into them. They were miles too big for her; they were shiny black leather lace-ups which squeaked every time she walked. Melissa gasped – they were Mr Hadleigh's shoes! Mr Hadleigh, the headteacher. The girl in Mr Hadleigh's big black shoes was in his office looking at all the papers spread over his desk. There were lists of children, lists of SATs results, lists of reading books; there were letters to parents, letters to governors, letters to the education office; there were columns of sums showing all the money that had been spent on books and paper and pencils and paint; there were bills for building repairs and school dinners, salary sheets for teachers and helpers and dinner ladies. No wonder Mr Hadleigh sometimes looked harassed with all that paperwork to do!

The cartoon girl jumped out of Mr Hadleigh's shoes and into another pair of black shoes which were standing still at the corner of the screen. They were small and rather like boots. Melissa recognised them as William's special shoes. The girl climbed into them as the classroom appeared on the screen. She tried to walk to the worktable, to the activity area, to the painting section, but it was very difficult and progress was slow. She tried to go to the library but there was a small ramp leading to it and she couldn't make her feet walk uphill. No wonder William sometimes had to use a wheelchair, and no wonder he didn't like comments about it.

The cartoon girl sat down and took off the small black boots. She turned round, and there, tiptapping across the screen was a pair of red high-heeled sandals. Melissa giggled. They were Miss James' shoes. The cartoon girl slid the shoes onto her feet. They were too big and too high but she click-clacked around the classroom on them as all the children appeared on the screen. The cartoon girl in Miss James' shoes went first to one table of children and them to another. She helped a group with writing, then a group with maths. She checked on the children in the painting corner and looked in on the children in the library. She dealt with two children from other classes as well as a visit from another teacher, and all the time she kept her eye on everyone, answered questions and gave encouragement. No wonder Miss James said she was always busy. No wonder she got cross with people when they wasted time.

The cartoon girl sat at the teacher's desk and dangled one of her red shoes from her toes. And just then, the real Miss James came out of the stock cupboard.

'Well, Melissa? Have you been thinking about putting yourself in other people's shoes?'

Melissa looked at the computer screen. It was blank. Completely blank.

'Er, yes, Miss,' she said. 'I think so.'

'You do know what I mean, Melissa, don't you?'

'Er, yes, Miss,' she said again. 'I think so.'

'Well, I hope you do. Now, go and join the others; they're all coming in from play.'

'Yes, Miss James,' said Melissa, and she looked again at the computer screen, but there was no cartoon girl, no shoes, nothing. The screen was blank.

I do wonder about that computer program! What you think? The story ends there, with Melissa joining the rest of the class at the end of playtime. You could write the next chapter in the story for yourself. Maybe the computer program helped Melissa to be more thoughtful about other people's feelings. Maybe Melissa's own imagination helped her to be more thoughtful. Whichever it was, I hope she started to be more considerate.

~

Help us, Lord, to be aware of other people's feelings. Help us to do nothing to intentionally hurt their feelings. Help us to remember to treat other people as we would like them to treat us. Amen

Theme 4

Choices

The two goblins

I wonder how many choices you've already made today. We're very lucky, because we have choice in so many things. I bet you've had some say already today in what to wear and what to eat; choices that were unheard of for children only a few years ago! And I suppose that at times during the day you'll choose what to do, who to play with, and what to watch on television. You'll probably help your mum or dad choose what do and where to go at the weekend, you may be allowed to choose what to buy, and you may even be asked where you'd like to go on holiday. You have a great deal of choices to make.

Of course, you also have choices to make about how to behave, and about your attitude. And you have choices to make about where to go for help if you need any. In fact, all through every day of our lives, we are all making choices of one sort or another all the time.

Some choices are easy to make. For example if you had to choose at lunchtime between a portion of delicious chocolate ice-cream and a piece of stale burnt dried-out bread and butter pudding, I think I know which you would choose! But other choices are more difficult to make, like what to do when you're solving a problem of some kind. Then you really have to think and weigh up the pros and cons of the choices on offer.

Just listen to the problem that occurred in today's story, and the choices that were made.

Once upon a time there were two hobgoblins. They were the most argumentative hobgoblins you were ever likely to come across, but nevertheless they were the best of friends. Most of the time!

On this particular day they were out and about looking for mischief, as hobgoblins do, when they came across a bag in the middle of the road.

'What do you suppose is in it?' said Mully, as he poked it with his foot.

'Dunno,' said Gatawny. 'We could open it and see.'

'It might be something scary,' said Mully and he backed away from it.

'Won't know 'till we look!' said Gatawny, and he carefully opened the bag. 'Doesn't look scary!' he said, and he tipped out an old tin box, a pair of green shoes and a stick.

'What is it?' said Mully, coming closer to see.

'It's an old tin box, a pair of green shoes, and a stick!' said Gatawny.

Mully picked up the stick and prodded the shoes. He poked the stick into the toes of the shoes.

'Here, stop faffing about,' said Gatawny, and he grabbed hold of the green shoes, pulled off his own, and put them on. Straightaway, the shoes shot into the air as though they were jet-propelled, with Gatawny still inside them. 'Hey, look at me, I'm *flying*!' he shouted. 'Wheeeeeeeeeeee . . . .' And he whizzed about in the sky right above Mully's head.

Mully stared. 'They're *magic*!' he whispered. 'Maybe the other stuff's magic too,' and he looked at the stick which was still in his hand. It didn't look magic. It looked like a perfectly ordinary stick with a few bobbly bits here and there. Mully ran his fingers along the length of the stick. Nothing. He touched the individual bobbles on it. Nothing. He waved it in the air and shouted 'abracadabra' at the top of his voice, but nothing happened.

Gatawny came down to earth. 'Maybe you have to *tell* it to do something,' he said. 'Beat it, stick!' he shouted, and the stick sprang into action. It leapt and danced and threw itself around the lane, thrashing everything it came into contact with. 'Hey, this is COOL!' yelled Gatawny. 'Just think what we could do with this!' But he was less enthusiastic a few seconds later when the stick came into contact with *him*! 'Stop it, stick!' he shouted, and fortunately, it did.

Mully picked up the old tin box and shook it to hear if there was anything inside. It sounded empty. They tried to prise the lid open but it was rusted tightly shut.

'Smash it open,' said Gatawny.

'You'll break whatever's inside,' said Mully.

'There's nothing in it!' said Gatawny.

'There might be,' said Mully.

'Give it to me!'

'No, I got it first.'

'Give it here.'

'No!'

The lid flew open and they both fell on the ground. The box landed between them and they peered inside. Nothing.

'Told you!' said Gatawny.

'I wish it had something in it,' said Mully, wistfully.

'What?'

'I don't know. Anything. Ten pence pieces!'

Suddenly, the box juddered. The lid snapped shut then jumped open again. The box was filled to the top with . . . ten pence pieces!

'Fifty pence pieces,' shouted Gatawny. Snap. Jump. And there they were.

'One pound coins!' yelled Mully. Snip. Snap. A boxful of pounds.

'A treasure chest!' bellowed Gatawny. Bang. Crash. And an entire chestful of treasure appeared out of the box.

'A castle!' screamed Mully. A crescendo of clatter and a glittering sparkling castle exploded from the box.

'Now what do we do?' said Gatawny.

'We share the stuff out,' said Mully. 'I want the tin box, you can have the stick. We'll toss for the shoes.'

'No, that's not fair!' wailed Gatawny. 'I want the box. You have the shoes and the stick.'

'NO, the box is mine. I don't want the other things.'

'Well toss for all three, that's fair!' said Gatawny.

'Can't do that, there are three things. It'll never be fair 'cos someone will get two and the other'll only get one.'

'Then we'll have to get someone to help us to decide,' said Gatawny. 'Who shall we get?'

They spent a great deal of time deciding who could help them. The owl was wise, and had been asked for advice before. The oak tree was also wise and trustworthy with it. Then there was the man of the mountain, or the old woman who lived by the lake; both were fond of giving advice.

As Mully and Gatawny were discussing who they should ask, a man came walking along the road. Unbeknown to them both, he had in fact watched all the events of the last few minutes.

'Good day, gentlemen,' he said. 'And a very fine day it is too, is it not?'

'Well, it would be, if we could decide what to do,' said Gatawny.

'Why? Would you be having a problem?' asked the man.

'You could say that,' said Mully, and he began to tell the stranger all about the bag and the shoes and the stick and the old tin box; all the time being interrupted by Gatawny who had to have the last word.

The man listened quietly and patiently. Finally he said, 'I think I may be able to help you to distribute the items fairly. I can help you both.'

Mully and Gatawny looked at each other and smiled a huge sigh of relief. Their problem was about to be solved.

'Now, where are the green shoes?' asked the man.

'Here, right here,' said Gatawny, and he set down the two green shoes in front of the man.

'And the stick and the box?' asked the man.

'Here, right here,' said Mully.

'Good!' said the man.

Mully and Gatawny smiled and watched as the man slowly took off his own pair of shoes. They waited in anticipation for him to solve their problem of how to share the magic things. They didn't have long to wait.

The man quickly grabbed the stick and the box then shoved his feet into the two green shoes which shot into the air as though they were jet-propelled. Mully and Gatawny stared as they watched their magic things disappear into a vapour trail in the sky.

'Oh well,' said Mully. 'It was only a tin box, an old pair of shoes and a stick. At least we've still got a castle and a chest of treasure.'

Those two hobgoblins could have made all kinds of different choices about how to share out the magic things. I wonder what you would have done. I think their biggest mistake was in their choice of an advisor, don't you?

～

Let us think, for a few moments, of some of the choices we are likely to make this week in school and at home. Let's think of some of those difficult choices we have to make which are about choosing between right and wrong, and about choosing the sensible thing to do. Let's also consider the best people we could turn to for help and advice when we have choices to make.

Leif the Lucky

Some choices are really difficult to make. Have you ever been in a situation where you know that it would be easier to do one thing, but that it would probably be better to do another? For example, when you're learning to swim, you might be given the choice of practising something you already know how to do, or trying to do something completely new. The new activity sounds interesting but you might be a bit scared simply because you've not done it before; whereas practising something you can do already is much easier. Of course, there was a time when that *activity was new, but you tried it and learned how to do it.*

We all need to try to do new things, otherwise none of us would ever learn or make progress. But choosing what to do can be hard. In today's true adventure story, someone had to make some difficult choices.

Leif Erikson was learning how to sail a boat so that he could be a famous explorer when he grew up, just like his father. But this was just over one thousand years ago, and sailing a boat was not like it is today. There was no engine, no radio or compass; just the sun and the stars and the sea currents to guide them.

Leif's father was Erik the Red, a fearless Viking leader who had already discovered lands over the sea from their native country of Iceland. Erik the Red had explored the east and south and west coast of Greenland and had set up Viking colonies there. And it was in Greenland that Leif was born and where he learned to sail. By the time Leif was 19, he was an accomplished mariner and was able to command a sailing ship with as many as 20 sailors, and he was not afraid of the sea or the wind or the weather.

At about that time, news reached Erik the Red of another sailor called Bjarni Herolfson who had been travelling from Iceland to Greenland when a fierce storm blew his ship off course. With no engine it was impossible to do anything but sit out the storm, and with no radio it was impossible to call for help. Bjarni Herolfson and his crew were at the mercy of the wind and the waves.

For several days the storm raged on and the boat was tossed about on the water like a toy. It was pushed further and further to the west, to an area of the sea they had not been in before. Through the rain and the clouds and the sea spray, the sailors *thought* they could see land. They *thought* they could see rocky cliffs and ice-covered land, but in the dreadful weather conditions it was hard to tell *what* they could see.

Eventually the storm died down and Herolfson managed to get the ship back on course. They returned to Greenland and told everyone what had happened. They described the land they thought they had seen.

Everyone turned to Erik the Red.

'You are our greatest explorer,' they said. 'You must lead an expedition to these lands and see them for yourself. You must claim them as Viking land.'

Eric the Red agreed to lead the expedition.

A ship was prepared and a crew of 35 sailors was hired. Provisions and supplies were loaded on board. All was ready. Then . . . disaster!

On the way to the ship, Erik's horse stumbled and fell. Erik was thrown off and landed on rocks at the side of the track. He damaged his back and could not go ahead with the journey.

All eyes turned to Erik's son, Leif, and he realised that they wanted *him* to go in his father's place.

'I can't do this,' he said. 'I know how to sail and I am not afraid of the sea, but I can't face the dangers of an unknown land. We don't even know that it really exists. I don't know how to be a leader of men and I can't take them on a journey from which they may not return.'

Erik looked at his son and said, 'This must be your choice. No one will force you to make this voyage. The choice must be yours.'

Leif thought.

'If I go, I will certainly be afraid. I don't know what I will have to face. I don't know what I will find. I don't know if I will succeed. But, if I *don't* go, I will never know what lies over the horizon of the sea. I will never know if there are new countries there, or what they are like.'

The he stood up tall and straight and said, 'I choose to go. I choose to lead the expedition.'

They set off from the southern tip of Greenland and sailed north, hugging the coast. These were seas that Leif knew; these were safe waters with land always in sight. Then, courageously, Leif turned west and headed the ship towards the western horizon, towards the unknown, towards either death or adventure.

They had no map, no chart. They headed west using just the sun and the stars to guide them. The wind was bitterly cold. Ice formed on the sails and the mast and even in the sea. Days passed. There was no sign of land.

'Shall we turn back, skipper?' asked the men.

It would have been so easy to choose to say 'yes', but Leif had his father's determination. 'I choose to continue,' he said.

Suddenly, a lookout shouted, 'Land ahead! Land!' Everyone looked. Sure enough there was land, but it was unfriendly and inhospitable. It was just rock and ice towering out of the sea.

'Is this it?' said the men. 'Is this the land that Herolfson spoke of? We cannot land here, or set up a colony. Should we not turn back, skipper?'

Leif looked at the rocky land, worn smooth by glaciers. They could not settle here. The land could not be farmed. 'I choose to continue,' he said, and the ship sailed on into the unknown.

Two days later, Leif looked out across the mist of the sea, and thought he could see green hills and trees. 'I must be dreaming,' he said, but the more he looked, the more real the green coastline became.

'Land ahead!' shouted the lookout.

They anchored the boat and went ashore. The earth was rich and fertile with pasture land and trees and rivers full of fish.

'This is the land,' said Leif. 'This is the New Found Land. We will stay here for the winter.' So they built wooden houses and spent the winter making a cargo of timber to take back to Greenland for use in their longships and houses.

The adventure didn't quite end there, because in the spring, when Leif set sail again for Greenland with his cargo of wood, he came upon a shipwreck and fifteen half-drowned sailors. He rescued them all and took them safely back to Greenland, where he was renamed Leif the Lucky.

Leif led the way for other sea explorers, hundreds of years later, to discover new lands and to begin the make maps of our world. But the story could have ended very differently if he hadn't chosen to go on the voyage in his father's place.

~

Dear God, help us to choose wisely when we have decisions to make. Help us to take opportunities when they are given to us. Help us to try new activities with courage. Help us to be adventurous but also to think ahead and be safe. Amen.

Two pots

Do you always do as you are told? Just as I thought! Some of you say yes and some say no!

Of course, it all depends on what you're being told to do, and who is telling you to do it. The people who care for you, like your parents and teachers, tell you what to do in order to help, guide and teach you. And because they care for you, they won't tell you to do anything that is foolish or dangerous. It's therefore a good idea, in those circumstances, to do as you are told.

But suppose someone tells you to do something that you think is not a good idea. Suppose someone tells you to climb up on the school roof and dance a jig then jump off. Or suppose someone tells you to play football in a busy road or jump into the swimming pool with all your outdoor clothes on. Or suppose someone you don't know tells you to go to their house. Then of course you're not going to do as you are told, and quite rightly so too. You will use your common sense and decide for yourself what to do.

Listen to this fable about two pots, and see what you think they should have done.

The two pots sat either side of a great gateway at the very edge of the king's garden. When they looked in one direction they could see the king's lawns and flower beds stretching up towards the palace, and when they looked the other way they could see the steps at the base of their plinth leading down into the river which flowed alongside the garden wall.

The two pots had been there, each on his own stone pillar, for as long as anyone could remember. One of them was round and fat and bulbous and made of brass which used to be shiny and golden but which was now a dull brown-green metal. It had two twirly handles near its top. The other was taller and thinner and had no handles. It was made of terracotta and used to have a lovely shiny green glaze on it with a pattern in white of a sleeping dragon. But the pattern and the glaze had long gone and the pot was now a dull green-brown clay.

The two pots had become friends over the years and spent their days talking and chatting, conversing and gossiping, since there was nothing much else they could do.

But, that was before the night of the great storm.

On that night, the wind whipped over the palace roof and scudded across the garden. It slapped against the pots and loosened the cement which secured them to their columns; it rocked and buffeted them until they were quite wobbly and in danger of falling off their pedestals. The rain joined in and beat down in torrents, raising the river level to the highest it had ever been. The water raged and tore past the king's garden wall, past the pillars with the two pots on top, until it found the steps of the gateway between the pots. And here it came into the garden.

It swirled and boiled between the pillars and climbed the steps one by one. It sucked and spattered and surged past the gateposts and raced into the garden beyond. And as the water level rose in the garden, it rose up the columns that held the pots.

'We'll drown,' the clay pot cried in the wind.

But the pots didn't drown and the wind and the rain died away. At dawn the following morning they could see the havoc that had been caused. The king's garden was completely flooded. The lawns and flower beds were under water, the river had reached the palace door, and instead of the water being at the foot of the columns the pots sat on, it was lapping up at the top. The pots in fact were sitting in water which loosened their cement even further.

'This is terrible,' wailed the clay pot. 'Whatever shall we do?'

'This is wonderful,' shouted the brass pot. 'What an adventure we can have. Come on, Clay Pot. Come with me. We can swim. We can play. Come ON!' and he pulled himself free of his last bit of cement and slid into the water.

'Come ON!' he said. 'It's fun!' and he bobbed about in the turbulent water, turning this way and that, laughing. 'Come on. Jump in.'

But the clay pot hesitated. 'It looks scary.'

'Come ON!' called the brass pot again. 'We might never get this chance again. Think about all those years when we sat on that wall with nothing to do but chatter. Now we can move about, be active, have FUN! Jump in. You know you want to.'

But still the clay pot hung back. 'I'm not sure . . . I don't think it's such a good idea . . .'

'Oh stop being such a wimp,' yelled the brass pot, as he twizzled and twirled and swivelled and swirled in the water. 'This is terrific,' and he did a dive, narrowly missing filling himself with water.

And still the clay pot dithered. 'It looks dangerous,' he muttered.

'Scaredy-pot, cowardy cowardy scaredy-pot' sang the brass pot. 'Come on in. I won't tell you again.'

So the clay pot, much against his better judgement, did as the brass pot told him to do, and slithered into the water. It was cold. Colder than he would ever have imagined. The water began to seep into the tiny cracks on his surface and he felt himself getting heavier and heavier.

'Brass Pot?' he called to his friend, but the brass pot was taking no notice, he was too busy trying out a new trick of bumping into anything and everything he could find.

'Come and do this,' he shouted to the clay pot, and he bashed into the side of the gatepost and bounced off again, making only a tiny dent in his round fat middle. 'Come on, have a go at this. It's great fun,' and he threw himself into the side of the post again.

But the clay pot suddenly saw the danger. The real danger was not only from the water itself but also from his friend Brass Pot. His metal body could withstand thumping and crashing against things; he was shatterproof, but the clay pot knew he was weak in comparison. His body was brittle and easily broken. He felt afraid of his friend.

'Come and play bumps with me,' called the brass pot, unaware of the danger to his friend; unaware that his friend was afraid. He folded his handles, pushed out his middle and thrust himself towards the clay pot.

'No! No, please,' spluttered Clay Pot as he struggled to keep his neck above water.

'Come and play!' ordered Brass Pot and he barged forward again. This time he bumped into Clay Pot . . . and smashed him into a hundred pieces. The pieces sank to the bottom of the water and only a tiny bubble of air escaped to the surface which broke with a tiny whisper of 'please, no'.

The brass pot was horrified. He hadn't intended this to happen. He only wanted to have a bit of fun. He turned and bobbed on the water. He drifted and floated downstream, then disappeared, never to be seen again. As for the clay pot, he sat on the river bed in pieces for the rest of time.

It's not a very happy ending is it? What do you think they should have done? I wonder who you think was most to blame. Was it the brass pot for telling the clay pot what to do in the first place? Or was it the clay pot for doing what he was told, and not thinking for himself?

~

Help us, Lord, to think for ourselves. Help us not just to follow others, but to use our own common sense and our own judgement, and make up our own minds what to do. Help us to think carefully before we tell other people to do something. Help us to think ahead. Amen

Theme 5

Bravery

The Pink Lady

There are many stories throughout history of people who acted bravely and heroically. Usually, those people did not set out to become courageous heroes; it often happened because they remained clear-headed when things went wrong. The heroes were usually the sort of people who kept their cool, used their brains and thought things through. They were the people who were determined not to be beaten, and we can all learn from heroes like that.

Today's true story happened just a couple of years ago, in the summer of 2005. A group of four men, all keen sailors, decided to row the 2100 miles across the Atlantic Ocean from Canada to England. They were going to attempt to break the world record for the fastest North Atlantic row. They had a boat – she was called the Pink Lady* and was sponsored by Pink Lady apples. They had an aim – they were going to try to beat the record. And they had a purpose – they were going to raise money for the British Heart Foundation. And now they were ready.

It was 30 June and the beautiful bright pink boat was bobbing in the sunshine in the harbour of St John's, Newfoundland. The crew of four men clambered on board. There wasn't much space! There was just enough room for the four of them to sit, one behind the other, to row the boat. At each end of the boat was a tiny covered area where they could take it in turns to sleep when they were not rowing, and where all their provisions were stored for the next six and a half weeks; for that was how long they thought it would take to row across the Atlantic.

---

* Further information can be found at www.gopinklady.co.uk.

With a great deal of noise and waving, clapping and shouts of 'Good luck!' they set off. Out of the harbour and into the open sea. Only 2100 miles to go and they would be home! They were all in high spirits.

They had, of course, checked the weather conditions before they set off. They had studied the maps. They had taken advice. They had looked at the long range forecast. Everything looked fine. But what neither they nor anyone else knew at that time, was that thousands of miles away to the south, in the warm tropical seas off Brazil, a tiny patch of turbulent weather was just beginning to form.

The four men made good progress. Rowing is hard work but they were making a steady progress of about 40 miles each day. For some of the time the sea currents were with them, pushing them forward in the direction of England. For most of the time the wind was behind them, pushing them east in the direction of home.

'We stand a good chance of beating the world record,' they said. 'We're in with a chance of doing it!' And they rowed on, determined to succeed.

But all the time, that expanse of turbulent weather, hundreds of miles to the south, was spinning, and growing, and moving nearer.

Day after day went by. The men were tired. They had now been rowing for over five weeks but they had covered almost 1700 miles of sea. There were just 400 miles to go. On and on they went, two or three of them always at the oars, one of them snatching a few hours sleep. But all the time, that worsening weather system grew and expanded and spread.

By 6 August the weather system had turned into a fully developed hurricane. It even had a name; Hurricane Alex. And it was heading straight for the Pink Lady.

On 7 August the hurricane struck. The winds whipped up the sea to a fury and tore at the men in the boat. They were tied by their safety lines to the boat and they hung on. Rowing was impossible in those conditions and all they could do was ride out the storm and hope they would survive. The waves rose up above them, as high as houses, lifting up the Pink Lady then throwing her down into enormous troughs. The noise of the wind and the water was terrifying and there was no escape from the stinging sea spray. The men were afraid. But the Pink Lady held firm.

Then . . . disaster. At 1.30 in the morning of 8 August a gigantic freak wave smashed down on the Pink Lady and split her in two. The four men were thrown into the sea. They struggled to keep their heads above water and to breathe. All four men believed they would drown.

But, the minute the Pink Lady broke apart, her emergency life raft hit the water and automatically inflated. The four men managed to struggle into the life raft. At least they were now out of the water even though they were saturated and bitterly cold.

And at the same time as the Pink Lady's life raft inflated, her emergency beacon was activated and it sent a satellite signal to RAF Kinloss in Scotland. The safety devices on the Pink Lady were working to help the men, even though the boat herself was broken and useless. As soon as RAF Kinloss received the satellite signal, they sent a Nimrod aircraft to search for the exact location of the damaged Pink Lady.

The Nimrod searched the heaving seas for signs of a life raft. Nothing. The raft was so small and the seas so huge that the searchers couldn't find it. Then . . . a sighting. It was the raft. Tiny and fragile, but there. The Nimrod crew signalled back to the RAF station.

'We have it. Position confirmed at 49 degrees north and 14 degrees west. Three hundred and seventy miles from the nearest land.'

The RAF station alerted the Cornish Coastguard who put out a radio signal to any shipping that might be in the area. At first there was no reply. Then, a signal from a Scandinavian Reefer – a huge refrigerated ship.

'Am in the area of the disaster,' said the skipper. 'Will go to the assistance of the men and try to pick them up.'

The Scandinavian ship changed course and followed the directions from the Nimrod, still circling overhead. At first the skipper could see nothing in the heaving waves. Then a glimpse, a brief sighting, of a tiny life raft. He edged his ship nearer, but the waves and the wind worked against him. The closer he got to the men, the further away the waves pushed the raft. It took all his skill as a skipper, learned through years and years of experience, to manoeuvre his ship close to the raft so that the men could be lifted off to safety. Once on the huge reefer, the men were safe, but were about to be rescued again, this time by the Falmouth air rescue team, who airlifted them to land where they were taken to hospital.

None of the men had suffered serious injury. All four of them were just glad to be alive, even though they'd not succeeded in beating the world record for rowing across the Atlantic. They knew they owed their lives to the Coastguard Service, to the RAF and the Nimrod crew, and to the extreme skill of the skipper and crew of the Scandinavian Reefer.

The story might have made a small article in a local newspaper, but all the time the Nimrod was circling over the Pink Lady's life raft, it was videoing the rescue. Soon, film from the Nimrod was broadcast all round the world, making headline news in every country. People were able to see for themselves the dreadful sea conditions, the tiny raft, the amazing seamanship of the Scandinavian skipper, and the rescued men.

It's difficult to know who showed the most courage and bravery. I wonder what you think. Maybe you think it was the four-man crew of the Pink Lady? Or the Nimrod crew? Or perhaps you think it was the skipper and crew of the Scandinavian ship? They certainly all showed bravery, and the story would have had a very different ending if they hadn't all worked together.

~

Let us think for a few moments of the bravery of the people involved in that story. They all worked together; they all thought clearly even though they were afraid; they all did their best; they were all determined not to be beaten but to succeed. Let us think of how we can learn from their actions.

The boy who wanted to ride a bike

All the time, every day, there are people acting bravely. Some of those brave deeds are heroic acts that could only happen once in a lifetime, like for example, the story of the Pink Lady; other acts of bravery are much smaller, more every-day, but nevertheless they show that the person involved is tough and strong and determined.

Determination can often lead to bravery, as well as success, as you can hear in today's true story.

Thomas is a boy, just like many of you. He likes all kinds of sport, he enjoys school, he's rather good at maths, he's very friendly, he's lively and fun-loving, and he can sometimes get into trouble. So you see, he's very much like many of you!

But, there is a difference. Thomas was born with a rare genetic disorder which affects his heart and his immune system. When he was only three he had to have two major heart operations and they were followed by several years of painful therapy to make his immune system work better. He spent weeks in hospital and months off school.

'He will always tire much more easily than other children,' the doctor told Mr and Mrs Hume, Thomas's parents. 'His heart is weak and has to work 50 per cent harder than anyone else's.'

When Thomas was small he used to look out of his window and see the other children playing outside, and say 'Why can't I go and play out like the others?' and his mum would try to explain about his weak heart and how he didn't have the same energy levels as everyone else. But as Thomas grew a little older, he began to think that maybe he could *train* his energy levels.

His mum spoke to the doctor about it.

'Well, it's true that he could build up his strength and his stamina,' said the doctor. 'The trouble is, he needs exercise in order to get stronger, but the exercise itself will make him tired. You could try taking him out for walks and building up his strength that way.'

'Walks!' said Thomas in disgust. 'But I want to play tennis and football. I want to go horse riding and swimming. But most of all I want to ride a bike. That's what I want. A bike!' But his mother and father looked at each other and shook their heads. He would never be strong enough to ride a bike. But Thomas had other ideas.

'Dad?' he said one day. 'Can we have a dog? If we had a dog I could take it out for walks.'

His mum said 'That's a good idea Thomas. The doctor said that walking would be good for you.' So they bought Thomas a dog. She was a beautiful Yorkshire terrier puppy. Thomas called her Molly and they soon became inseparable. Thomas took her out for walks every day, just to the corner of the street at first, then past the shops, and eventually over to the park. His tolerance to exercise grew each day.

'But I still want a bike,' he told his dad.

When the doctor saw how well Thomas was progressing and how his strength was increasing, he suggested that his parents take him swimming. Thomas loved it! Within only a few sessions he had gained his first Dolphin award, then his second, and was working towards his first full length of the pool.

'But I still want a bike,' he told his mum.

The next time Thomas had a hospital appointment one of the nurses said to his dad, 'You know, it might be good for Thomas to go horse riding. He's a lot stronger than he used to be, and horse riding would build up his stamina even more.'

'Can I, Dad?' said Thomas. 'But I still want a bike!'

So Thomas went horse riding and was soon doing it really well. He progressed from just sitting in the saddle and being led around by a trainer, to being able to ride properly himself. And with every activity he took part in, he was getting stronger.

Then, Thomas saw an advert in the local paper for the council's cycle training scheme. This was just what he'd been waiting for.

'Can I go, Mum? Can I? Oh go on, let me go. I know I can do it.'

And his mum said yes.

After just five lessons Thomas was cycling on his own. No stabilisers. No helpers holding on to the saddle.

'He's brilliant,' said one of the trainers. 'Thomas should be proud of what he's achieved. Cycling is a wonderful way for people to improve their fitness levels, and it's good for the environment.'

'Well, it's been an ambition of his for a long time, to ride a bike,' said Thomas's mum. 'He's been determined to do it ever since he was small.'

'I think he's just the sort of boy we could do with for our poster campaign,' said the trainer. 'He can advertise our council scheme to encourage youngsters to get on their bikes for our summer programme of children's cycle training.'

'How about it, Thomas? Do you fancy being the star of our poster campaign and having your photo on all our posters?'

'Cool!' said Thomas. 'As long as I can keep on riding my bike.'

So Thomas became a poster child for the local council. Later in the summer he had to go back to hospital for further surgery, this time to repair a leaking valve in his heart.

'But he should make a good recovery,' said the doctor. 'He's certainly fitter and stronger than he was last time he came to me for surgery. And it's all down to him. He's a brave and determined lad.'

Thomas might not have beaten any world records with his sporting activities, but for a boy with the problems he had, he did well. It would have been so easy for him to sit back and say to everyone, 'Well I can't do that, because I'm not strong enough.' But he didn't say that. He showed bravery and determination in trying to overcome his problems. And his bravery and determination made him succeed.

~

Help us, Lord, to do our best in everything we do. Help us not to give up easily, but to try as hard as we can. Help us to face difficulties with courage and determination, and to know that courage and determination can help us to succeed. Help us to remember that we won't succeed if we don't try. Amen

Sherpa Tenzing and the Everest expedition

Often, we read in the newspapers of someone doing a brave and heroic act. For example, there was recently a fireman who rescued someone from a burning building and saved their life. Or there was the case of the policewoman who climbed up some really dangerous and unsafe scaffolding to rescue a small child who'd climbed up there and got stuck. And then there was the cave rescue team who spent days in difficult conditions getting people out of an underground cave when the water levels rose and cut off their escape route.

Reading their stories, I've noticed that they all have something in common. The rescuers were all very modest afterwards, and they all said that they were not really brave, but that they were just 'doing their job'. Of course, they were 'doing their job' but they added something to it. They added something that we call 'above and beyond the call of duty'; they added something extra special, some extra courage, some extra bravery, because they were determined to help whoever it was in difficulty.

You may already know of the famous Mount Everest Expedition in 1953*, when Edmund Hillary and Tenzing Norgay became the first people ever to climb to the top of the world's highest mountain. But you may not know this story of something that happened whilst they were still building the base camps.

It was the spring of 1953 when the expedition arrived in Nepal to try to be the first to reach the top of the world's highest mountain – Mount Everest.

But before the climbers could begin their attempt, the first camp had to be set up at the starting point of the climb. Three hundred and fifty sherpas, led by Tenzing Norgay, helped to carry tons and tons of equipment – tents, food, clothing, ropes, axes, even lightweight ladders – up to Camp 1. The sherpas were people from the countries of Nepal and Tibet, who lived on the foothills of the Himalayan Mountains. They knew the mountains and were used to the harsh conditions of snow and ice.

Once Camp 1 was set up, the climbers and some of the sherpas had to set up eight further camps, each one closer to the summit of the mountain. And to do this they had to find a safe route through the dangerous and unstable rocks and ice.

On 25 April, Edmund Hillary, Tenzing Norgay and three other climbers roped themselves together and set off from Camp 1 to find a route across the

---

* Further information can be found at http://teacher.scholastic.com/activities/hillary.

Khumbu Glacier; a river of very slowly moving ice. The movement of the glacier makes the ice break and fracture, and forms enormous blocks and splinters and spikes of ice. It creates huge deep fissures, cracks and crevasses.

They began to climb the glacier.

It was slow going. They painstakingly cut steps in the ice with their ice axes and gripped each step with their crampons – the needle-sharp steel spikes fastened to their boots.

Soon, they came to their first crevasse. It stretched wide, eerie and deep, down, down into the depths of the glacier. They looked at each other and knew what to do. They changed direction and followed the deep dark crevasse until they found a place where the ice had formed across it. An ice bridge! But it was fragile and brittle. Would it hold them?

Edmund Hillary tested it for strength. He lengthened the rope between him and Tenzing Norgay and carefully edged his way across the ice bridge. It held. The others followed, one by one, until they were all safely across. Success! They clapped each other on the back and cheered.

They continued up the glacier, metre by metre, hour by hour, cutting more steps in the ice, slowly, slowly making progress. Then . . . another crevasse. This time a massive one, and even worse, one with no ice bridge. They searched and searched, using up precious time and energy, but no bridge.

'Then we'll have to make a bridge,' said Hillary.

'I think it's too wide,' said one of the others.

'We'll try,' said Hillary.

Three of the men were carrying sections of aluminium ladders in their huge backpacks, and they unpacked them and fastened them together, sure that they wouldn't be long enough. They secure one end of the ladder to one side of the crevasse and pushed the other sections out over the wide abyss. Surely they wouldn't reach that far! But, with only 30 centimetres to spare, the ladders spanned the crevasse. The climbers crawled, one by one, across the fragile metal bridge.

At the other side they cheered and shouted. This was a huge success. And the success gave them confidence. In fact, Edmund Hillary felt *over*-confident.

'If we can do that, we can do anything,' he declared. And they set off again.

In no time at all they reached another crevasse in the ice, but this was a small fissure in comparison with the last huge crevasse.

'It's small enough to *jump* across,' said Hillary.

'Don't be stupid. Don't be foolhardy. Let's look for an ice bridge,' said one of the others.

But Edmund Hillary was still feeling the confident glow of the last successfully crossed crevasse. This one was *tiny* compared with that. This one would be a doddle! And he jumped.

He leapt clearly over the yawning gap and landed heavily on the other side, laughing and feeling exhilarated. But his laughter stopped abruptly when he heard the loud CRACK of splintering ice and felt himself plunging into the depths of the glacier. He saw the broken block of ice he'd landed on, fall and shatter at the bottom of the crevasse. Hillary knew that he had to stop his fall or he, too, would crash to the bottom and be killed and, worse, he would pull Tenzing Norgay with him as they were still roped together.

In the split second it took to think, Hillary slammed his feet against the side of the crevasse and the spikes of his crampons dug into the ice wall. He braced his shoulder against the other wall. The pain was incredible but he had stopped his fall.

And in the same split second, Tenzing Norgay realised that Hillary could plunge to the bottom of the crevasse; could pull him, Tenzing, with him, and could kill them both. He quickly pulled his ice axe out of his belt, and jammed it into the ice at the top of the crevasse. He grabbed the rope and secured it round the handle of the axe.

Then he looked down the crevasse.

Hillary was stuck fast, half way down. There was no way he could climb out on his own. But, he was alive.

Tenzing began to pull on the rope. Slowly, slowly, inch by inch, he pulled up the rope, telling Hillary to 'walk' up the sides of the ice wall. Slowly, slowly, inch by inch the rope shortened. At last Hillary reached the top.

'Thank you, my friend,' he said. 'I'm sorry. I shouldn't have done that, I could have killed us both. I'm sorry. But thank you. Without your brave action, we might both be dead.'

Tenzing grinned at him. 'All in a day's work!' he said.

Afterwards, when that story became known, and when Edmund Hillary and Tenzing Norgay had successfully climbed to the top of Mount Everest, everyone said how brave and courageous they were. Tenzing, however, was always very modest about his part in the achievement. He always said he was simply doing his job. He was a sherpa, he said, and it was the job of the sherpas to support the expedition. And that, he said, was what he'd done. Because it was his job.

I wonder what you think. I wonder if you think he had that extra something 'above and beyond the call of duty' that made him extra brave and courageous? I know I do.

~

Let's think for a moment or two, about the courage of Tenzing Norgay and Edmund Hillary. They were courageous because they accepted the challenge of Mount Everest in the first place. They were brave in the way they tackled difficulties and obstacles. Tenzing showed bravery in his quick thinking, and fast action.

Let's think about ways in which we can do things to the best of our ability. Let's try to follow Tenzing's example by trying to do a bit extra on top of what is expected of us.

Theme 6

Bullying

Arion and the dolphin

Bullying is unpleasant. The people who bully and the people who are bullied both end up unhappy if nothing is done about it. But, as you know, we have a policy against bullying in our school, like all other schools, and we work hard to deal with bullying when it happens. The important thing is to tell someone if you are being bullied, or if you know that someone else is being bullied. Then, the person being bullied can be helped, and the person doing the bullying can also be given help to deal with their problem and to help them to stop.

The sad thing about bullying is that it has happened for as long as people have lived here on the earth. Today's story is from the time of the Ancient Greeks, who lived almost 3000 years ago.

Arion was a brilliant songwriter and a musician. In fact he was so good at composing songs and making music that the king of Corinth, King Periander, gave him a job in the palace as royal musician.

But Arion, despite being so talented and gifted, was a shy and quiet young man. He spent much time entertaining the king and courtiers and guests with his music, but his favourite time was when he was on his own, perhaps outside in the countryside, making up songs and poems and putting them to music which he played on his harp. It was said that his singing and playing was so good that even the birds and wild animals stopped what they were doing to listen to Arion's music.

One day, news came to Corinth that there was to be a music festival over the sea on the island of Sicily, and everyone said to the king, 'You must send Arion. He is such a wonderful musician that he's bound to win.'

But the king said, 'I don't want him to go. I shall miss his music too much whilst he's away.'

'You must let him go,' said the king's advisers. 'Just think of the honour! Just think of the glory that *you* will have. After all, you are his king. It is you who has encouraged him, nurtured him, employed him. You must send him to the festival.'

So, reluctantly, the king gave his permission for Arion to go to the music festival and take part in the competitions. And, of course, Arion won *all* the prizes. He was awarded with gifts and gold coins, cups and trophies and medals. He won so many prizes that people had to help him back to the ship with them all when it was time to go home.

The sailors started to grumble about him. 'Who does he think he is? Coming on board our ship with his medals and trophies. He's a stuck-up little twerp,' they said. 'Just look at him! Sitting there playing that harp!' And they started to bully him.

At first they just hid a few of his things, and tied his blankets in knots. Then they tipped him out of his hammock and kicked him when he fell on the deck.

Then they threatened him. One of the sailors held a knife to his throat and said they were going to kill him.

'Don't hurt me,' pleaded Arion. 'You can have all my money, my medals and trophies, but please let me go.'

'We'll let you go all right!' laughed the sailor. 'We'll let you go right to the bottom of the sea,' and they held the quivering Arion over the edge of the ship's rail.

'Let me go,' cried Arion. 'I'll give you anything you want when we get back to land.'

'Oh yes, you say that *now*, but you'll change your mind when you get back home, and no doubt tell the king.' And they dangled him over the waves.

'Plea . . . . . se,' said Arion, but his voice died away as he fell in the water and disappeared under the foam.

'And that's the last of *him*,' gloated the sailors as they went away to steal all Arion's things.

Arion sank beneath the sea and used up his last breath of air. Then, in a flurry of foam and a burst of bubbles something pushed underneath him. It hoisted him up and propelled him forward, up, rising towards the surface, pushing him towards the air, the beautiful clear clean *breathable* air. They broke the surface together, Arion and the dolphin that had saved him.

'But why . . .?' asked Arion. 'How . . .?'

'I've listened to your music,' said the dolphin. 'This is to repay you. It's the least I can do. Now! Next stop – Corinth!' and he swan with Arion on his back all the way to the harbour and the king, who was standing on the jetty waiting for Arion's ship to come home.

King Periander was overjoyed to see him and listened carefully to the whole story that Arion and the dolphin told him of the bullying sailors and the dramatic rescue.

Three days later, when the ship came into port, the king sent for the captain and the crew.

'Where is he?' he demanded. 'Where's Arion?'

'Oh, I'm sorry, Sir,' said the sailors, smiling at each other with lies in their eyes. 'Arion had such a good time in Sicily at the music festival that he decided to stay. He wouldn't come back with us no matter how much we tried to persuade him.'

'Is that so?' said the king.

'Oh yes, Sir,' they answered. 'We wanted him to come back, but he wouldn't. We *pleaded* with him to come, because we knew how much you'd want to see him, with all his medals and that, but he just kept saying no. There was nothing else we could do. Sir.'

'Then how do explain *this*?' asked the king as he opened a door and ushered Arion into the room. The sailors stood there, dumbfounded. 'I . . . that is . . . we . . . well, we . . .' they stammered, but of course, they had no explanation other than the truth.

'You are bullies!' said the king. 'And bullies will be punished in my kingdom!'

And that's exactly what he did!

The story doesn't tell us what the punishment was. I wonder what you think it should have been. The story, however, because it's so old, does tell us that bullying was around even 3000 years ago. What a dreadful thing! Three thousand years of bullying! I wonder why no one has stopped it before now.

But we are in a fortunate position. We know what a ridiculous thing bullying is. It doesn't make the victim or the bully feel good. We can put a stop to bullying by making sure that we tell someone of any bullying, and then the problem can be dealt with.

~

Let's spend a few moments thinking about playing our part in making our school a no-bullying school. Let's make sure we tell a responsible adult if we know of any bullying going on. Let's ensure that we respect each other's differences as well as our similarities. Let's ensure that everyone in our school feels valued and important. Let's be tolerant towards each other.

The biggest bully

Today's story is a traditional fable from China. It's about bullying, but there's a rather interesting twist at the end of the tale.

Xiang Zhou (pronounced *Shiang Jhoe*, with a soft *J*) was a bully. He was bigger and stronger than all the other people in his village and he terrorised them. He enjoyed nothing better than throwing his weight around and making other people look small and inadequate. He frightened the children, poked fun at the old folk, laughed at the ones who were ill or disabled. He got what he wanted by shouting and yelling and never took no for an answer. And if ever anyone was brave enough to stand up to him, Xiang Zhou would fight them. The trouble was, he always won!

One day, when Xiang Zhou had bullied the shopkeeper into giving him an enormous bag of sweets, the shopkeeper's wife said, 'Something has got to be done! This cannot go on. We've foolishly put up with all this for far too long.'

'There's nothing we can do,' said her husband. 'He's too big, too strong, too much of a bully. If we try to do something, he'll only get worse.'

'Rubbish!' said his wife, and she went to see the wise woman of the woods.

'A bully, you say?' said the wise woman. 'I'll come to the village and meet him for myself.' So she did.

The next day, Xiang Zhou was in the sweet shop again. His tactics of the previous day had worked, so now he was trying them out again, this time to get some chocolate.

'If you don't give me some, I'll smash up your shop,' he shouted to the shopkeeper.

The shopkeeper hesitated and Xiang Zhou banged his fist down onto the counter, making all the bottles and jars rattle and shake. Just then, the small, frail and wrinkled wise woman of the woods came in to the shop. She prodded Xiang Zhou with her stick.

'Young man!' she said, peering up at him through short-sighted eyes. 'You might be able to help me!'

Xiang Zhou spun round and looked down at her in astonishment. 'Help *you*,' he said.

'Yes! I need someone fearless and strong, like you, to help me deal with a couple of bully beasts up the mountain! Can you do it?'

'Sure can!' said Xiang Zhou. 'If it's fighting you want, I'm your man!'

'Come on then,' she said, and they set off together for the mountain.

'Now,' said the little wise woman, 'there's a bully-boy dragon living up there in that cave. He's fierce and he's dangerous and I want him dead! Can you do it?'

Xiang Zhou leapt up the mountain. He found the dragon sharpening his teeth on some juicy bits of bone in front of a roaring fire. Xiang Zhou hurled his axe but it bounced off the dragon's thick skin. He fired a quiverful of arrows but they danced like pins off the dragon's back. So he threw himself at the dragon, grabbed it by the jaws, grappled it to the ground and strangled it with his bare hands. He swung the dead dragon over his shoulder and carried it down to the tiny wise woman of the woods.

'Well done,' she said. 'Now! There's a bully-girl sea monster living down there in that lake. She's fierce and she's dangerous and I want her dead! Can you do it?'

Xiang Zhou leapt down the mountain and swam across the lake. When he got to the middle he found the spiky-backed sea monster thrashing the surface of the lake until the water churned like a boiling cauldron. Xiang Zhou hurled his axe but it bounced off the monster's slimy skin. He fired a quiverful of arrows but they danced like pins off the scales of the monster's back. So he threw himself at the monster, darted underneath it, found its soft yellow underbelly and stabbed it with his knife. He dragged the dead sea monster to the edge of the lake, hoisted it over his shoulder and carried it back to the wizened little woman of the woods.

'Well done!' she said. 'Now! There's just one more. I want you to conquer the fiercest and biggest bully of them all!'

'Tell me where it is!' shouted Xiang Zhou, brandishing his axe. 'Tell me where to find it. I'll stop it in its tracks and kill it DEAD!' and he rattled his quiver full of arrows in front of the wise old woman of the woods.

'It's here,' said the little old woman. 'The biggest bully of them all is standing here, right in front of me.'

Xiang Zhou looked round. There was no one there. The only person standing right in front of the wise woman of the woods was himself. Xiang Zhou. The biggest bully of them all.

He stared at the woman. He almost felt like bullying her. He began to puff himself up with his usual bluster, then, like a balloon losing its air, he shrank back to his normal size. He felt embarrassed and ashamed. He felt humbled and disgraced. He felt red-faced and sheepish and small.

'You see,' said the old woman, 'No one likes a bully, and because no one likes them, they have no friends. That's what you need – a friend. And so do I. So how about it, amigo?'

And that's how the little wise woman of the woods and the big strong

Xiang Zhou became the best of friends for the rest of their lives. And the strange thing was that as soon as Xiang Zhou stopped being a bully, he found he made other friends as well.

Maybe Xiang Zhou didn't realise he was being a bully, although I do find that hard to believe. I think the old woman was right and that Xiang Zhou needed a friend. I think his bullying behaviour was because he couldn't get attention any other way, so he decided to get it by being horrible to people. The trouble is, that being horrible doesn't work; it certainly doesn't get you friends. I think everyone here knows that to have a friend you need to be a friend. And no one wants to be friends with a bully.

~

Dear God, help us to remember that in order to have a friend we need to be a friend. Help us to be friendly to each other. Help us to be friendly and helpful to new people in our school and neighbourhood. Help us to act in a friendly and responsible way towards people who are younger than us, or who need to be cared for. Amen

A famous author

Bullying, as I'm sure you know, doesn't always mean physically hurting someone; it doesn't always involve physical injury. Bullying can be extreme teasing, or name-calling; it can be not letting someone join in, or constantly picking on someone. Bullying is always unpleasant and hurtful, which is why we in school always take it so seriously.

If someone is being bullied, one of the best ways of making it stop, apart of course from telling a responsible adult, is to try not to let the bully see that their behaviour is having any effect. That way, the bully no longer has any power, and if they have no power there's no point in them doing the bullying. But, trying to ignore hurtful behaviour is very difficult. Even more difficult is trying to turn the unpleasant experience of being bullied into something positive. That's very difficult to do, though not impossible.

The person in today's true story had to put up with some very unpleasant behaviour from adults and children, but she used those experiences to help her. In fact she turned them to her advantage.

Maybe you can guess, as the story goes on, who it's about. You already know that it's someone female.

She started school when she was five, and although she was rather quiet and shy she quickly settled in and made friends. School was fun! She learned to read, which she liked, and to write, which she liked even more. She was very good at making up stories and she used to make up games to play with her friend, Ian Potter.

When she was nine, the girl's family moved house and she was sent to a different school. Her teacher at the new school was very different from the old one. This teacher was extremely stern and strict and everyone in the class was scared of her. The girl was so nervous most of the time that she never seemed to do anything right.

One day, the teacher decided she was going to reorganise the classroom. She would sort the children out into those who were clever and able, and those who were not. Then, she would put the clever children in one half of the room and the not-so-clever ones in the other half. And to help her to decide which part of the room each child should sit in, she set the class a test.

But, unfortunately, the teacher did not explain the test very well, and the girl didn't understand what she had to do. She put up her hand to ask but was told to sit still and be quiet. When the test papers were marked later that day, the girl had scored no marks at all. She was put with the other children who had not done well.

After school that day, the girl made up a story about a magic hat; she called it the 'sorting hat'.

The girl, despite being not so happy in her new class, worked hard and tried to do her best, and eventually the teacher realised that she had put her in the wrong section of the room, and she moved her.

'You're a bright girl, after all!' she said.

Two years later, when the girl was 11, she moved school again, but this time to the local comprehensive high school, and this time with all the other children in her class. She was still rather quiet and shy but she liked her new school and quickly settled in.

'What's your favourite subject,' a dinner lady asked her one day.

'English,' said the girl, without any hesitation. 'I'm going to be a writer,' she added.

The girl continued to work hard at school, but, oddly, this started to cause some problems for her. There was a group of girls at the school who were not interested in working hard, or doing their best, or making progress; they were only interested in messing about and laughing and giggling together. But even worse, they didn't want anyone else to work hard or do their best either. They used to pick on the more serious students and call them names.

'Swot!'

'Teacher's pet!'

'Boring brain-box!' they used to shout.

The girl tried not answering questions in class, so that the other girls wouldn't pick on her, but it was hard *not* to give the right answers, especially in English which she was good at. It wasn't however, quite so difficult in science. She felt she wasn't very good at science, so when the teacher asked her something, it was easy (and truthful!) to say 'I don't know'.

One day the bullies were picking on her again.

'Goody two-shoes,' they shouted. And this time she retaliated. She suddenly turned and started fighting with the girl who'd called her names, even though the bully was much bigger and taller than her. Of course, she got into terrible trouble; fighting was not allowed in school. But at least the bully didn't pick on her for the rest of that week.

After school that day the girl made up a story. In it she had a science teacher making up magic spells and potions, and a small boy being unable to answer his questions.

The girl continued to do well at school, despite the pupils who didn't want to learn. She passed her exams at 16 and achieved her A levels when she was 18. Then it was time to go to university. She worked hard and got her degree. She got a job. But all the time she still dreamed of becoming a writer, and she still wrote stories in her spare time, just as she had done at school.

One day she was sitting on a train from Manchester when she quite suddenly had an idea for a new story. It would be about magic. It would be about a boy who got a place at a school of witchcraft and wizardry. The characters for the story came tumbling into her imagination. The boy – he would be named after her childhood friend, Ian Potter. The school – it could be old fashioned and dark like the primary school she went to when she was nine. She would call it . . . Hogwarts. The teacher of spells and potions – well, he would have to be based on her science teacher at high school. And so it went on. As the view from the train window sped past her, the story and characters flew into her mind.

By the time she got home, the ideas were teeming in her brain. She grabbed a notebook and wrote down all the ideas in her head. And that notebook became the very beginning of the . . .? Yes, you've guessed it. The Harry Potter books. That notebook formed the foundation of *Harry Potter and the Philosopher's Stone*. And the girl in the story . . .? Yes, of course, she's J.K. Rowling.

And J.K. Rowling is a brilliant and gifted story-teller. But, like many writers, she uses things that have happened in real life and changes them to fiction, to fit in with the story.

J.K. Rowling didn't have an easy time of it when she wrote the first Harry Potter books. But she used many of her experiences to her advantage. She may not even agree that the behaviour of the strict teacher in her primary school, and the behaviour of those girls at her high school, was actually bullying. (I wonder what you think.) But those experiences cannot have been pleasant, and they can't have been easy for the young Joanne to deal with.

~

Let's think for a moment of being kind and helpful to the people in our school and our neighbourhood. Let's think of ways we can be helpful and friendly. Let's concentrate on making sure that we don't allow any bullying behaviour of any kind.

Theme 7

Doing your best

Guitar man

I wonder how many times you've had people tell you to 'do your best'. Hundreds, I imagine! The people who look after you at home, and your teachers and helpers here in school, not me mention me, are always telling you to do your best.

We not only ask you to do your best, we also ask you to work hard, at whatever you're doing, because it's by hard work that we make progress. When I was little, if my mum found me playing around when I should have been doing my homework, she'd say, 'You won't do well if you waste your time!' Or, if I was daydreaming when I should have been doing my piano practice she'd say, 'You won't learn to play the piano by looking at it!' And she was right! To succeed, we all have to work hard. When you think of the people who are successful at something, like famous footballers, or tennis players, or dancers, or singers; or the people who are really successful in their jobs and professions; they all have something in common; they have all worked extremely hard at what-ever it is they do.

The person in today's story thought he could still succeed, even if he didn't work hard. See what you think about him!

His name was Bradley, and he was a fisherman like his father before him, and his grandfather before that. His father and grandfather both loved their job. They liked the sheer hard work of going out to sea; of dealing with the boats and the nets and the weather. The liked the challenge of catching fish, the exhilaration of full nets, and the work involved in getting the fish ready for market.

Bradley, however, had a problem. He didn't like hard work.

Oh, he liked the wages that fishing brought him! But he didn't like the work. Especially the hard work.

What he did like, was playing his guitar. Whenever he had any spare time, which wasn't very often, he would go to his bedroom and pretend to be a famous pop star. He'd even got himself a name. He would call himself Brad, and his boy band would be The Barnacles. Brad and The Barnacles. Yes, he liked the sound of that.

He would stand in his room and play that guitar for all he was worth. And actually, he was quite good at it. Unfortunately, almost every time he started to practise, someone would want him.

'Bradley? Come down here and help mend these nets.'

'Bradley? Where are you? Come and salt these fish.'

'Bradley? Come and hose the decks.'

'Bradley? Where are you? It's time for work!'

It was always work! work! work!

Sometimes when he was down by the sea and didn't have his guitar, he would play an imaginary guitar.

'Look at Bradley,' the other fishermen would say. 'He's at it again. He doesn't half fancy himself as a pop star.'

'But he *is* quite good, isn't he,' someone said, one day.

'He ought to be! He gets enough practice,' grumbled his father.

'Yes, he *is* quite good!' agreed the fishermen. And Bradley overheard.

'Yes, I *am* quite good!' he thought.

One day, just after that, Bradley was down by the edge of the sea, standing on a huge rock, playing air guitar. He pretended the rocks behind him were his boy band, the Barnacles. He imagined the surging sea in front of him was his adoring audience, screaming and shouting at him for more. He strutted and strummed and posed and played. And of course, he was very very good.

Suddenly he had an idea.

'I *do* play well,' he thought. 'Everyone *knows* I do. They said so. So, suppose I play my guitar here by the sea. Suppose I play to the fish. They'll hear how good I am and they'll swim closer to listen. If I spread a few nets over the sand, and stand at the far side of them, the fish will jump into the nets in their eagerness to get nearer to me to hear my music! They'll put *themselves* into my nets and I won't have to do any work. Brilliant! I can be a fisherman without doing any fishing! All I have to do is play my guitar, which is what I like doing anyway, so it won't seem like work. I don't know why I haven't thought of it before. It's a wonderful plan!'

So, early next morning before the sun was up, Bradley went down to the sea with a few fishing nets and his guitar. He spread the nets on the sand, found a good solid rock to stand on, and started to play. The music was good.

He played whilst the sun came up over the horizon.

He played as the tide went out and uncovered pebbles and rock pools shimmering in the light.

He played as the sun climbed to the highest part of the sky.

He played as the tide washed in and lapped against the base of the rock he stood on.

He played as the sun dipped down in the west and turned the sea crimson, vermillion and orange.

And he played as the moon rose and painted the sea silver and black.

And not one single fish jumped out of the sea and into his nets on the sand.

'Oh, well,' he thought. 'They must all be somewhere else. They'll come tomorrow. Tomorrow will be a better day and they'll throw themselves into my nets.'

But of course, the next day was exactly the same, and the next, and the one after that. Bradley did not coax a single fish out of the sea and into his nets.

'You're a fool, Bradley,' said the fishermen. 'You can't catch fish if you don't go fishing!'

'Yes, I can!' said Bradley. 'The fish are just not here in this part of the sea at the moment. They'll come. Just you watch!'

The fishermen watched and waited, and Bradley spent the best part of a month playing his guitar to the sea. And, not one single fish jumped out of the sea and into his nets on the sand.

Eventually, Bradley's father insisted he go back to work on the boat.

They sailed out to the open sea and lowered the nets. Then they drifted with the ocean currents, all the time working on deck; checking the nets, working the sails, preparing fish boxes, checking navigation, cleaning equipment, working, working, all the time.

After several hours of hard work, Bradley's father said, 'Now, pull in the nets,' and Bradley started to haul in the huge heavy fishing nets.

'Hey! Look!' he shouted, astonished. 'They're *full*!'

'Of course they're full, Bradley,' said his father. 'They're full because of our hard work. They're full because we used our skills as fishermen. We succeeded because we *worked*!'

And at last Bradley understood that hard work brings rewards. To succeed we have to work, not play.

I wonder what you think of that fable. You may not agree with it. You may think that Bradley ought to have worked hard at being a musician, since that was what he wanted to be. He clearly wasn't very keen on being a fisherman. But I wonder if you agree with the moral of the story – the message it's trying to tell us – that in order to do anything worthwhile, we have to work at it.

~

Let's think for a few moments about doing our best in the work we're going to do today. Let's think of the work and activities we have on our timetable for this morning and this afternoon, and think of how we are going to do them. What sort of attitude are we going to have? How hard are we going to work? How much effort are we going to put in? Let's remember that in life, it's generally true that we get out what we put in! In other words, if we put a lot of effort in to something, we are likely to get a lot of reward and satisfaction back.

The new boy

Those of you who are in the cubs will know that the cub promise and law both say that cubs will always do their best. Do you think doing your best is always easy? I don't. There are times when it's quite difficult to do your best. I'm think-ing of those times when things are not running as smoothly as they might, or when we're feeling a bit out of sorts with everyone, or when everything seems to be going wrong. We all have times like that and it's hard then to be upbeat and cheerful and to do our best. But, if we can persevere, and continue to do the best we can, then things usually work out in the end.

In today's story, someone was having a difficult time of it, and doing his best was the last thing on his mind.

George was not pleased!

He and his dad had just moved from the house where they used to live in the town, to the village where his dad had a new job as estate manager at a big country house. George had just started at the village school, but he missed his old friends, his old school and his old way of life. He didn't know anyone and didn't much feel like going out of his way to get to know anybody.

'You need some new friends,' said his dad. 'I know, you can join the cubs, you'll make new friends there.'

'Cubs!' said George, scornfully. 'I'm not joining them!'

'It'll be good for you,' said his dad. 'It's good fun in the cubs and scouts. You'll soon make friends and you'll do all kinds of activities. I had a brilliant time in the scouts when I was only just a bit older than you are now.'

'I don't want to,' muttered George, but his dad insisted, and the following Thursday they went to enrol George in the local cub pack.

'Well? How did it go?' asked his dad when he went to collect him at the end of the evening.

George was not pleased!

'It was 'orrible!' he grumbled. 'They've got *girls* in the cubs! You never told me they'd have *girls*! And one of them can't even walk properly. She's got this chair thing so she shouldn't even *be* there!'

George's dad was just about to tell him off about being unkind, when Akela – the cub scout leader – interrupted.

'You're right George,' she said. 'We do have girls in our cubs. It's because there's no Brownie pack for them in the village, so we have girl cubs as well as boy cubs here. We have six girls altogether and fourteen boys. And you're right about Sarah, too. Sarah can't walk easily, so she needs a wheelchair some of the time. But, you're wrong about how she shouldn't be here! Sarah has as much right as anyone else to join in and be accepted. In fact, she's a great asset to our cub pack because there are some things she's very good at.'

George muttered 'sorry', but he didn't say anything else because he wasn't convinced. How could a girl, and a girl in a wheelchair at that, be good at things the cubs did? He didn't believe it. And he wasn't pleased.

George continued going to the cub meetings for the next few weeks, not because he enjoyed going, but because his dad said he must. 'You'll soon settle in,' he said.

But George didn't feel as though he was settling in at all. He didn't make any friends, mainly because although the other children were friendly to him, he wasn't friendly back. He didn't join in the games and activities unless he was made to, and he continued to be quite rude to people, especially to Sarah, and especially when she was using her wheelchair.

Akela was beginning to lose patience with him. 'The other children are doing their best to be welcoming, George, but you have to do your best to meet them half way, you know.' But George was unrepentant and unresponsive. He was also unhappy. He didn't want to be here. He didn't want to be part of the pack, or the village, or the village school. He wanted his old school back, his old friends, his old life in the town.

But George brightened up a little at Akela's next comment. 'We're having a bus to take us to the swimming baths next Saturday, George. Would you like to come?

'Nearly everyone's put their name down.' And George said yes, although at that stage neither he nor Akela knew just how things were going to change on that Saturday!

The bus arrived at the village hall at 9.30a.m. and everyone clambered on. George was dismayed to see Sarah there as well, being helped up the steps by her mum and Akela.

'Don't see why *she* has to come,' he said to himself. 'We'll all have to wait for her, and she'll just be a nuisance to everyone,' and he barged into her with his sports bag as he walked past her seat. But, when they got to the baths, he forget all about Sarah in his excitement of getting changed and getting in to the water. He liked swimming. He used to go to the baths every week at his old school and he'd been awarded his 10 metre certificate just before he left.

Akela put the children into groups. She asked George if he could swim and he proudly told her about his 10 metres. She told him to join the beginners group in the shallow end of the pool.

'But I don't want to go with the beginners,' he complained. 'I can swim. I've got my 10 metres!'

'Well, we'll just start you off in that group,' said Akela, and she went to supervise the top group, leaving George with the swimming instructor.

The children were all told to get into the water, to hold on to the bar, and to practise their leg kicks for breast stoke.

'I'm not doing that,' muttered George, and as soon as the instructor wasn't looking, he edged away from the shallow end into the middle of the pool where the intermediate children were swimming.

At first, wading into the deeper water was easy, but just as the water was up to George's shoulders, someone bumped into him and knocked him off his feet. George disappeared under the water and then bobbed up again, spluttering and coughing. He frantically moved his arms and legs and tried to swim. This wasn't a bit like swimming his 10 metres in the shallow end. This was scary and frightening and all too real. His head went under again; his eyes filled with water and the sound of it rushed in his ears. George thrashed the water with his arms and tried to swim faster but the faster he swam the slower he went and the more tired he got. He tried to shout but the water filled his mouth and he coughed and spluttered again.

Then suddenly, he felt something at his side. Someone was there. They got hold of the back of his head and started to tow him along. They told him to be still and to stop struggling. They swam strongly, holding his head above the water, all the way to the edge of the pool where other hands caught hold of him and pulled him out, laid him down on the poolside and let him cough the water out of his mouth.

He heard voices saying, 'Well done, Sarah. What a good job you saw him. What a good thing that you're a strong swimmer; that you know how to do lifesaving; that you could rescue George.' And he turned to look at the person who'd saved him. Sarah. The girl who was not very good at walking, but who was the best swimmer in the cubs and the school and the village.

'Thank you, Sarah,' he said.

'It's all right,' said Sarah. 'I just did my best. It's what cub scouts do. You should try it sometime!' she added, with a grin.

'I will,' said George, in an ashamed sort of voice. 'I'm sorry! I'll do my best from now on.'

I think George learned several important things that Saturday, and I'm sure you could tell me what they were. Doing your best doesn't just apply to work and school and games and sports; it applies to everything *that you do all day long. No one can ask you to do more than your best, and it makes you feel good to know that you've done the very best you can.*

~

Dear God, please help us to do our best in everything we do, every day. Help us to give our best to our families, our friendships, our work. Help us to do everything to the best of our ability, and to take pride in doing things well. Amen

The footballer — we work hard

As you know, your parents and carers and teachers all expect you to do your best all the time. And as you also know, doing your best every single minute of every single day is not easy. But, if we want to succeed, if we want to do well, it's what we all have to do. Of course, if we have a definite aim, something we really want, then that determination can help us to do our best to work hard and to succeed.

The person in today's story had a great deal of determination, right from being very small. He was determined to do his best to reach his goal, and he never stopped doing his best until he reached it. In fact, he's still doing his best even now, at what he's involved in.

It's a true story, but I'm not going to tell you the real name of the person in it until the end. By then I'm sure you'll have worked out for yourself who it is.

The boy (he needs a name so I'm going to call him Robert) was born in the East End of London in 1975. His parents were not wealthy, but that didn't concern Robert, because the thing he enjoyed doing most, actually cost no money at all. He liked to go with his dad to the park and play football.

The very first time they went was when Robert was only about two and a half. He was just big enough to run about and kick the ball. He loved it!

'I'm a footballer!' he shouted.

'Right!' laughed his dad.

They started going to the park every week, and the more he played the more Robert loved the game. He grew a bit bigger, a bit older, and he said, 'I really *am* going to be a footballer when I grow up. *And*, I'm going to play for Manchester United.'

'We'll see,' said his dad, and they carried on, week in , week out, going to the park to practise. And at every practice session, Robert did his best to improve his ball skills and playing skills; and at every session Robert dreamed of one day playing for Manchester United.

When Robert went to junior school he joined a local team called the Ridgeway Rovers, and it was there that a talent scout saw him play one day and spotted his talent and potential. The scout told some of the big London football clubs about him and the next thing that Robert knew was that the Youth Academy were talking to his dad about signing him up.

'It's brilliant news!' said his dad. 'You're only 11 and Tottenham Hotspur want you in their youth team.'

'Yeah, but it's not Man U is it!' said Robert, and he turned up to his very first day at the Spurs Academy, in a Manchester United kit!

Robert continued to work hard and to do his best. During the summer in the school holidays, when the other lads were playing around in the park, Robert went to soccer school and worked hard through the whole holiday. He was asked to take part in a football skills competition and he got through to the final. He was really excited to discover that the final was to be held at Old Trafford – the home of Manchester United. He became even more determined to do his best and to win.

The competition final was held during the half-time of a Manchester United and Tottenham Hotspur match; Robert's dream team and his home team. Robert won and it made him even more determined than ever to play eventually for Man U.

Two years later, two more years of working hard and doing his best,

Robert was spotted by a Man U talent scout and he was given a trial at the club by its manager – Alex Ferguson. And on Robert's thirteenth birthday, on May 2nd 1988, he signed up with Manchester United. His dream had *almost* come true. He now belonged to his dream club, but had yet to play for them.

At only 13, Robert was still living at home in London with his parents. He still had to go to school. He put up with school work, which he didn't much like, and lived for the holidays when he could go back to Manchester and train.

At 16, Robert left school and went to live in Manchester as a trainee. It was hard at first, being away from home and his old friends. But the thought of his dream to play for Man U kept Robert going. One year later Alex Ferguson let him play in his first big match. It was an important day, but also a bit disappointing because the manager didn't invite Robert to play permanently in the first team. But Robert didn't give up. He kept on doing his best and working as hard as he could, in the hope that he would be chosen to play permanently in the first team. Another year went by and still he wasn't chosen.

'I think he's going to tell me to leave,' said Robert. 'That's why he's not choosing me for the first team.'

'It's not that; it's because you're too small,' everyone said. 'That's why!'

'You need to toughen up!' said Alex Ferguson. 'I'm sending you to a third division team for a month for extra experience,' and so Robert went to Preston for a month, and was so relieved not to have been given the sack that he worked even harder than before.

The manager's plan worked, and Robert came back one month later a better player for his experience away.

And at last, he saw his dream come true. He was picked for a permanent place in the Manchester United first team. That dream he'd held, even since he was a tiny boy playing football in the park with his dad, had come true, because of his determination, his hard work, and the fact that he did his best all the time to *make* his dream come true.

Well, I wonder if you've worked out by now who 'Robert' is.

Yes, I knew you would! He is of course David Beckham. David Robert Joseph Beckham; Robert is one of his middle names.

As you probably know, David went on to Captain England, and to play for Real Madrid in Spain. Now he's moved to the USA with his family. He's still an excellent footballer and these days is a fashion icon as well. He spends a good part of his time encouraging young people, especially those from poorer homes, like him, to realise their dreams of being good footballers. And I think as well as teaching them about football, he also teaches them, and the rest of us, about determination and doing our best.

~

Let's think for a few moments of the way that David Beckham did his best and worked hard in his determination to reach his goal, to fulfil his dream of playing for Manchester United football club. Even when things were not going smoothly, he didn't give up, he kept on doing his best and kept his dream in sight. Let's think of how we can each do our best and be determined to achieve the things we want to achieve. Let's remember that doing our best in small things can help towards the bigger things we want to achieve.

Theme 8

Honesty

Mercury and the woodman

What would you say if I asked you what the word 'honest' means? Yes, you'd say it means telling the truth, it means not stealing things, it means not keeping things that are not yours; it's to do with not telling lies, not deceiving people; it's to do with being loyal, truthful, responsible, and honourable. Honest, trust-worthy people are the kind of people that we would all like to be. They're the sort of people that every society and community wants and needs.

I don't think we have anyone in our school who would be deliberately dishonest; who would tell lies on purpose or steal things from others. But supposing you were tempted with something? Supposing a shopkeeper gave you too much change, and you knew they'd given you too much – what would you do? Or supposing someone gave you something that wasn't yours but they thought it was. What would you do then? This happened in today's story. I'd like you to listen and decide what you think should have happened.

A woodman lived in the forest with his wife and their children. He was a hardworking man, always trying to do his best and to earn enough for his family to live on and to have a few extra treats from time to time. His job was to work in the forest, cutting down any old or dangerous trees, planting new ones, thinning out the growing saplings, and cutting mature trees for wood to be made into furniture and for building.

One day, he was working beside a deep fast-flowing river, when he slipped and almost fell in. He grabbed hold of the branch of a tree to save himself, but in doing so he let go of his axe and it fell to the bottom of the river.

'Oh no!' he cried. 'I'll never get it back now, and it's my favourite axe. I've had that axe for years and years; I can't work without it,' and he broke off a tree branch and started poking around in the water at the edge of the river in the hope of finding it in the mud at the bottom. But it was useless. The axe was gone. 'Oh no!' he said again.

Unbeknown to the woodman, Mercury, the winged messenger of the Gods, was watching and listening. He knew the woodman to be a good and honest man, and he wanted to help. He touched the golden wings on his heels and flew down to earth, dived deep into the river, and came up with a wonderful axe made of pure gold.

'Here,' he said to the woodman. 'Here's your axe. Take it!' and he held it out.'

'That's not mine,' said the woodman. 'Someone else must have dropped it in the river. Mine's just an ordinary axe with a plain wooden handle, but I'd really like it back if you can find it.'

So Mercury dived to the bottom of the river again. He was gone several seconds before coming up again, this time with a beautiful silver axe.

'Here! Here it is,' he said. 'Take it!' and he held out the silver axe to the woodman.

'That's not mine, either,' said the woodman. 'I can't take what doesn't belong to me. Mine's just an ordinary axe with a plain wooden handle and I'd really like it back if you can find it.'

So Mercury dived into the river again and this time emerged with the woodman's old worn plain axe.

'That's it! That's my axe,' cried the woodman excitedly. 'Oh thank you, thank you for finding it. It really is my favourite axe and I was so upset to think I'd lost it. Thank you again,' and he took his axe from Mercury and started to climb back up the river banking to the path from which he'd slipped a few minutes before.

'Hang on! Just a minute!' called Mercury, who was so impressed with the woodman's honesty, he wanted to reward him. The woodman turned back. 'Here,' said Mercury. 'These other two axes are mine, but I want you to have them. For being an honest man. Here, take them,' and he gave the woodman the gold and the silver axe to keep.

The woodman was delighted with the gift; he thanked Mercury, then hurried home to tell his wife and children all about his adventure in the forest and how he came by the axes. And soon, the story of what had happened was all over the forest and the neighbourhood. Another woodman came to hear of it and decided that he, too, would try to get a gold and silver axe from Mercury, the winged messenger of the Gods.

He waited until no one was about, then went to the part of the river where he'd heard the first woodman had been working. He threw his own axe into the middle of the river, and then made a great fuss about losing it.

'Oh, whatever am I going to do,' he wailed, at the top of his voice. 'I've dropped my axe in the water and I won't be able to work again. We'll all *starve*,' he yowled. 'I need HELP! Someone help me, PLEASE,' he howled.

Mercury, of course, was watching and listening. He knew this woodman to be a dishonest good-for-nothing, and was determined to teach him a lesson. He touched the golden wings on his heels and flew down to earth, dived deep into the river, and came up with a wonderful axe made of pure gold.

'Here,' he said to the woodman. 'Here's your axe. Take it!' and he held it out.'

'Yes! YES!' yelled the dishonest woodman, punching the air. 'It's mine, MINE! Give it to me! Quick!' and he lunged forward for the axe, missed his footing and sprawled headlong and face down in the stinking mud at the side of the river.

'Yours, is it?' said Mercury. 'I think not!' and he hurled the golden axe into the deep fast-flowing water of the middle of the river, to join the woodman's own axe which lay there, unreachable, on the river bed.

'Dishonesty gets you nowhere,' said Mercury, leaving the woodman to extract himself from the mud and struggle home, wet and defeated.

Well, what do you think of the two woodmen? Should the first one have accepted the gift of the gold and silver axes, and if so, why? And what about the second woodman? What do you think of his behaviour?

Sometimes we are all tempted to try to 'get away with something'. But if we want to be responsible people, to be loyal friends and good citizens, we need to be honest and for others to know that we're honest and truthful.

~

Dear God, help us to be honest people. Help us to be responsible and loyal. Help us not to give in to the temptation of telling lies or taking something that doesn't belong to us. Help us to remember that it's always better to tell the truth and own up if we've done something wrong. Help us to forgive other people when they admit doing something dishonest towards us. Amen

Anansi's bald head

I'm sure everyone here already knows of Anansi. He's the famous spider of African folk tales, who was God's helper when the world was new. But Anansi, although very lovable, was extremely naughty! He got into all kinds of trouble because he was mischievous, he told lies, he sometimes stole things, he could be very greedy, and he liked to play tricks on people. The trouble was, he usually meant well; perhaps that's why everyone likes him so much.

Let's see what happened to him in today's story.

Anansi woke up one bright summer morning and all was well with his world. He felt good! In fact he felt so good he decided to go and help someone. But who?

He looked out of his window and there, across the valley, he could see old Mrs Frangipan planting seeds in her garden. 'I'll go and help her,' he said, and without further ado he set off.

'Mrs Frangipan!' he called as he approached her garden. 'I've come to help!'

'Oh, Anansi that *would* be kind. You've no idea how hard I find digging and planting these days. My poor old back isn't what it used to be. Now, if you could dig some furrows here and plant these beans for me, it would be an enormous help. And whilst you're doing that, I can go and get some dinner ready and then pick some tomatoes for tea.'

So, Anansi started digging and planting and Mrs Frangipan went to her kitchen and began to prepare the meal. She made a bean and vegetable casserole – a sort of stew. Into the pot went beans and peas, meat and onions, tomatoes and peppers and herbs and spices. The pot was put on the stove and left to simmer away to itself whilst Mrs Frangipan went to see to her tomatoes in another part of the garden.

Anansi carried on working.

But soon, the delicious aroma of cooking casserole wafted past his nose. He sniffed the air. Mmmm! Exquisite! No one could cook bean casserole quite like Mrs Frangipan. Anansi moved nearer to the kitchen. He sniffed again. Mmmm! Delectable! He moved nearer still. Sniffed again. Mmmm! Indescribably appetizing! He wanted some!

Anansi looked around. No one was watching. No one was near. Mrs Frangipan was round the other side of the house. He could do it! He could steal some of the casserole!

He quickly ran into the kitchen, grabbed a spoon, lifted the lid of the cooking pot and tasted the stew. It was hot, too hot, but rich, succulent and juicy. He tasted more. Even better with each mouthful. 'But what if some-one comes,' he thought. 'It would be dreadful to be caught stealing food! But, I want more!' He suddenly had an idea. He took off his hat and began spooning great dollops of stew into it. He ladled in more and more until his hat was almost full to the brim with burning boiling bean casserole. 'Now, I can eat it later and no one will know,' he grinned.

But, just as Anansi was turning to leave, Mrs Frangipan's neighbour knocked on the door.

'Hello,' she called, expecting Mrs Frangipan to be there. 'May I borrow your weighing scales? I need to weigh my marrows.' And she pushed open the door.

Anansi froze. Whatever was he to do?

Quick as a flash he jammed the hatful of hot stew on to his head. But those beans and tomatoes and onions and peppers were still boiling. That casserole was burning. It was HOT! The pain was excruciating. But Anansi dare not take off the hat. If he did, it would be obvious that he was a thief! Better to burn than to be found out!

But, it *hurt*! Anansi began to jump around the kitchen with the pain. He clutched his head and shook his head from side to side.

'Whatever's the matter?' asked the neighbour. 'Are you all right?'

'I'm fine,' groaned Anansi. 'Just fine,' and he clutched his head even tighter.

'You don't look fine,' she said. 'Why are you shaking your head like that?'

'Shaking my head?' moaned Anansi. 'No ... it's just ... um ... I'm ... I'm doing this ... um ... I'm doing ... er ... the hat-shaking dance. Yes, that's what I'm doing, it's the hat-shaking dance!'

'Hat-shaking dance?' said the neighbour. 'I've never heard of it!'

'Oh yes, it's famous,' said Anansi, still dancing round the kitchen, still clutching his hat, still shaking his head. 'And, not only is it famous, but I'm going, straight away, now. To the hat-shaking festival. In my father's village. I've got to go. Now! He's waiting for me. Bye!' and Anansi danced out of the kitchen, into the garden and down the lane.

But he reckoned without the curiosity of the neighbour.

'Wait for me!' she shouted. 'I want to come and see the hat-shaking festival, too,' and she followed him, running, down the lane.

Mrs Frangipan joined the neighbour. 'What's going on? Why are you running after Anansi?'

'We're going to the hat-shaking festival. Come on. You can come too.' And as she ran through the village, the neighbour shouted to everyone else,

'Come on! Join in! We're going to the hat-shaking festival. Anansi's taking us. Come on!' And soon, the entire village was running along behind Anansi who was still clutching his burning head under his hat.

Suddenly, Anansi could stand it no longer. He stopped and pulled off his hat. Stew spilled everywhere. Boiling beans and peas, piping hot peppers and onions, sizzling spices, herbs, tomatoes and meat poured from his head and scattered all over the lane. He was found out! Everyone knew what had happened.

And everyone suddenly roared with laughter. The hot casserole had burned every hair from his head. Anansi was as bald as an egg.

He felt ashamed. Ashamed and embarrassed.

He said not a word but crept away into the long grass which took pity on him and hid him in its damp green blades so that his head would cool and be soothed.

And so it is, even today, that spiders are bald and like to walk in long grass, to remember the time when Anansi stole stew and felt ashamed.

Lots of traditional folk tales, like the Anansi stories, were told not only because they were amusing and entertaining, but also because it was a way of teaching people how to behave, how to belong to a community. Do you think stories like that still have something to teach us today? Do you think it was wrong of Anansi to steal Mrs Frangipan's casserole? Do you think it's always wrong to steal from people? I'm interested to hear what you think. Maybe next time you see me around school today, you can tell me what you think.

⌒

Let's be quiet for a moment and think about times that we might have been temped to take something that wasn't ours. Let's remember that every action we make has an effect on other people. Let's try, today, to make sure we do nothing to have a bad effect on someone else. Let's try, today, to make sure that whatever we do helps someone else in some way or another.

Katy and Baz

Do you know the story of the boy who cried wolf? I think you probably do. He was the shepherd boy who was always telling lies. He used to get very bored doing his job of looking after the sheep and in order to liven things up a bit he used to pretend that a wolf was attacking the sheep. Time after time he shouted 'help' and the villagers all came running, only to discover that there was no wolf, that they'd been tricked. Then, one day, a real wolf came. The boy shouted and shouted for someone to come and help him, but of course, no one believed him and no one came to help. Lots of the sheep were killed and the boy was more frightened than he'd ever been in all his life. He never told lies again after that.

Today's story is about a girl. It's not a story from years ago, it's a story of now. And she's a real girl. Let's hear what happened to her.

Her name was Katy. She was eight years old and lived with her mum and her older sister, Jenna who was fifteen. Katy had a *very* vivid imagination and was always making things up. Normally this wasn't a problem, in fact when it came to writing stories at school, it was a positive advantage.

'You've got a good imagination, Katy,' her teacher often said. 'You could be a writer when you grow up.'

But Katy's mum was less enthusiastic about her imagination. 'I just wish you wouldn't let your imagination run away with you,' she used to say. 'We never know whether to believe you or not, we never know whether it's just another of your stories!' And Katy quite liked that. She liked the fact that she could often trick people, that they never knew whether what she was saying was real or fantasy. And because she liked it, she began to tell stories more and more.

One day she told her mum that she had a new friend. 'He's called Baz,' she said. 'He's just started at our school 'cos he's just moved house. He lives two streets away in Belmont Avenue. And he lives with his mum and older sister just like I do. And he's my best friend now. And I play with him every playtime.'

'That's nice, Katy,' said her mum, not quite sure whether to believe her or not. 'What do you play at?'

'Oh we play at spaceships or we go diving in submarines or we go exploring in jungles, you know, stuff like that.'

'She's lying,' said Jenna.

'Am NOT,' said Katy.

'Don't argue,' said their mum. 'It's time for tea!'

The next day when Katy came home from school she asked if she could go round to Belmont Avenue to play with Baz at his house. 'It's OK with his mum,' she said.

'I don't think so,' said Katy's mum. 'I don't know this boy, or his mum. Why don't we ask him round here tomorrow for tea.'

'Don't want to,' said Katy.

'She doesn't want to, because he's not real,' said Jenna. 'She's lying. I asked some of her friends about him, yesterday when I picked her up from school, and nobody's ever heard of Baz.'

Katy just smiled to herself and went to play in her room.

For the next few days she told her mum of all sorts of adventures that she and Baz had got up to at playtimes at school. She even told her mum that they went out of school at lunchtime and caught a bus into town then went back to school in time for afternoon lessons.

'That's enough, Katy,' said her mum. 'There's no way you'd have gone out of school because it's not allowed. And if you had, then Mrs Webster would have telephoned me, so I *know* you're not telling the truth. So just *stop* telling these stories!'

But Katy continued. She told her mum about going to play in an old boarded-up house at the end of Belmont Avenue, at home time when she'd been trusted to come home on her own.

'And Baz pulled this bit of board away from the door and we went inside,' she said. 'And it was all dark and creepy in there. The builders are going to knock it down you know, and build some flats instead.'

This piece of information had Katy's mum worried, as she knew there was a boarded-up house, and that it was going to be developed and made into apartments.

'You'd better *not* be going to play in there on your way home from school!' she said. 'You're certainly not allowed to do that. If you can't be trusted to come that small distance between school and here on your own, then I'll have to take you and collect you every day.'

'It's all right,' said Katy. 'Just joking!'

But once again, Katy's mum was not sure whether to believe her or not. She decided to go and talk to Katy's teacher.

'She's always making things up,' said her mum. 'I'm really worried about it because I never know when she's telling the truth. I mean, it's like this boy, Baz, her new friend. *Is* there a new boy in the class?'

'Well, we do have a new boy, but he's not called Baz. His name is Danny, so I think that perhaps Baz might be Katy's imaginary friend.'

'That's what I thought,' said Katy's mum.

The next afternoon, Katy burst into the house in tears. 'You have to come,' she cried. 'It's Baz. He's fallen down the stairs in the old boarded-up house and he's hurt his leg. I think it's broken. Come on. Quick!'

'Now Katy, this has gone far enough!' said her mum. 'You really must control your imagination. I know perfectly well that there *is* no Baz. I spoke to your teacher only yesterday and she told me. All this story telling has got to stop. I . . .'

'But, Mum,' interrupted Katy. 'It's true! He's fallen and he's hurt! You've got to come and help!'

But Katy's mum refused to be drawn into the story. 'Katy, ENOUGH!' she said, sternly.

Katy ran out of the house, down the next two streets and into Belmont Avenue to Baz's house. She hammered on the door.

'You've got to come, quick!' she said to the woman. 'It's Baz. He's fallen down the stairs at the old house. He's hurt his leg.'

'Baz?' said the woman. 'Who's Baz?'

'Oh, Danny then,' said Katy, irritably. 'It's just that I call him Baz. Come on! Quick!'

And the woman, together with Katy, hurried to the old house where they found Danny the new boy, lying in a heap at the bottom of the stairs. Katy's mum was not far behind.

Danny, or Baz, as Katy still insisted on calling him, was taken to hospital where he soon had his broken leg put in plaster. His mum was pleased with Katy for coming to get her so quickly, but both mums were cross with the children for playing where they'd been told not to go.

And that's where the story ends!

I wonder what else Katy's mum said to her? I wonder what you think of Katy's imagination. Do you think she was telling lies, or telling stories? Do you think there's a difference?

I think it's important to tell the truth and to be honest. I don't think it's a good idea to trick people so that they don't know whether you're telling the truth or not. The trouble with tricking people, as we saw in the story of the boy who cried wolf, and the story of Katy, is that the tricks have a nasty habit of backfiring, of going wrong.

~

Let's think for a few moments about being honest. Let's think about being honest with the words we use, about telling the truth and about being trustworthy so that people know that we're being honest. Let's remember that trying to trick people into believing something is true when it's not, can be cruel and can even be dangerous. Let's try hard to be honest, truthful people, so that we make our school and our communities the best they can be.

Theme 9

Loyalty

The animals, the birds and the bat

I bet lots of you here this morning support a team of one sort or another. Maybe you support a football team or a cricket team. It might be a small local team or it could be one of the big international teams. If you support a team you'll think of yourself as a loyal supporter, and you'll know that loyal means to be firm and faithful, to be true to your team.

Of course, there are many other ways of being loyal as well as to a sports team. You can be loyal to your friends; you can be loyal to your school or a club or group you belong to; you can be loyal to a cause or a charity. But whoever you are loyal to, it means the same thing: it means being supportive, faithful and true.

During our lives, we are all entitled to change our minds about things. If you start off as a Liverpool supporter, it doesn't mean that you can never ever change! You might move house and go and live in Manchester and want to support Man United because they've become your local team. The important thing about being loyal is that you don't keep swapping sides for the sake of it, or even worse, swapping sides depending on who's winning at the time!

There's a famous fable about swapping sides. Let's find out what happened.

Once, a long time ago, the birds and the animals were at war. They could not agree on who should live where, who should eat what, or who should be in charge. They had the fiercest arguments and the most dreadful fights. There was hardly a day went by that some creature was not injured or killed.

Sometimes it seemed that the animals were winning the battles. They would lie in wait until the birds were eating or sleeping, then rush in and attack them. The birds tried posting look-outs to watch for raids, but somehow the animals always surprised them.

At other times, the birds seemed to be winning. They too would wait until the animals were off-guard, sleeping or eating, but their attacks were always from the air. They would swoop down from the treetops or sky, always downwind and in line with the sun so that their enemy would not sense them or see them clearly. Then they would attack the animals with their beaks and claws.

But there was one creature who was always on the winning side. He was never on the side of the losers. He was the bat. He was in a unique position of course, for he had the body of an animal but he also had wings and could fly. He constantly changed his mind as to which side he was on, depending on who was winning at the time. When the birds were apparently doing well, the bat became one of them and fought on their side. But when the situation reversed and the animals emerged triumphant, he stopped being a bird and joined the animals.

At last the war ended. The differences were settled, the arguments ended, the fighting stopped and peace was restored between birds and animals. There had been too many hurt, too many injured, too many killed, for the war to continue.

'Enough is enough!' they all said, 'We must learn to live in harmony together in the world that we share.'

The bat was pleased that the war was over. 'Now everyone will be my friend,' he thought. 'They will *all* know how much I contributed to the war. After all, I must be the only creature who was on both sides! They'll *all* be pleased with me. In fact, I'll probably be hailed as a hero. I shall probably be given medals and certificates. They may even want to have a special celebration for me, a wonderful end-of-war party to thank me for all I did for the animals *and* the birds,' and the bat smiled to himself at the thought of the splendid times ahead.

He was, therefore, rather surprised when things didn't turn out as he thought they would. In fact, far from being greeted like a hero, the bat discovered that the animals wanted nothing to do with him.

'We don't want you here!' they said. 'You're nothing but a traitor. You were not fighting on our side, you were on the side of the birds!'

'No I wasn't!' said the bat. 'Well, at least not all of the time. I was on your side as well!'

'And that's just it!' said the animals. 'You kept changing your mind. You kept swapping sides. You were on our side, then theirs, then ours again. We never knew who you were supporting. You were a hypocrite. You pretended to be on the side of whoever was winning at the time. You didn't really truly support either side. Well, we don't like that. So go away. We don't want hypocrites here! Clear off!'

The bat felt that this was all extremely unfair, but said 'Well, see if I care! I'll go and join the birds. They'll want me. They'll appreciate me. They'll know how helpful I was to them in the war.' And off he flew to see the birds.

But here, to the bat's dismay, he found that things were no different.

'We don't want you with us!' the birds said. 'You betrayed us. You're nothing but a double-dealing, two-faced turncoat! You were not on our side at all, you were with the animals!'

'No I wasn't!' said the bat. 'Well, not all the time anyway. I was on your side as well!'

'And that's the problem with you!' said the birds. 'You were always changing your mind. You didn't actually believe in *either* side. In fact, you only believed in saving your own skin, you weren't bothered about saving the birds, *or* the animals. You betrayed us, you back-stabbing bat!' and the birds all turned their backs on him and flew away.

'Well! I like that,' grumbled the bat. 'After all I've done for them and that's how they treat me! Well, they can all please themselves. From now on I shall have nothing to do with any of them!'

And that's how it's been ever since. The bat is now a species apart; not quite accepted by the birds even though he can fly, and not quite accepted by the animals, even though he is in fact a mammal.

So the poor old bat ended up being loyal to no one and as a result he ended up with neither side accepting him. We can all learn something from that story: it's important to be loyal to our beliefs and not to keep changing our minds about things in order to try to stay on the winning side. We won't keep our friends by being disloyal to them.

~

Dear God, please help us to be loyal to our friends, our family, and the groups we belong to. Help us to stand by our friends. Help us to stand firm for what we believe is right. Help us to be honest and fair, truthful and steadfast. Amen

Greyfriars Bobby

Loyalty means being faithful. It means that you don't deliberately say or do anything to hurt your friends. It means standing by someone even when things are difficult or when they need you. It means not abandoning a friend because someone more interesting or exciting comes along. It means standing by them no matter what.

You may have read stories of animals who have shown great loyalty to their owners, and one of the most famous of these is the story of Greyfriars Bobby.* You may, in fact, know the story, as it's recently been made into a film. Here's what happened.

John Gray lived in Scotland with his wife and his son. He worked on a farm, but times were difficult; there'd been months of bad weather with storms and floods and ruined crops. The farmer John worked for had to sell up and John Gray was left without a job.

'There's nothing else for it,' he said to his wife. 'We'll have to move from here to the city. There's bound to be jobs in the city.'

So the family moved to Edinburgh and John set about looking for work and somewhere to live. But many other people were doing exactly the same thing. There were no jobs to be had.

After a whole day of trudging round the streets, John found himself outside Edinburgh Police Station. He went inside.

'I'm looking for work,' he told the police officer behind the desk. 'I'm fit and I'm strong; I could work for the police.'

'How old are you?' asked the officer.

'I'm 40,' said John Gray.

'Too old!' said the officer. 'We're taking on men only half your age.'

John Gray left the station, but he didn't give up. He knew he could be a good police officer, so he went back the next day and asked again. Then he went back the day after that, again and again, until at last they said he could work for them, but only on three conditions: he had to pass a medical check-up, live in the area where he would work, and get a dog!

'You'll need a watchdog,' said the police. 'Get yourself a good dog. It needs to be alert, quick and a bit fierce when it needs to be!'

John Gray went for a medical and was passed fit and healthy by the doctor. He and his wife rented a small house in the city centre near the

---

* Further information, together with a photograph of the statue of Bobby can be found at www.greyfriarsbobby.co.uk.

police station. And John bought a dog. It was a tiny, six-month-old Skye terrier puppy whom he called Bobby.

'Call that a watchdog!' laughed the other policemen. 'We've seen bigger rabbits! Just look at its legs! They're only six inches long! And look at that little stumpy tail, and that long silky fur! It's a funny-looking watchdog, John Gray!'

But John took no notice of their teasing banter. He knew that Skye terriers are tough little dogs who eat almost anything and who can lie still for hours if they need to. And, somehow, right from the start, John Gray had sensed something special about that little dog.

Soon, John and Bobby became inseparable. Bobby was a loyal companion, fearless and tough. Together they walked the streets of Edinburgh during the long, cold winter nights, checking that all was well, that everything was safe. Each evening they would call in at a city centre café where John would have a hot meal. There was always a bowl of food for Bobby to eat under the table. John knew he had found a friend for life, but he didn't know that his life was to be all too short.

John began to feel ill and had to stop work. The doctor was sent for and said that John had a disease called tuberculosis. It was a lung disease caused by the dirty damp air of the city. The only cure was to live where the air was clean and warm, but that was impossible. John's illness became worse. He was so weak he had to stay in bed, and Bobby sat by his bedside day and night.

In February 1858 John Gray died. The funeral was held in Greyfriars churchyard, and although Bobby had been fastened in the house and told to stay there, he got out and followed the small procession to John's grave and watched as John's coffin was placed carefully in the ground.

Mrs Gray took Bobby home and shut him in again. But Bobby didn't want to be fastened in. He howled and howled to be let out, and at last John's son let him out. Bobby ran straight to the churchyard and spent the rest of that night sitting by the side of John's grave. In the morning Mrs Gray took him home again, but that night the same thing happened, and Bobby returned to Greyfriars churchyard. After that, they gave up trying to keep Bobby indoors and he spent most of each day at John's grave.

Eventually Mrs Gray and her son moved away from their house in Edinburgh.

'I don't know what we're going to do about Bobby,' she said. 'He'll be heartbroken if he has to leave Greyfriars.'

'He can come and live with me,' said a neighbour. 'I'll look after him.'

So the Grays moved away, but Bobby refused to go to the neighbour's house. They tried picking him up and making him go with them, but he barked and snapped until they had to leave him alone.

By now Bobby was spending all his time at the Greyfriars churchyard. He only left once a day, and that was when he heard the one o'clock gun sound from the Edinburgh castle walls. The gun sounded every day so that the ships in the nearby harbour could set their clocks to the accurate time, but now, the gun was announcing the time to Bobby, as well. As soon as Bobby heard the sound, he left John's graveside and he made his way to the café where he and John used to eat their meal in the evening. Here, the café owner gave him a bowl of food, every day, without fail. 'You're a loyal and faithful friend to John, that's for sure,' he said. 'You've become a true watch-dog.' And as soon as Bobby had eaten his meal, he would go back to the Greyfriars churchyard and keep watch over John's grave.

Bobby's routine never varied. Days and weeks and months passed. The months became years. News of Bobby's loyalty to John Gray had spread far and wide, and people started coming to the gates of Greyfriars to see the small dog set off for his meal, or to see him come back to keep watch again.

Bobby grew old. He struggled to walk to the café and back, and one day he simply stayed by the graveside, loyal to John Gray until the end. They found him next morning, and buried him next to John.

Bobby made such an impression on the people of Edinburgh that they had a statue made, in memory of him. You can still see it today, if you visit Candle-makers Row in Edinburgh. There's also a website dedicated to Greyfriars Bobby, so that people from all over the world can know of the loyalty of one small dog to his owner.

You could perhaps read the story for yourself. There's a Young Puffin Book and a Puffin Classic of the story, which you could look for in the library.

Let's think about the story for a few moments. Bobby's example of loyalty to John was exceptional, and although it is a story from a long time ago, it still has something to teach us today. Loyalty is important. Let's try to be loyal to our family and friends and stand by them if things go wrong. Let's not do or say anything to hurt them, or leave them behind if more interesting and exciting people come along. Let's remember the importance of friendship.

When did you last see your father?

Loyalty means being true and faithful. It means not doing or saying anything to hurt the person you're being loyal to. Yet sometimes that loyalty can be tested. For example, if your friend, or someone in your family has done something wrong, and you are questioned about it, what should you say? Should you tell the truth, or should you lie to save them getting into trouble? What do you think? It's a difficult question isn't it? It's important to tell the truth, and it's important to be loyal.

There's a famous painting about exactly this. The picture is called 'When did you last see your father?'* and was painted by an artist called William Frederick Yeames. The picture tells a story from English history, from the time of the English Civil War, over 300 years ago. Oliver Cromwell's men (the Roundheads) were fighting against the king's army (the Cavaliers). Every family in the land supported either the king or Cromwell; the Cavaliers or the Roundheads.

The painting shows a young boy about to be questioned by some of Cromwell's men. The boy's father is a Cavalier, an officer in the king's army, and the Roundheads want to find him, to kill him.

The boy is very young, probably only eight or nine. He is brought into the family dining room where his mother and sister are waiting. They are both crying. The Roundhead soldiers have burst into their house.

'Where is he?' they shout. 'We know he is hiding! Where is he?' but the boy's mother and sister say nothing. They know that if they tell the Roundheads where the boy's father is, he will be killed.

The Roundheads then try a different approach. They sit down at the table, leaving the boy, his mother and sister standing at the other side. One of the soldiers gets out a pen and paper and starts to write. Another begins to read through letters and papers he has found. Other soldiers begin to search the house, perhaps the boy's father is hiding in another room. They search in cupboards and chests. One Roundhead finds the family's box of money and brings it to the dining room. The boy is told to come forward to the table, but he is so small that the Roundhead at the other side of the table can barely see him.

'Bring him something to stand on,' he says. A footstool is brought and the boy is made to stand on that.

---

* The painting can be seen at www.liverpoolmuseums.org.uk/walker/collections/lastseefather.

The Roundhead in charge leans across the table on his elbows. He tries to look friendly but the boy is not fooled. He is on his guard. He knows he must be loyal to his father. He knows he must say nothing that will betray him or let these Roundheads know where his father is hiding.

The Roundhead leaning on the table tries to look kindly at the boy.

'Now!' he says, in a gentle-sounding voice that the boy knows is not genuine, 'when did you last see your father?'

The boy looks round. His mother is at the far side of the room, looking anxious. His sister is behind him, waiting her turn, knowing she will be next to be questioned. A guard is ready to push her forward to the table. The boy turns back to the Roundhead.

He must keep calm. He must not appear afraid, even though he is. He must tell the truth. He must be loyal to his father. How can he be all those things all at the same time? The question is impossible.

The Roundhead repeats the question, more firmly this time.

'Tell me boy, when did you last see your father?'

The boy looks past the Roundhead to the wall behind the dining table. There, hanging in front of him is a portrait. The portrait of his father that was painted only a short time ago. The boy had an idea.

'I last saw my father yesterday,' said the boy.

'That's more like it!' said the Roundhead. 'Well done, boy! So, you saw your father yesterday?'

'Yes sir,' said the boy.

'And what was the last thing your father said to you?' asked the Roundhead.

The boy thought carefully. He must be honest, yet he must be loyal.

'The last time my father spoke to me, he said I must be loyal to my king and country.'

'Yes, I suppose he would say that, being a Cavalier,' replied the Roundhead, sarcastically. 'But, what else did he say?'

'My father said that one day the war will be over, and that we will then rebuild our country to make it even better than before,' answered the boy.

'Yes, yes,' said the Roundhead, growing impatient with the answers. 'But you say you saw your father yesterday? Where was that? Where did you see your father?'

And the boy pointed to the painting on the wall. 'He is there, sir. The last time I looked at the painting was yesterday when we had dinner. So that was the last time I saw my father. I looked at it for a long time and I remembered the last words my father said to me. He told me to be loyal to my king and country and that the war would one day be over. Sir.'

'And when did he say those words to you?' asked the Roundhead, angrily.

'It was almost a year ago,' said the boy. 'It was just before he went away to fight for the king's army in the war. That was the last time my father spoke to me.'

'You are wasting my time,' shouted the Roundhead, who knew that the boy had been clever enough to tell the truth, yet give nothing away. 'Get out of my sight! Get them all out of my sight!' he shouted, before getting up from the table and storming out of the house. The rest of the Roundheads went with him, and the boy, his mother and sister were left alone for the time being at least.

The boy stayed calm, he kept his head, he told the truth and managed at the same time to keep his father's hiding place a secret. I'm sure his mother was extremely proud of him.

Maybe you could look for that painting by William Frederick Yeames, and see the story for yourself in the picture.

~

Let's think about loyalty. Sometimes it can be difficult to decide what to do or what to say if our loyalty is tested. In those situations we need to think for ourselves and listen to our conscience – that voice inside us that tells us what is right and wrong. We need always to try to do what we believe is right, and never be tempted to do what we know is wrong.

Theme 10

Keeping your word

A promise of safety

What is a promise? Yes, it's when you give your word that you will definitely do what you say you will do. It's a pledge, an assurance; a promise. And of course, like many other things, promises come in all different shapes and sizes! Some promises are small, easily made and easily kept. You might be able to think of a promise that you've made recently that was easy to make and not difficult to keep.

But other promises are much bigger. They need to be made with care because they may be extremely difficult to keep, especially if things don't go exactly according to plan.

In today's true story, someone made a promise that could *have cost them their life, but they made it just the same.*

Trudi Schönberg was just sixteen years old. And she was happy! She was doing well at school, she had lots of friends, and she was enjoying the winter. She *loved* winter in Austria where she lived, and she especially loved winter in her home town of Vienna. She loved the mountains in the distance, and the snow, and the cold and the ice; especially the ice because there was always an ice rink in the centre of the town and she could go skating with all her friends. The only problem in her life was that she sometimes had to take her younger sister, Hansi, along wherever she went, and Hansi could be a bit of a pain.

Trudi's parents, however, were not so happy. They had worries and concerns that they were careful to hide from Trudi and her sister. You see, the Schönbergs were Jewish, and to be Jewish in Austria at that time was difficult. It was 1938, just a few months before the start of the Second World War. Adolf Hitler had been in power in Germany for five years. Hitler hated the Jews and wanted rid of them.

One day, Mr Metzger, who was not Jewish, but who was Mr and Mrs Schönberg's friend and neighbour, said to them, 'You should think about leaving Vienna. It's no longer a safe place for Jews and their families.'

'Why should I leave?' said Mr Schönberg. 'It's my home. I was born here. It's where I belong.' And he wouldn't consider leaving his home town, even though many of his Jewish friends were selling up and moving to Britain or America.

But soon Mr Schönberg was to regret his decision to stay.

On the night of 12 March 1938, Nazi soldiers marched into Vienna and took over the city. They claimed Austria as part of Germany. Hitler was now in charge.

Immediately, new laws were issued. Jewish shops, cafés and restaurants had to have the word 'Jew' painted across the front of them. People who were not Jewish were forbidden to go in. The Jews were made to wear a yellow star on their clothes so that everyone would know they were Jewish. The Jews of Vienna, almost one-sixth of the city, had all their rights taken from them. They were not allowed to go to work or school, they had their homes and businesses taken away from them, they were not allowed to go to the cinema or theatre, or to go to cafés or restaurants, they were not even allowed to go to the park or ride on a bus.

It was no longer possible to hide all this from Trudi and Hansi.

'But why can't we do what we normally do?' asked Hansi.

'Why have we got to move out of our house?' asked Trudi.

'Because Hitler believes the Jews are inferior people,' replied Mr Schönberg. 'And because of that he wants to get rid of us.'

'But it's not fair,' said Hansi.

'You're right,' said Mr Metzger, who was with the family on that occasion. 'It's *not* fair! It's not fair that I am breaking the law just by being here with you. I have been your friend and neighbour for years, yet now I am supposed to have nothing to do with you. But, I am your friend. I *will* help you, I promise.'

The next day, things in Vienna became even worse. The Nazi soldiers began to arrest Jewish people then beat and humiliate them. Some Jews were forced on to trains then sent out of Vienna to camps where they were shot or starved to death.

'You *have* to leave!' said Mr Metzger. 'I give you my word I will help you,' but he knew it would not be easy. Mr Metzger also knew that if the Nazi soldiers found out he was involved with a Jewish family, then he too, would be killed.

Mr Metzger contacted a business friend in England and asked for his help. Yes, said the friend, he could arrange for Trudi and Hansi Schönberg to escape to Britain, but no, he was sorry, he could not help Mr and Mrs Schönberg to go. The British authorities had placed restrictions on the number of immigrants they were prepared to accept into the country. And, Trudi and Hansi would have to have someone to sponsor them, and they would have to have jobs to go to; otherwise they would not be allowed in.

Mr Metzger passed on this information to Mr Schönberg.

'I have no choice,' said Mr Schönberg, sadly. 'I must save my two girls. They must have the opportunity to escape. My wife and I will try to follow them later, if we can.'

And so Mr Metzger secretly became the girls' sponsor, knowing that he would be killed if the Nazis discovered this, and he found jobs for the girls in England. Hansi was to work in a hospital, and Trudi was to become housekeeper for an old lady.

The day came for the two girls to leave. Mr Metzger took them by car to the Austrian border, where they were met by someone else who took them to Holland and the ship for England. The girls were afraid. They didn't know what their new life in England would be like, or if they would ever see their parents again, but they knew they had to be brave and they promised to look after each other.

But when the ship arrived in England they were separated. Hansi was taken away but Trudi was not allowed off the ship. People tried to explain to her what was happening, but she didn't understand English and no one on the ship spoke German.

She tried to tell them that she had her papers, her passport, that she had a job to go to and that everything was arranged. But no one listened. Then, to Trudi's horror, she realised that the ship was turning round and heading right back for Holland.

Somehow, a message was sent to Mr Metzger.

'I have to help her,' he said. 'If she is brought back to Austria she will surely be arrested and killed.'

'But you have risked so much already,' said Mr Schönberg. 'If the Nazis know you have helped, *you* will be arrested and killed!'

'I know, but I gave my word,' said Mr Metzger.

He contacted the immigration authority in England and discovered that the old lady whom Trudi was to have worked for had died. Trudi therefore had no job to go to, and with no job she had not been allowed to land in Britain. Mr Metzger contacted some more people to find another job for Trudi. He had to work fast. He *had* to find a job for her before her ship arrived back in Holland otherwise it would be too late. At last he had it!

A nursery school in the north of England needed a helper to work with children. Mr Metzger arranged for Trudi to have the job.

She was kept on board when the ship docked in Holland, and she stayed on the ship as it headed back for the English coast. This time plans went smoothly and Trudi was allowed to land and to start her new life in England. The sisters were safe.

Sadly, their parents never escaped from Austria. The Nazis sent them to one of the death camps in Poland, where they were both killed. Trudi and Hansi both stayed in England for the rest of their lives. Trudi eventually became a teacher and Hansi trained to be a nurse. Mr Metzger continued to live in Austria and helped almost 50 other Austrian children to escape from the Nazis.

When Mr Metzger gave his word to help Trudi and Hansi, he knew it was an enormous promise to make. But he knew the importance of the promise, and that once it was made, he had to keep it, even though it could have cost him his life. There are many accounts of promises made and kept, and acts of bravery, during the Second World War; maybe you could find out about some more of them?

~

Dear God, help us to know the importance of keeping our word. Help us to think before we make a promise, and never to make a promise that we are not going to keep. Help us to be loyal and trustworthy to our friends. Amen

A wolf goes on trial

Everyone knows that it's important to keep a promise; that once it's made it shouldn't be broken. And why? Because if we make promises and then don't keep them, people won't be able to trust us. We'll be like the boy who cried wolf. People won't know whether to believe us or not. They won't be able to rely on us because they won't know if we mean what we say.

In today's traditional Jewish story, an animal made a promise then tried to be clever and get out of the promise he'd made. Listen to the story and see what you think.

Once upon a time all the animals of the world became so fed up with the wolf's cruelty that they went, all together, to see the lion.

'We have come to you,' they said, 'because you are the king of the beasts and you will know what to do. We just cannot cope with the wolf any longer. He is a monster. Everywhere he goes he attacks and kills. He is fierce and cruel and bloodthirsty. He kills young and old alike. He attacks us all, from the smallest to the largest animal. Not one of us is safe. You *have* to help us. Please!' It was clear that the animals were desperate.

The lion sat up on his haunches. He shook out his mane. He thought long and hard. And then he spoke.

'The wolf must be brought to justice,' he said. 'But he must have a fair trial. He must have the opportunity to put *his* side of the story. He must be given the chance to speak.' And the lion called for the court to be in session. He himself would be the judge. Everyone seated themselves in position and the trial began.

'These animals say you have been unbelievably cruel,' said the lion. 'They say you attack and kill without just cause. What have you to say for yourself?'

'I need food to eat,' whined the wolf. 'I kill for my dinner like everyone else; like you, for example, Your Excellency,' he snivelled.

'I kill only what I need to eat,' roared the lion. 'But you! You kill for the thrill of the chase, the enjoyment of the hunt. You kill far more than you need to. You kill for the sake of killing. Is that not true?'

And the wolf agreed that it was.

'Then you shall be punished!' thundered the lion. 'Nothing I say to you will bring back the animals you have slaughtered. But you will kill no more! Your punishment is this: for two whole years you will kill *nothing*. Not one single creature.'

'But sir, I shall *starve*,' whimpered the wolf.

'You should have thought of the consequences before you went on your killing sprees,' growled the lion. 'Now! Two years with no killing! I need your word. I need your promise.'

'I promise,' whispered the wolf.

'Court dismissed!' bellowed the lion, and the animals all went their separate ways.

The wolf slunk off to his lair but on the way he saw a small lamb contentedly grazing in a field. The wolf's mouth watered. He so much wanted to taste the warm blood of the lamb, even though he wasn't particularly hungry.

'But what am I to do?' he said to himself. 'I made a promise! A promise not to kill any living creature for two years. Two years! That's 24 months! It's 104 weeks! That's 730 days! How can I go without 730 dinners!' And he began to think. To cogitate. To rack his brains. To mull over the problem.

'I need to keep my promise, but I need to eat!' he pondered. 'I need to keep my word, but at the same time, wriggle out of keeping it!' he mused. 'I need to think sideways!' he said.

'730 days! And what is a day? A day is a sunrise and a sunset. A day is a light-time and a dark-time,' and an idea began to form in his mind. 'If I open my eyes, it is light. If I close my eyes, it is dark,' and he quickly opened and closed his eyes just to check.

'Yes! That's it! When I open my eyes it is light; therefore it is daytime. When I close my eyes it is dark; therefore it is night-time. Open – day. Close – night. Open, close, day, night. Every blink is a whole day. That's it! I've solved the problem!' And the wolf began quickly to open and close his eyes, counting carefully every time he did so.

'Open, close – one day. Open, close – two days. Open, close – three days.' On and on he counted. 'Open, close – 396 days. Open, close – 397 days.' And he kept on opening and closing his eyes and counting until he got to 730 days.

And then he stopped. And he opened his eyes wide.

The lamb was still grazing in the field.

The wolf licked his lips.

'I have kept my promise,' he whispered. 'For two whole years, for 730 days, I have killed nothing. For two whole years, for 730 days I have eaten nothing. I have kept my word. I have kept my promise. So now I can do as I like!' and the wolf pounced on the unsuspecting lamb and killed it.

Well! The poor lamb! I wonder if you expected the story to end like that! I wonder if you think the wolf really did keep his promise, and what you think of his explanation. Maybe you think he cheated; that's certainly what I think. The story was originally told to teach people that they won't be accepted if they lie and cheat. It was also told to warn people that scoundrels cannot be trusted because they will always find a way to get round a promise.

I believe it's important for each of us to keep our word, to keep a promise if we make one. I think it's unfair and unjust to try to wriggle out of a promise. I think a good motto is 'say what you mean and mean what you say.' It's what I try to do. Another good motto is 'never make a promise that you don't think you can keep'.

~

Let's think for a few minutes about keeping our word. Let's remember that when we promise someone that we'll do something, that person relies on us to keep our word. Let's remember not to let people down. Let's think for a few moments of promises we've made recently. Let's consider whether we've kept those promises, or whether we still need to do anything about any of them.

The underground railway

Keeping a promise is important. If you make a promise, the person to whom you've made it expects you to keep it. But what if you make a promise to yourself? What then? Does it matter if you break a promise you've made to yourself? After all, no one else probably knows about it, so no one else is likely to know whether you've kept the promise or not. What do you think? Should you keep a promise you've made to yourself?

I wonder whether you think it's easier or more difficult to keep a promise you've made to yourself? There are pros and cons, things for and against, making a promise to yourself.

I'm going to tell you a true story of someone who made a promise to herself. The story is called 'The Underground Railway' though it has nothing to do with a railway at all!

Harriet Tubman* was a slave. She was born around 1820, though she never knew exactly when her birthday was. Her parents were black slaves in Maryland, one of the southern states of America. In those days it was legal there for black people to be enslaved and to have to work for white people. From being a tiny child, Harriet had to work on a white man's plantation, in his cotton fields. All the slaves, including the smallest children, were often whipped; the owners thought the slaves could be kept under control if they were whipped or beaten and made to feel afraid. None of the slaves could read or write, none of them went to school.

When she was twelve, Harriet saw one of the slaves being dragged back after trying to escape.

'Here, get this rope and tie him up,' shouted the overseer to Harriet, throwing her a huge heavy rope. But Harriet refused. The overseer was furious and tied up the man himself, then turned on Harriet and hit her hard across the side of her head. Harriet was knocked unconscious. No one was allowed to help her and she lay there in the dirt in a pool of blood

---

* Further information can be found at www.nyhistory.com/harriettubman/life.htm.

for hours before she regained consciousness. When she woke up she made herself a promise, 'One day I will escape from slavery. One day I will be free.' She made this promise even though she knew that slaves never did escape. They were captured and brought back and either beaten or killed.

Harriet didn't forget her promise to herself, but it was another thirteen years before she got her chance to escape. She heard that she and other slaves from the cotton fields were to be sold to another plantation owner further south. Harriet knew that the only way to escape was somehow to travel to north America, where black people were not held in captivity, but could be free. She knew she had no time to waste. She knew she must escape now. But how?

A white neighbour saw her looking at the fence that surrounded the plantation. He noticed how furtively she looked, as though she were looking for a gap, a hole, a space. The neighbour did not agree with slavery. He hated the way the black people were mistreated and beaten. He caught Harriet's eye and he nodded to a part of the fence near a tree. Then he walked away into his own house.

Harriet looked round to see whether anyone was watching. The overseer was at the other end of the field. The other slaves were busy with their work. No one had seen the look that passed between the neighbour and Harriet. She dropped down onto her stomach and crawled towards the fence. There, sure enough, was a gap, just wide enough to squeeze through. Harriet hid in the bushes at the other side of the fence. She waited. The neighbour came out of his house and walked past the bushes. He didn't look at her but quietly told her the way to a safe house.

'They will show you the way to the *next* safe house,' he said. 'You have just begun your journey to freedom,' and he went back inside his house before anyone could realise what was happening.

Harriet waited in the bushes until dark and then followed the instructions to the first safe house. Here, she was put onto a wooden cart and covered with old sacks, then the cart was driven to the next destination where she was hidden overnight.

'You'll be put on the Underground Railway,' she was told.

Harriet was puzzled. She didn't think there was a railway nearby, she hadn't heard one, and she certainly couldn't imagine there being an *underground* railway. The next day a guide arrived and Harriet was taken on foot to another safe house, then another and another. Day after day, travelling usually on foot, sometimes hidden on carts and wagons. But never, ever, on a railway!

Harriet's journey continued, bit by bit, stage by stage, until eventually she arrived in Philadelphia in the north of America, and the Underground Railway was explained to her.

'It's not a real railway,' they laughed. 'It's a secret network of safe houses, routes and roads, that has been organised by people who want to help slaves escape to freedom, people who want to see slavery abolished. We help slaves from the south to get here, to reach freedom.

'I'm here?' said Harriet. 'I'm free?'

'You have to register yourself as a free person,' they told her. 'Then you're free to do as you please.'

Harriet could hardly believe it. She was no longer a slave. She'd kept the promise she had made to herself all those years before. But her happiness was tinged with sadness at the thought of all her family and friends she'd left behind in the cotton fields of Maryland. And so she made a new promise to herself. 'I'll set them free as well,' she said.

But the abolitionists of the Underground Railway said, 'No! Be careful! If you set foot in the south again, you will be recaptured and returned to slavery. You can't go back!'

But Harriet took no notice. She had a promise to keep. She went back along the Underground Railway, back to Maryland. She knew what would happen to her if she were caught, but, fearless for her own safety, she rescued two more slaves and travelled with them until they were safely in the north.

'Well done, Harriet. You're safe again. Stay here, don't risk going back south again!' the abolitionists said.

'I can't stay here,' said Harriet. 'I have a promise to keep.' And she went straight back along the Underground Railway, back to Maryland, to rescue more slaves.

Over the next ten years, and often in enormous danger, Harriet Tubman helped more than 300 slaves to escape from the plantations of the Deep South. She became famous for her work, and not one of the slaves she helped was recaptured. Harriet went on to help even more people during the American Civil War, when she worked as a soldier, a spy and a nurse. After the war ended Harriet built, and ran, a home for elderly black people. Eventually, she herself was cared for in the home, and she died there in 1913, aged about 93.

What a remarkable lady! And what a promise to try to keep. She made that first promise about escaping from slavery when she was just 12 and it took another 13 years for her to keep it. Then she made another promise to help others to escape, and really she spent the rest of her life keeping that promise.

Harriet Tubman is an example to us all; her life shows us about bravery, about perseverance, about caring for other people, and about keeping promises. Maybe you could find out more about her life?

~

Thank you, Lord, for people like Harriet Tubman; for their bravery and courage, for their steadfastness and perseverance, for their concern for others, for their belief in rights and freedom, for their example of keeping their word. Help us to have some of the qualities of people like Harriet Tubman.

Theme 11

Right thinking

Sat Nav

When I say to you 'Use your common sense!' what do you think I mean? After all, it is something I say quite often! I think 'common sense' is a very important thing, and something that's often not used enough! So, what do I mean?

Yes, of course you know what it means. I looked it up in the dictionary this morning, and there it says that common sense is 'normal understanding; practical sense in everyday things'. In other words, you're quite right, it means 'Use your brain!' Think for yourself!

Using your brain means thinking for yourself, and of course that can bring its own problems, because so often we are all told what to do. Parents, carers and teachers tell children what to do; bosses, officials and the government tell adults what to do; so it's not always possible to think for yourself and use your own brain. But you should still keep thinking! You should still check that what you're being told to do is sensible.

I have a story for you today which is absolutely true. It was reported in the newspaper not so long ago. Someone in the story did exactly what they were told! I'll leave it to you to decide whether you think they used their common sense!

Dave the driver climbed up into the coach.

'Morning all!' he said to his passengers as they settled into their seats. 'Nice day for our trip out, isn't it?' and each one of his 38 passengers agreed that it was. They were all elderly people and they were looking forward to their day out.

'Now,' said Dave. 'What's on the agenda? I see we've a nice drive to Barcroft and lunch at the country pub, then a stroll by the river, and off to

Aireminster for a look at the shops and afternoon tea. Everybody ready?' and they all said they were.

'Off we go then,' said Dave, and he started the engine. 'I don't know this route,' he added, 'but not to worry! We've got Sat Nav on board,' and he patted the small screen mounted on the dashboard of his coach.

'What does he say?' asked Mrs Evans who was hard of hearing.

'We've got satellite navigation on the bus,' said Mr Evans. 'It shows him the way so's we don't get lost.'

'Oh good!' said Mrs Evans. 'I wouldn't like us to get lost.'

'No chance of that!' laughed Dave. 'I just have to do what the Sat Nav tells me!'

At first it all went well, then Dave consulted the satellite navigation to tell him the best route to Barcroft. The Sat Nav directed him along the main road, through a couple of small villages, then down a narrow road called Bramble Lane.

'It's a bit narrow for a coach, isn't it!' said Mr Evans.

'Yes, but it'll be right,' said Dave. 'I just have to do what the Sat Nav tells me,' and he continued to drive the coach down the lane. Soon, it became narrower still. It was clearly not often used as there was grass growing down the middle of it.

'Are you sure this is right?' someone said.

'Bound to be right,' said Dave. 'The Sat Nav says it is.'

'The Sat Nav could be wrong,' said Mr Evans.

'Nah!' said Dave. 'It'll be right!'

'I think maybe we should turn back whilst we still can,' said someone else. 'Sat Nav is all very well, but it can't see what *we* can see! It can't think for itself, but *we* can.'

'Don't worry! It'll be right,' said Dave. 'I just do what it says!' and he carried on driving the coach down the lane.

The road became even more narrow. Brambles scratched and scraped at the sides of the coach as it went by. Tree branches rasped and rattled against the roof. Stones jutted out from a broken down wall and jolted the wheels as they passed. Suddenly, a woman ran out of a farmhouse at the side of the lane. She waved her arms and shouted something.

'What does she say?' asked Mrs Evans, but no one seemed to know.

A little further down the lane a man started to wave at the coach, then two more people. Dave waved back.

'Cheerful lot, aren't they?' he commented.

'Are you *certain* this is the right way?' asked Mr Evans.

'Course it is!' said Dave. 'All I have to do is follow the Sat Nav!' But just as he said that, the coach juddered against a tree trunk, a boulder and some bushes, and stopped. It was stuck fast! The satellite navigation system said 'Drive on! Drive on!' but it was impossible.

The people who had waved at the coach further back down the lane, now came running. They had to squeeze past the bushes and climb over the stones to get on board.

'What on earth do you think you're doing?' shouted the farmer. 'Can't you *see* that the lane is too narrow for a bus? Where's your common sense, man?'

'We tried to warn you,' said the woman. 'We waved and tried to tell you!'

Dave felt foolish. He knew he should have used his brain; thought for himself. But he hadn't. 'So what do I do now?' he asked.

'Well, I can pull you out of the bushes with the tractor,' said the farmer. 'But I can't tow you all the way back to the main road. You'll have to drive across the fields.'

'I can't take a coach across fields!' said Dave, aghast.

'You should have thought of that before,' said the farmer, and he hitched a tow rope to the coach.

But pulling the coach out of its jammed position proved to be much more difficult than anyone believed. It took *hours*. The farmer's wife helped all the passengers off the coach, to make it lighter and to give them the chance to stretch their legs. She took them to the farm, gave them sandwiches, hot drinks and cakes, and let them use her bathroom.

At last the coach was free and the farmer towed it as far as the gateway to his fields. The passengers all got back on and Dave set off once more, but this part of the journey was almost as problematic as before. The coach swayed and jolted over the uneven ground, as it mowed its way through three fields of recently harvested barley. The passengers felt sick!

At last, they reached the main road again and this time Dave switched off the Sat Nav and used his common sense and the road signs to get to the country pub at Barcroft.

'You're a bit late, aren't you?' said the landlord. 'We expected you at twelve o'clock and now it's nearly five!'

'Sorry!' said Dave. 'We had, um, a bit of a detour.'

'Bit of a detour!' exclaimed Mr Evans, who was none too pleased. 'Bit of a detour in his brain, more like!' and they all sat down to tea instead of lunch.

Now don't get me wrong! Satellite navigation is very good, I like it, but with Sat Nav, like everything else, you still have to use your brain. You still have to think for yourself. It's no good just following instructions if you don't think they're right.

As I said earlier, we are all told what to do all the time. People who care for us tell us what to do usually for our own good, to keep us safe, to teach us. People who care for us will not tell us to do something which is unsafe, or dangerous or foolish. But, we still have to think! We still have to use our brains. We still need to have common sense.

And everyone here knows that I don't react very well when someone gets into trouble and says, by way of excuse, 'Well, so-and-so told me to do it!'

Think for yourself!

Dear God, help us to think for ourselves. Help us to think clearly and to decide for ourselves what is right, what is wrong, and what is the proper thing to do. Help us to have the confidence and the strength to say 'No' when we are encouraged to do something that we know is wrong. Amen

A fair-minded wolf

I wonder if any of you have said today, 'It's not fair!' Unfairness is something that annoys all of us. No one likes it when we think we have been unfairly treated, but we can all put up with something we don't particularly like if we can see that the reasoning behind it is fair.

Take for example some children playing a game. The first one has had his turn and is getting a bit bored. But, even though he doesn't like the fact that it's not his turn, he can see that it's only fair for the other children to have their turn. Or take the example of two children in a family. One of them is getting a special treat. The other one thinks it's not fair because she's not getting the treat, but underneath she knows it's fair because she had something special on an earlier occasion.

It's good to be fair. It's good to play fair in games and sports, and it's good to be fair-minded. We sometimes call that being 'open-minded'; it means being prepared to see the other person's point of view, being prepared to weigh things up before making a decision, making a decision based on facts and not just on impressions.

Let's listen to this fable by Aesop.

Once upon a time a wolf was prowling about looking for something to eat. He wasn't in fact particularly hungry, but felt he could just nibble something nice. Over in the distance he could see a sheep, a rabbit and a small boy. 'Mmmm,' he thought to himself. 'A bite of boy would be tasty. That's what I'll have,' and he dropped down onto his stomach and began to stalk the boy.

The boy, oblivious to the wolf, was playing with a ball. He threw it and caught it, threw it and caught it, then threw it . . . and missed. The ball rolled over the grass and stopped against a tree stump. The boy ran across to it and suddenly found himself face to face with the wolf. The wolf growled and bared his teeth. The colour drained from the boy's face and he started to tremble with fear.

'Please don't hurt me,' pleaded the boy.

'Hurt you?' sneered the wolf. 'I'm not going to *hurt* you. I'm going to *eat* you!'

'Then please don't *eat* me,' whimpered the boy.

The wolf, who had been ready to kill the boy immediately, hesitated. He knew he wasn't hungry, so decided to tease the terrified boy instead. It would while away an hour or so, and if he got fed up with the game, he could always eat the boy anyway.

'OK,' said the wolf. 'I won't eat you if you can tell me four things that are so absolutely true that I cannot possibly disagree with them. If you can't do that, I shall kill you and eat you.'

The boy shook with fright. He knew that the wolf was toying with him, playing with him, teasing him. But he also knew that the wolf could kill him at any moment. Wolves were known for their cruelty and their unfairness. He could only hope that *this* wolf would be fair-minded. The boy searched his memory for truths that the wolf would accept. This would be difficult. Wolves were notoriously clever at twisting the truth.

The boy thought and thought.

Eventually he said, 'It's very unlucky that I was in the same field as you.'

'It's not unlucky for *me*!' replied the wolf.

'No, but it's unlucky for *me*,' said the boy, as calmly as he could.

'That's true!' answered the wolf. 'I cannot argue with that! Now, tell me your second truth.'

The boy thought again, then said, 'It's very unfortunate that you saw me.'

'Not unfortunate for *me*!' laughed the wolf.

'No, but it was unfortunate for *me*,' answered the boy slowly.

'That's true again!' answered the wolf. 'I cannot argue with that! Now, tell me your third truth.'

The boy thought again. He knew his life depended upon his keeping a clear head and giving answers the wolf couldn't disagree with. He took a deep breath.

'I don't like wolves,' he said.

The wolf roared with laughter. 'No, I don't suppose you do,' he said. 'I really can't argue with that. That's three good answers. Now, what is your fourth truth?'

The boy felt a little more confident now. He had given three acceptable answers. Only one more to go. He thought again, then said in a rush, 'It's not just me who doesn't like wolves. No one likes them because they eat sheep for no reason at all.'

The wolf was silent. Then he spoke. 'That is not an acceptable answer. It's not true. People may not like wolves, but as for eating sheep for no reason at all, that's ridiculous. Of course there's a reason. There's always a reason. We eat sheep because we're hungry, because we like to kill them, because we *want* to. I'm sorry, little boy, but you have failed to tell me things that are so true I cannot disagree with them. Therefore I shall eat you!'

The boy trembled but tried to stay calm. Then he said, 'Mr Wolf, you have misheard me. I said that "*in my opinion* it's not just me who doesn't like wolves; but *in my opinion* no one likes them because they eat sheep for no reason at all".'

'You're quite a clever boy, aren't you!' said the wolf. 'I suppose what you have told me is true from your point of view, even though it differs from mine. And since I am a fair-minded fellow, I can see your point of view, even though I don't agree with it. So, little boy, we must agree to differ! You may go!' And the wolf turned and slunk away, leaving the boy in the field with his ball; and his life.

Aesop wrote his fables hundreds of years ago to try to teach people the difference between right and wrong, and to try to teach them how to live successfully together in a community. What do you think he was trying to teach people in this story?

Yes, to be fair, to be open-minded, to see the other person's point of view, to accept that we all have opinions and that those opinions might not always be the same as ours. He was trying to teach people to be tolerant of others and to respect their different views. Aesop's stories were written hundreds of years ago, but do you think that what he was teaching applies just as much to us today?

～

Let's spend a few moments thinking about fairness and tolerance. Let's think about respecting other people's opinions and beliefs, ideas and thoughts. Let's remember that everyone has a right to their own opinions, and that those opinions might not always be the same as ours, but let's remember that everyone's opinion counts.

If you can keep your head

There's a famous poem by Rudyard Kipling called 'If'. Perhaps you've heard it. It begins:

> *If you can keep your head when all about you*
> *Are losing theirs and blaming it on you . . .*

The poem goes on to speak of being sensible and level-headed, of being positive, grown up and brave. It ends by saying that if you can be all those things, then you can do almost anything. And I think that's true.

What do I mean when I say 'level-headed'? Yes, of course, I mean thinking in a balanced way, using common sense, keeping cool, not flying off the handle. People who are level-headed are usually reliable people; people who are good in emergencies because they keep cool when things are difficult.

There are five children in today's story. One of them was totally irresponsible, two of them were unreliable, one got into a complete panic, and one kept his head. I'll leave it to you to sort out who was who!

Three of the children were best friends. Jacob, Hulley and Lewis were all in Year 6 and had been allowed to go to school and back on their own for quite some time. Ellie and Tom were in Year 4. They were twins and Jacob was their big brother. Ellie and Tom were always taken to school by their mum, who would have liked Jacob to walk with them as well, but he always wanted to be with Hulley and Lewis.

One day Ellie and Tom asked their mum if they could walk to school on their own as well. 'It's not fair, Mum,' said Ellie. 'Jake's been going on his own since he was in Year 4, so why can't we?'

'Go on, Mum, say yes,' pleaded Tom.

'Well I don't know,' said their mum. 'I like to keep an eye on you. I need to know that you behave.'

'We *will*, Mum,' said Ellie. 'We won't get into trouble. Anyway, Jake can look after us.'

So their mum reluctantly agreed that the next day the twins could come home on their own, on condition that Jacob came with them and looked after them. 'I know I can trust you, Jacob,' she said.

When the children came out of school the next day, all five started to walk home together, then Ellie started running on ahead.

'I'm going to the old playground,' she shouted to the others.

'You can't!' yelled Jacob. 'You've got to come home with us. Anyway, that old playground's all boarded up. It's derelict. It's not safe. It's waiting for the council to rebuild it.'

'My dad says they've got some lottery money to do it,' added Hulley.

But Ellie ran round the corner at the end of the road and towards the boarded-up playground. There were huge signs saying DANGER and KEEP OUT.

'Ellie! Come back!' called Tom. 'We'll get into trouble!'

'We won't if you don't tell!' shouted Ellie, and she squeezed and scrambled through a narrow gap in the boarding and into the playground. She looked around. It really *was* derelict. There was crumbling old tarmac on the ground, with weeds and grass poking through. There were rusty old swings with seats missing and broken chains dangling down where the seats had been. There was a saggy old roundabout with broken metal struts and rotten wooden boards; and a tall twisted old slide with broken steps and banisters leading up to a tiny tower teetering on the top.

'Wow! Come and look at all this!' she shouted to the others.

Jacob, Hulley, Lewis and Tom all crowded into the gap in the boards at the edge of the playground.

'Come out!' yelled Jacob. 'It's not safe.'

'You come *in*!' shouted Ellie. 'It's *fun*!' And she started to climb up the wobbly broken steps of the slide.

'Come out now, that's enough,' ordered Jacob, and he squeezed through the gap to go in and get her. The other children followed him.

'You can't catch me!' chanted Ellie from the slide, and she climbed even higher.

'Ellie, come down, I don't like it,' said Tom, beginning to cry. 'Make her come down, Jake.' But Ellie climbed up the last few steps and waved to them from the little tower perched on top. Lewis ran to the bottom of the slide, grabbed hold of the metal poles supporting it and started to shake them. 'I'll shake you out of there,' he grinned at her.

'No you won't 'cos I'm the king of the castle,' she laughed, and she leaned right out of the tiny tower and looked down on him.

Suddenly, there was a dreadful grating noise, a sort of screeching and tearing of old metal then, as though it was all happening in slow motion, the four children on the ground saw the entire slide begin to lean and then topple and then fall.

'Watch out!' screamed Hulley as he jumped away from the base of the slide just as it crashed to the ground in a shower of rusty particles and metal debris.

'This is your fault, Jake. You should have stopped her!' yelled Hulley. 'Well, I'm off! Come on Lew, before we get into trouble!' and he grabbed Lewis's sleeve and they both ran as fast as their legs would carry them, over the playground, back to the gap in the boarding, out onto the road, and away.

Tom started crying and shouting hysterically. 'She's trapped, she's dead, she's under there, get her out. Ellie! ELLIE! She's dead, I know she's dead.' And he started running up and down, along the now mangled slide lying on the ground, screaming at the top of his voice.

Jacob, who had watched the fall of the slide with horror, ran to where he could see Ellie, trapped underneath some of the metal. He could see she was alive, but hurt. She was barely conscious.

'Ellie?' he said. 'Ellie?' She mumbled, 'Mmm.'

He then turned and grabbed hold of Tom. 'Go and get the first grown-up you see. Understand? Go back through the fence and stop the first grown-up that's there. Get help! Do it. Now!' And he turned back to Ellie. Somehow he knew he had to keep her awake. He talked to her. 'Ellie, count for me!'

'What?' she murmured.

'Count! Go on! Count. In twos. Do it with me!' and he started to count 'Two, four, six, eight . . . What's next Ellie?'

'Ten, twelve,' she whispered.

They'd just got to 30 when Tom came back with a woman whose child went to their school.

'My goodness me! Whatever's happened?' she said, realising straight away and taking out her mobile phone to ring 999. Tom kept talking to Ellie. They were counting in fives now.

'We'll soon have you out of here and safe again,' she said to Ellie, then she turned to Jacob. 'Well done for staying calm, and for keeping your sister calm too. Now, here's my mobile, ring your mum whilst I talk to Ellie. Do you know your number?'

'Yes,' said Jacob and he rang his mum.

She and the ambulance arrived at the same time, and Ellie was taken to hospital. She had a broken leg and cuts and bruises, and was kept in hospital for a week before being allowed home again.

Later, Ellie's mum wanted to speak to all five children, and she had plenty to say to all of them!

The story ends there and doesn't tell us what Ellie's mother said, though I'm sure you can guess! I'm also sure that you've managed to sort out which child was irresponsible, who was unreliable, who got into a panic and which one kept his head when it all went so horribly wrong.

I wonder what you think of Hulley and Lewis's behaviour? And what about Ellie's actions in the first place. I wonder what you think should have happened.

~

Let's think for a few moments about being responsible, about being reliable and behaving sensibly. Let's think about being calm and level-headed, and facing problems without getting into a panic or losing our temper. Let's remember that we need to think before we do anything.

Theme 12

Determination

Anansi and his stories

I'm going to ask you what the word determination means. I wonder what your replies will be? Yes, I knew you'd be able to give me some good definitions, because we have a whole school full of people who are determined to work hard and do their best. So, determination means sticking to something, not giving up, being resolute, firm and steadfast; it means being strong, persevering, and not being side-tracked. It means having the willpower to carry on and see something through to the end. It means stickability!

Often someone can succeed with something, not because they're especially clever, or because they've got some inside knowledge, but because they're determined to do whatever it is. They have an inner conviction, an inner confidence, that tells them they are going to do it. Determination is a very powerful motive.

Today's story is about Anansi. You've met him before! He's the spider god of the Ashanti people of West Africa. He's a bit of a trickster, a bit of a culture hero, a lovable rogue. He doesn't take himself too seriously, he's able to laugh at himself.

In this story there's something Anansi very much wants.

Anansi loved stories. He could never get enough of them. He loved them all; the scary ones, the adventure stories, the sad ones, the funny ones. He loved the way that stories could teach people things like being brave, or being caring, being good or doing the right thing. He liked the way stories could make people laugh or cry. There was only one thing he didn't like about stories. They mostly belonged to someone else! Anansi wanted to own the world's stories. He wanted to be king of all the stories that had ever been told.

He went to see the God of Everything. 'I want to buy the stories,' he said. 'I'll pay anything you want!'

'Ah, you're not the first to want to own all the stories in the world,' said the God. 'But the price is high. Many have tried but no one has succeeded in bringing me what I want, in exchange for the world's stories.'

'But, I'll do anything,' said Anansi.

'Then you must bring me three things,' said the God of Everything. 'You must bring me the python who can crush anything, the hornets who sting like fire, and the fairy that no one can see. Bring me these, and the stories are yours. But, I warn you, no one else has ever succeeded.'

'Maybe no one else has been as determined as me,' grinned Anansi. And he set off on his mission.

First, he took a long, long pole to the edge of the river.

'Good morning, python!' he called. 'Could you come here and talk to me? I need you to settle an argument.'

The python slithered out from the reeds at the water's edge. 'What do you want?' he grumbled.

'I want to know how long you are,' laughed Anansi. 'My friend says you're not as long as this pole, but I say you are. I say you're much longer. Which of us is right?'

'That puny pole?' said the python. 'No contest! I'm much longer.'

'Then come and be measured. Come and lie down next to it and then I can see,' said Anansi.

The python snaked forward and lay next to the pole. He extended his body and stretched as far as he could.

'Let me look at your head,' said Anansi, and quick as a flash, he tied the python's head to the pole. 'And, let me look at your tail,' he added, and quick as a dash, he tied the python's tail to the pole. With his head and his tail tied fast, the python was unable to wrap himself round Anansi to crush him to death.

Anansi took him to the God of Everything.

'Mmm, I'm impressed!' said the God. 'But you haven't finished yet!'

Next, Anansi took a jug of water and the two halves of a coconut shell, and went deep into the forest to look for the hornets. He found them clustered together on the branch of a tree, buzzing wildly. Anansi threw the jugful of water on them then leapt out of the way to safety, shouting as he went, 'It's raining, it's pouring, the old man is snoring!' The hornets dived after him, angry that they'd been disturbed, but Anansi waved half a coconut shell at them. 'Fly here into my coconut shell and I'll keep you dry,' he said. The hornets hated to be wet, so they flew into the shell and no sooner had they settled there with the last one safely in, than Anansi clapped the other half of the shell on top and trapped them all inside. The noise of their droning was deafening.

Anansi took the hornets to the God of Everything.

'Mmm, I'm impressed!' said the God. 'But you haven't finished yet!'

Anansi went back to the forest and thought about the fairy that no one could see. If no one could see her, how would he find her? Who would know where she was? How would he know where to look? He decided to sing to her. If he sang her a beautiful song, then maybe, just maybe, she would show herself to him. Then, he could catch her.

Anansi sat in the forest and sang. The birds sang back to him.

Anansi climbed the mountain and sang. The wind moaned back.

Anansi sat in the fields and sang, and the grass shivered and sighed.

Anansi sat by the sea and sang, and, as the sea whispered back, Anansi felt a breath as light as a feather on his face, a touch as soft as a dandelion clock, a sensation as soft as a fairy's wing.

He stopped singing and hurried to the shoreline. He gathered big bunches of grasses and straw, tied them together in the shape of a man and stood him on the sand. Then he covered the grass man with tar. Black, sticky, gluey tar. Then Anansi hid.

For a while he did nothing. Then he started to sing. He sang a love song in which the grass man wanted a kiss. A kiss from a beautiful fairy. A kiss, without which he would be sad for the rest of his days.

Anansi couldn't *see* the fairy, but he was sure she was there. He was sure that she would kiss the grass man and stick fast to his gluey black tar. He kept on singing. He thought he saw a tiny movement of the sticky black tar; a slight indentation on the grass man's face. But he couldn't be sure. He continued singing. The daylight faded and still he sang. Then, when the darkness came, he finished his song and carefully picked up the grass man by its toes, and took it to the God of Everything.

'Mmm, I'm impressed! And astonished!' said the God. 'No one has ever caught the invisible fairy. And who knows? Maybe you haven't caught her now?'

'Maybe I haven't!' answered Anansi. 'But maybe I *have*!'

'You're a very determined fellow,' said the God. 'You've shown that with a lot of determination and a little bit of wit, you can achieve what you want. Well done! The world's stories are yours!'

And that's how Anansi came to own all the stories in the world.

And so you see, determination is a very powerful motivator. With a good dose of determination almost anything becomes possible; even catching an invisible fairy! Do you think Anansi really did catch her? But, whether he did or whether he didn't, he achieved his ambition and bought all the stories he wanted. And the message in this story is that just about anything is possible with determination.

~

Dear God, please help us to show determination in the things that matter. Help us to know that we can achieve so much if we show determination and perseverance. Help us to be determined to work well and to do our best. Amen

Hannibal's journey

Motivation – wanting to do something – is a huge part of actually getting something done. If you want to do it, you are well on the way to success. If you are determined to do it, you are even nearer being successful. I once heard a famous writer say that success is 99 per cent determination and 1 per cent perspiration; in other words 99 per cent of being successful in anything is being determined to be successful, and the other 1 per cent is sheer hard work. I wonder if you agree with that.

Whether or not you agree with those figures, I think you'll agree that being determined to do something helps you along enormously in doing it. In today's story from history, someone was determined to do something that had never been done before. No one thought he would succeed. Let's hear what happened.

Hannibal lived in Carthage in North Africa over 2000 years ago, and he became one of the greatest military leaders of the Ancient World.

One of his best known expeditions involved travelling from southern Spain to northern Italy with his army. The easiest and most direct route was by sea, but the entire coastline was guarded by Roman ships, so it was impossible to go by sea. But Hannibal was determined.

'If we can't go by sea, we'll go overland,' he said to his generals.

'But it's *miles*!' they said. 'We'll never be able to get together the number of horses we need for such a journey!'

'Then we'll take what horses we can, and we'll take elephants as well,' answered Hannibal.

'Elephants?' said the astonished generals.

'Elephants!' said Hannibal.

'But it's impossible! A journey like this has never been done with elephants,' the generals argued.

'Then ours will be the first, won't it!' said Hannibal.

And so the expedition was prepared. In May, BCE 218, the army set off. There were 40,000 soldiers, hundreds of horses and 37 elephants. Most people thought Hannibal was mad.

The army marched north through Spain and into France; the elephants lumbering along beside the soldiers, carrying the equipment they needed for the journey. All went well for the first 1000 miles, then the army came to the wide and deep River Rhône.

'We'll never cross that,' said the generals.

But Hannibal was determined. He persuaded local fishermen to ferry some of the soldiers across in their boats. He had other soldiers make rafts so that they could float across, towing the horses behind; the rest of the men and the horses had to swim across. The problem was the elephants. They were too heavy for the rafts and boats, and although they would go to the water's edge, they refused to wade into deep water and swim.

'They need some help!' said Hannibal, and he emptied out some of the bladders that were storing water, wine and vinegar, and refilled them with air. He then tied several bladders together with string and tied these bunches of what looked like balloons to the elephants' backs.

'There!' he said. 'They can float with these!' and sure enough, when the elephants went into deeper water the bladders of air acted like elephant water wings, and the animals floated across the river to the other side.

A short time later, Hannibal and his army reached the foothills of the Alps. The mountains loomed above them. Hannibal had planned that the army would reach the Alps in the summer time, but by now it was autumn and each day brought rain and fog, which made progress up the mountains difficult and dangerous.

It was the fog that caused the next problem.

Unbeknown to Hannibal and his men, attackers were stalking them. There was suddenly an ambush and the whole of Hannibal's army was forced into a gully. There was no way out. They were trapped. To one side of them was a sheer mountain face, stretching up to the sky. At the other side was a sheer drop, down to the valley floor. In front of them was a solid wall of rock and boulders. Behind them were the attackers. But Hannibal was determined not to be beaten. He turned his army round and they faced their enemy. Men, horses and elephants surged forward.

That same fog which had hidden the attackers from Hannibal had also hidden the elephants from the attackers. The attacking group were astonished then dismayed to be faced by not only soldiers and horses but by warrior elephants as well. They turned and fled down the mountain.

Hannibal continued the journey over the Alps. They encountered snow and ice, rain and fog, wild animals and raiders. But at last, the plains of northern Italy were in sight. Only a few more days of travel and they would reach Rome. They began the downhill climb from the highest reaches of the mountains.

Then, suddenly from above them came the rumbling sound of falling rock. The men, horses and elephants came to an abrupt stop. They all pressed themselves into the side of the mountain as the avalanche of rock came crashing past them. The sound was deafening but lasted only a few minutes, then all was quiet again. But now, there in front of them, blocking their only way forward, was a landslide of stones, earth and rock, and one enormous boulder. Again Hannibal was determined not to be beaten. He ordered the men to start clearing the way.

The earth, small rocks and stones were easy to move aside and push over the edge of the precipice. But the boulder! How could they ever move the boulder! The men tried to push it. The horses were harnessed to pull it. The elephants were positioned to move it. But all to no avail. Nothing worked.

'We're beaten!' said the generals.

'If we can't move it, we need to break it up!' said Hannibal, and ordered more men to attack the boulder with hammers and chisels, axes and cleavers. But nothing worked. Nothing they did would move or smash the rock.

'We *will* break it!' vowed Hannibal. 'Think! What breaks rock!'

'Heat?' someone said.

'That's it!' shouted Hannibal. 'Heat and acid together will break rock!'

'He's mad!' said the generals. 'Anyway, we have no acid.'

'Yes we have!' exclaimed Hannibal. 'We have vinegar! We have wine! We have beer!' And he ordered his men to build an enormous wooden framework round the boulder, pack it with straw, cover it with earth and stone, and set fire to it. Soon the boulder was red hot.

'Now,' said Hannibal. 'Push aside the fire and pour everything on to it!'

The men did as they were told and almost instantly, the boulder shattered into splinters and fragments. The way was cleared and the army marched on into the plains of northern Italy and then Rome.

The 'impossible' journey had succeeded, just as Hannibal was determined it would.

What an adventure! Hannibal travelled almost 2000 miles on that epic journey and most of it was down to his determination to succeed.

∽

It's good to have determination and the will to succeed, but it's also important to use our determination for things that matter. Let's think about being determined to work hard, to put our best effort into the things we are asked to do, and to do the best we can. Let's also be determined to help others, to stand up for what we know is right, and to do nothing to hurt anyone else.

The wooden horse of Troy

Sometimes, when a problem needs solving, determination on its own isn't enough; you need some good ideas as well. There's a very old proverb, a saying, that goes 'Necessity is the mother of invention'. It means that when you really need to do something, you can often have very original and inventive ideas.

I'm sure that in your class when you've all been involved in a project, you've often started with a brainstorming session, or an ideas map, where you've all put down every idea you could think of, no matter how unusual or far-fetched. And sometimes it's the most original ideas that lead to something that works.

Determination and inventiveness together can lead to extraordinary solutions. Take today's story, for example.

Once, long ago in Greece, there was a beautiful queen called Helen. Her husband, the king, loved her very much and showered her with gifts of gold and silver, jewels and ornaments. She lived in a magnificent palace, and had servants and maids to do everything for her. But, one day, Helen met a handsome prince called Paris. She fell in love with him and they ran away together, to the City of Troy where Paris came from.

The king was distraught. He summoned his army and commanded the men to march to the city of Troy and bring Helen back. The army set off. The soldiers quickly surrounded the city. But Troy was a fortified city. It had high strong stone walls all around it with turrets and look-out posts. The four gates of the city were guarded by Trojan soldiers. Getting into Troy to recapture Helen was not going to be easy.

The Greek soldiers tried every way they could think of to gain entry to the city, but nothing worked. The Trojans beat them back every time. Nevertheless, the Greek soldiers didn't give up, they were determined to enter the city of Troy and bring back Helen to their king.

The siege went on for ten long years. Yet, after all that time, the Greeks were no nearer getting into the city. The soldiers were beginning to feel defeated. They were tired. They wanted to go home.

Odysseus knew that they could not succeed without the will and determination of the ordinary soldiers.

'Just let's have one last attempt,' he said. 'One more try,' and he sat down with some of the soldiers to talk it through.

'But it just doesn't work,' said one of the soldiers. 'We've tried every war-like attack on the city and *nothing* works. We can never break their defence.'

'Every war-like attack . . .' echoed Odysseus. 'Every attack . . . But that's *it!*' he suddenly shouted. 'All this time we've been *attacking* the city!'

'Yes,' said the soldiers, patiently. 'That's because we're soldiers. That's what we do.'

'But we need a new strategy,' said Odysseus. 'We need to do something different,' and he began to scribble a plan on the soil with a stick.

'Suppose we let the Trojans think we've given up. Suppose we pack up camp and let them believe we've left. And then suppose we leave them a gift, a present, to say "You've won, we've gone home". Then suppose they take that gift into the city.'

'And what good's that going to do,' said the soldiers.

'Suppose that gift is a horse,' answered Odysseus.

'A horse?' said the soldiers, thinking that Odysseus had suddenly gone mad.

'Listen,' said Odysseus. 'Here's the plan.'

The next day, out of sight of the Trojans, Odysseus and some of his army began to make an enormous wooden horse. At the same time, the rest of the Greek soldiers began to pack up their camp.

'Hey, look!' said one of the Trojan look-outs. 'They're leaving!'

'No!' said others, disbelievingly. 'After all this time? They're surely not giving up!'

The Trojans watched with interest to see what would happen next. They saw the camp being completely dismantled. They saw the Greek soldiers preparing to march away. Then, several days later they saw the entire Greek army march away over the hills and out of sight.

'They've gone!' a Trojan said.

'It's a trap,' said someone else.

'No, I think they've really gone!'

'I don't believe it! Let's wait and see!'

So the people in the city of Troy waited to see what would happen next, but nothing did.

'They really have gone!' the Trojans said. 'The Greeks have gone! We're free of them at last!' and they began to prepare the biggest party the city had ever seen, to celebrate the end of the siege of Troy.

The party was in full swing when a guard looked out from his tower, and saw what seemed to be a huge horse outside the city gate. But the guard was rather drunk and couldn't really rely on his eyes! He staggered down the steps of the tower and opened the city gate just a crack. Just enough to peep through. It really was a massive wooden horse. He clanked the gate shut and ran to tell the others.

'What *is* it?' they asked. 'Why is it there? What is it for? Who put it there? Does it belong to the Greeks? Is it a trick? Is it a trap? Should we bring it in?'

'NO!' someone shouted. 'It could be a trap.'

They sent for officials to help them decide what to do. Even Queen Helen came to look at the strange horse. Eventually they decided to bring the horse into the city so that they could examine it more carefully. The gates were opened and the gigantic wooden horse was wheeled in.

The officials and Queen Helen took long poles and prodded and poked the horse. It didn't seem to be a trap of any kind. They wheeled it forwards and backwards. Nothing happened.

'I know what it is,' laughed Helen. 'It's a gift! It's a present to us all from the Greeks to say they've given up and gone home. It's quite safe. It's just a gift!' and with that, they all laughed at the peculiar present the Greeks had left for them, and they all went back to the party.

The wooden horse stood, all alone, in the square in front of the city gates. It waited.

Then, as the cockerel crowed at the start of the next day, when all the Trojans were sleeping off the effects of the party, a small trapdoor in the underside of the horse, carefully, slowly, opened. A ladder poked down to the ground. A foot stepped on to the ladder. Odysseus climbed down. More Greek soldiers followed him from their hiding place inside the wooden horse. They ran to the gates and began to pull back the bolts. The Trojans slept on.

Suddenly, as soon as the gates were fully open, hundreds of Greek soldiers poured into the city from their hiding places in the hills. The city of Troy was captured, and with it, Helen, who was taken back to the king of Greece. Odysseus was hailed as a hero for his extraordinary idea of building a wooden horse, which for evermore has been known as the 'Trojan Horse'.

What a clever idea! Though I wonder what you think of Helen being brought back to the king by soldiers?

The idea of using a wooden horse to hide in was also used by some prisoners of war during the Second World War. The men were determined to escape and get back to England, and they used a sort of wooden horse to hide in and to get rid of soil that they'd dug out of a tunnel they were making. You could look up their story and find out how they did it. It's another example of people being very inventive and determined.

Let's think for a moment about determination. It's good to be determined, but it's not so good to be stubborn. Determined people think of ways round problems, and think of alternative solutions. Stubborn people have only one idea and refuse to alter their thoughts. Let's make sure we are determined and open-minded people, who can see the value in other people's ideas as well as our own.

Ourselves and Others

Theme 1

Respect

Annie's biker to the rescue

Can you tell me what the word 'respect' means? Yes, it means to treat someone with consideration, to value someone. It means to treat someone with politeness and courtesy; to avoid insulting them, or offending them, or hurting them in any way. It means to be thoughtful towards them. In other words, to respect someone is to treat them as a valuable and worthwhile person, in the same way that you would expect them to treat you.

I wonder if you think everyone deserves respect? What about homeless people or people in prison? Do you think they deserve respect? Or what about people who live in other countries and have a completely different way of life from us; do they deserve respect? What about people who are not as clever, or not as well off, or people who are disabled in some way? Do they deserve respect? I'm interested to know what you think, because I think that everyone, no matter who they are, deserves respect. I believe that everyone is valuable as a person, and that everyone is worthwhile.

Let's see what you think about the people in today's story, and how they reacted to each other.

Annie Umpleby got her bike out of the shed and set off on her cycle ride as usual. She was 76 now, but had ridden her bike almost every day for as far back as she could remember. She'd been given her first two-wheeler when she was six and her dad had taught her how to ride it. When she was a bit older they'd gone out on long rides together. Then, in her teens she'd joined a cycling club, and as a young woman she'd ridden for Yorkshire and then for Britain. She had a cupboard full of medals and trophies and prizes.

Now, she was too old for competitive cycling but she certainly wasn't ready to give up cycling for pleasure, even if some of her neighbours did think it a bit odd that she should still enjoy riding her bike at nearly 80!

Annie had a good ride that morning. She'd cycled a ten-mile circuit from her village along the surrounding lanes. The sun shone, the air was fresh and clear, and on her bike she could appreciate the sounds and smells of the countryside that were not apparent from inside a car. She loved being outdoors.

She was just zipping along the last stretch of roadway leading back to the village, when phsssshhhh . . . the front tyre went down.

'Oh no! A puncture,' groaned Annie. She climbed off the bike and looked in dismay at the front wheel. The tyre was as flat as a bin bag.

'It could have waited 'till I got home,' she grumbled, but there was nothing for it but to tip the bike upside down on the grass verge and set about mending the puncture. Luckily, being an accomplished cyclist, she knew exactly what to do and always carried a repair kit for just such an occasion. She was just in the middle of scrabbling about in the saddle bag for the repair kit when a car came along the lane.

It belonged to Mrs Brook who was a teacher at the local school and who was dashing home at lunchtime to collect a parcel she'd been expecting. She noticed the woman at the side of the road with the upturned bike, and thought she recognised her as the old lady who went out cycling most days. But, Mrs Brook was in a hurry. She really didn't have time to get waylaid by anything, least of all an old woman with a bike!

'She'll be all right!' Mrs Brook said to herself. 'Anyway, there'll be loads of other people passing, and they'll be able to help her if she needs it.' So she drove on.

Annie found the repair kit in the saddle bag and took out the tyre levers. She was just in the process of levering off the tyre, when the local vicar came past in his car.

The Reverend Thomas was on his way to an important meeting with the bishop. He was already a few minutes late because of a telephone call that came in just as he was leaving the vicarage, and he really couldn't afford to lose any more time. He glanced at the woman at the side of the road and thought he recognised her from one of the village fêtes, but she didn't go regularly to his church and he couldn't be sure she was who he thought she was. So he drove on.

'She looks all right,' he said to himself. 'It's not as though she's injured or anything. Anyway, there'll be other people driving along here any minute, and they can help her if she needs it.' And his car disappeared over the hill.

Annie removed the inner tube of the tyre and began to look for the puncture. She was just in the middle of getting out the sticky patches to put over the hole when another car came by. It belonged to the local doctor who had finished his rounds and was on his way back to the surgery for his lunch before doing his clinic in the afternoon. He noticed the woman mending a puncture at the side of the road and realised it was Annie Umpleby.

'Maybe I should stop,' he thought, but then remembered what a hurry he was in. 'I'm sure she doesn't need any help. She knows what she's doing where a bike is concerned,' he said to himself, and with a cheery wave to Annie, he drove on.

Annie carefully stuck on the patch and dusted it with chalk. She was just about to push the inner tube back inside the tyre when a powerful motorbike came screaming along the lane, going much faster than it should, and probably breaking the speed limit.

The driver wasn't from the village, but he was looking for the pub, where he'd heard they did a good steak pie and chips. He saw the elderly woman at the side of road with her upside-down bike and thought she might need some help. He screeched to a stop.

Annie looked up. The biker was big. He looked fierce and intimidating in his black leathers and helmet. Annie glanced around. There was no one else about; no houses nearby, no other traffic on the road, no one walking a dog or taking a stroll. The lane was deserted. There was no one in sight except her and the tough-looking biker.

'Need any 'elp, luv?' he shouted.

Annie grinned at him. 'You're a bit late,' she laughed. 'The job's nearly done.' Then she said, 'I'm fine. I had a puncture but it's almost mended. Thank you for stopping to help.'

'No problem,' said biker. 'Here. Let me,' and he fitted the inner tube back into the tyre and pumped it up. 'There! How's that?'

'That's fine,' said Annie. 'Thank you.'

'Now, can you tell me where the pub is, that does really good steak pie and chips?' he asked.

'I certainly can,' replied Annie. 'It's just down the road. In fact, I might go there myself and have some lunch.'

'Great! See you there then,' said the biker, and he roared off down the lane.

I wonder if she did meet him at the pub, and what she had for lunch?

And I wonder what you think of that story and the people who were in it? Do you think Annie should have still been going cycling at her age? And what about the teacher, the vicar and the doctor who all didn't stop to help? What do you think Annie was thinking when the biker first pulled up beside her? Were you surprised that he turned out to be so helpful? What do you think could have happened?

Those are interesting questions and interesting answers. We often think we know how people are going to react or behave, but we're not always right. It's important to remember that everyone is different and that everyone deserves respect. We shouldn't lump people together and think we know what they're like. They may surprise us.

~

Dear God, help us to remember that everyone is important, that everyone has something to offer. Help us to remember that everyone deserves respect and to be treated with consideration, no matter what country or religion or background they are from. Help us to make the world a better place by treating everyone with courtesy and fairness and respect. Amen.

Guns into art

Assembly preparation: you will need various objects that can be recycled, e.g. plastic bottle, glass jar, newspaper, cardboard packaging, potato peelings, an apple; and a toy gun.

If I asked you what the word 'recycling' means, what would you say? Yes, I knew you would all know what it means. If we don't want our world to disappear under a heap of rubbish we need to get used to the idea of recycling. I know that at home I try hard to put my rubbish in the appropriate bins so that the council can recycle my glass and newspaper and plastic and packaging. I'm sure you do the same at home as well.

Maybe you can tell me how all these items can be recycled? (Hold up objects in turn, leaving toy gun until last.)

And, finally, what about this? Some people in a country called Mozambique, in Africa, are recycling their guns into ploughs, or sewing machines, or bicycles, or something even more exciting still.

Here's the story of Sousa Manuel Goao.

Sousa lives in a small village near Maputo in Mozambique. When he was 23 years old, he was kidnapped by rebel soldiers who were fighting against the government. The soldiers had guns and threatened to shoot Sousa if he didn't go with them. Sousa was very scared.

They rounded up other young men who lived in and around Sousa's village, and they forced Sousa and his friends to walk for 150 miles, in their bare feet, to a place in the middle of nowhere, which was to be their training camp. Sousa and his friends were going to be forced to be rebel soldiers, just like the men who had kidnapped them.

During the march, some of Sousa's friends tried to run away, but the soldiers caught them, dragged them back, then lined them up in front of the others and shot them dead. This was to make the other young men too afraid to try to escape. It certainly worked; Sousa and the others were terrified and were too frightened to do anything but what the soldiers told them to do.

After days of walking, Sousa and the others arrived at the camp. Life was difficult and hard. They were taught how to raid farms and attack the people who lived there, in order to steal food or anything else they needed. They were made to kidnap other young men, just as they had been kidnapped, so that more rebel soldiers could be trained. They were taught to kill. They killed men, women, and even children; it didn't matter to them who they killed. Soon, this way of life became normal for Sousa and the other young men who had been forced to join the rebel army.

Then, in 1992, the rebel army came to an agreement with the government. The fighting stopped and all the rebel soldiers were asked to hand in their guns. But most of the men didn't want to do this. They felt they needed their weapons in order to survive. Sousa didn't want to give up his guns. He needed them to help him get food and money.

The government needed to find a way of encouraging men like Sousa to give up their guns. The country of Mozambique needed to find a way of helping their people live without guns. So a group of people got together and created the Christian Council of Mozambique. They were given support and money by Christian Aid. They believed that if they could persuade the men to swap their guns for tools, they would be able to support themselves and earn a living, without having to resort to violence. So the Christian Council began to give sewing machines or ploughs or even bicycles to anyone who was prepared to hand in their guns.

Sousa heard of the Christian Council of Mozambique and of their system for swapping tools for guns.

He says, 'I heard about the Christian Council of Mozambique. It was offering to give people tools, like ploughs and sewing machines, in return for their guns. I was hopeful. I wanted to stop running. I wanted to stop attacking people. So I nervously took in some guns.'

Sousa handed in some of his guns. And was amazed at what happened next.

Sousa was treated with respect. The people at the Christian Council spoke to him politely and courteously. They didn't ask him any questions about why he had the guns or what he'd used them for. They didn't want to know what he'd been doing with his life, or how he'd got the guns in the first place. They didn't judge him. They simply accepted the guns he brought them and handed him a sewing machine in their place.

'I was amazed,' says Sousa. 'I was treated with respect. They gave me a sewing machine. No questions asked. Now I had a chance to earn a living.'

Sousa took the sewing machine away and learned how to use it. He set up a small workroom and began to make clothes which he sold in the local market. Later, he gave up more of his guns and was given two more sewing machines in return. Now, he works with his brother and his uncle, making clothes to sell at the markets.

'I am so happy now there is peace in my life,' he says.

Well, how about that for recycling? Sousa swapped his guns for sewing machines; other rebel soldiers swapped theirs for ploughs and bikes; but what do you think happened to the guns that the Christian Council of Mozambique ended up with? Yes, they were in a way turned into something else, but not perhaps quite as you might think. They were turned into art!

In seven years the Christian Council has collected and destroyed more than 200,000 guns! They are cut up, and artists make them into wonderful sculptures. One of the sculptures is called the 'Tree of Life'.* It's made entirely of guns and it stands 3 metres high and weighs half a tonne. It is currently on display in the British Museum in London, and so if you visit London between now and 2010 you could go and see it. It really is spectacular. If those guns hadn't been recycled they could still be used to kill people, but by recycling them the Christian Council is helping to bring peace to Mozambique.

As well as Sousa being given his sewing machines, he was given something even more important. I wonder if you can guess what that was? He was given respect. Everyone deserves respect, no matter what their background is. Everyone deserves a chance to live a better life.

～

Let's think about Sousa giving up his guns to do more peaceful work. Let's think about how the people who gave him the sewing machines treated him with respect, despite the things he'd done in the past. Let's think about how good we

---

* The 'Tree of Life', Mozambique, can be found at www.thebritishmuseum.ac.uk

feel when everything is calm and peaceful. Let's think about how we can bring peace to our school.

Story © Christian Aid, London, UK (2003). Adapted by the author.

Pachchai Mutthu's dances

Everyone is different and everyone is the same! You've heard me say that before, and I wonder if you agree with me.

We are all the same because we all belong to our world family of people. We all want to be loved and cared for. We all want enough to eat and somewhere to live.

Yet we are all different. We all look different from each other. Even identical twins are usually slightly different from each other. In our world family we come from different backgrounds; we believe different things.

Just as we need to respect other members of our family at home, we need to respect other members of our world family.

In today's story, which is from some studies and research carried out by Christian Aid, someone is helping other people to respect his culture and background.

Pachchai Mutthu is a father and a grandfather. He has ten children; five sons and five daughters who are now all grown up, most of them with children of their own; and he has nine grandchildren. It's a big family.

Pachchai Mutthu and his family live in Sri Lanka, which is a country at the southern tip of India. Everyone in his family, except the very smallest children, work on the tea plantations. The weather in Sri Lanka is exactly right for growing tea, and there are many plantations. But Pachchai Mutthu's family hasn't always lived in Sri Lanka.

More than 150 years ago, Britain ruled over both India and Sri Lanka. British people owned the tea plantations in Sri Lanka, but there were so many plantations, because there was so much demand for tea, that the British owners could not find enough workers on the island of Sri Lanka itself, so they brought hundreds of workers across from India to live and work on the plantations. Pachchai Mutthu's family were some of the Tamil Indians who were brought over to live in Sri Lanka.

At first, the British owners allowed the Tamil Indian workers to keep their own traditions and beliefs that they had held when they lived in India. They allowed them to build temples on some of the plantation land. But, gradually, the Tamils were discouraged from keeping their old culture, and many of their old traditions began to die out.

In 1947, Pachchai Mutthu was born. He was a clever boy and when he was old enough he was allowed to go to school. He learned quickly. Of all the things he learned as a child, his favourite activity was dancing. Some of the people in his community taught him the old traditional dances of their past. But Pachchai Mutthu's childhood was soon over and when he was eleven he had to leave school and start work as a tea picker. The hours were long, the work hard, and the conditions were often difficult. There was very little spare time, and hardly any time, or energy, left over after work for dancing, but Pachchai Mutthu was determined that the dances of his people should not be allowed to die out.

Then, in 1991, an organisation was started called the Institute for Social Development, which everyone called the ISD. It was a partner organisation of Christian Aid, and it was set up to make sure that the traditions and the culture of the Tamil Indian people were not forgotten; and to make sure that everyone knew just how hard the Tamil Indians had worked for Sri Lanka.

Pachchai Mutthu was invited to help teach the folk dances.

'Often we have not had the time to devote to our cultural practices,' says Pachchai Mutthu. 'Work as a tea picker is very tiring. But we must not let these folk dances die. Our children and grandchildren must learn and pass them on to the next generation.

'I have taught my children some of our traditions,' he says. 'I am keen to impart what I know to the rest of the community, especially to the younger generation so that our traditions will be carried forward into the future.

'The two most traditional dances I teach are the Karagam and the Kavadi.

'The Karagam is performed to the woman God Mariamma. It involves balancing a decorated pot of rice weighing 5 kg on the head. It requires great skill so we start off with a small pot so that the young people get used to it. Sometimes a troupe of around ten of us do this dance. This is my favourite dance, but I have yet to learn it properly.

'The Kavadi involves the wearing of peacock feathers. My daughter Sathyarani is particularly good at this dance,' says Pachchai Mutthu.

Enthusiasm for the dances grew and grew, and eventually the ISD arranged for the dancers to perform at festivals and events. One of the spectacular festivals has dozens of dancers and a parade of elephants through the streets of the city.

The dancers are all paid a small amount of money and given travelling expenses to get to and from the festival.

'We are thankful to ISD for taking on this project of enabling us to revive our culture and make us proud of our history,' says Pachchai Mutthu. 'My hope is that these songs and dances will live on and inspire our community and others.'

The ISD have promoted the idea of respecting this cultural heritage even further. In 2006 they opened a museum called 'The Plantation People's Story'. It's a place where anyone can go to discover more about the traditions, folklore and culture of the Tamil Indian people, and find out more about the way they have helped the country of Sri Lanka.

I think it's important that the ISD and Christian Aid are keeping alive the history of the Tamil Indians. By keeping those traditions going, we can all learn to respect each other's culture and background.

We all have a slightly different background; even here in our school, where in fact we are so much alike. We might come from a different country from our neighbour, or we might just come from a different part of town. We all have different favourite food, even if we get it from the same shop. We all have similarities and differences but we all deserve the same respect.

~

Let's think for a few moments about how we are the same, yet different from the people we know. Think about someone you know well and think of something that makes you the same as them; and think about something that makes you different from them. Let's respect each other's differences. Let's celebrate our differences. It's the differences that make our lives so interesting and diverse.

Theme 2

Tolerance

Nasrudin's coat

Do you know what tolerance means? That's right, it means being sympathetic and understanding to other people. It means letting other people have their own opinions and ideas, their own culture and religion, without interference. It means not jumping to conclusions about people before we've had the chance to get to know them.

Sometimes we're all guilty of jumping to conclusions about people. Sometimes we judge people by what they look like, or what they wear, or how they speak, instead of getting to know them before we make decisions about them.

Today's story is about Nasrudin; you may have heard of him already. Nasrudin is a popular folk hero of the Muslim world; he can sometimes be a bit foolish, but nevertheless he teaches people how to behave. Let's hear what happens to him in this story.

Nasrudin had lived in his village for a long time, and he was well liked and much respected by his neighbours. They would ask his advice, or go to him if they wanted to know something, and Nasrudin would always do his best to help them.

One day a rich merchant, who lived in a huge house at the edge of the village, decided to throw a party. He invited all the villagers to dinner, followed by entertainment. It was to be a very grand occasion.

'Are you going to the party, Nasrudin?' asked one of his neighbours.

'Of course I am,' answered Nasrudin. 'Everyone's going. Don't worry, I won't forget.' But Nasrudin did forget. He became so involved in working in his fields that everything else went clean out of his head.

Later that week the neighbour came hurrying by. He was dressed in his best clothes and was on his way to the party.

'Hey, Nasrudin!' he called. 'What are you doing? You should be on your way to the party by now. You surely haven't forgotten have you?'

'Oh the party!' said Nasrudin. 'I completely forgot! I'll have to come as I am! I haven't time to go home and get changed, and if I'm late Rashid will think I'm very rude. I'm coming now!' and Nasrudin put down his tools and hurried out of his fields, along the road to Rashid's house, still in his working clothes.

When he arrived, he went straight in through Rashid's front door with lots of other guests, but he noticed that no one spoke to him. In fact, it was as though everyone was deliberately ignoring him. People he had known all his life were turning away from him when he went near them. Even Rashid, who had invited him to the party, walked past him without speaking.

When it was time to sit down to dinner, things became even worse. There was not a place set for Nasrudin. There was nowhere for him to sit.

'But why?' said Nasrudin to himself. 'Why is everyone treating me like this? What can I possibly have done to make them ignore me?' and he looked around at all the beautifully dressed guests, and then he looked at himself. He saw his old, ragged, dirty, worn working clothes; his mud-caked shoes; his battered old hat. And he knew the answer to his question.

Nasrudin left the dining room and crept out of the back door of Rashid's house. He hurried back to his own house and quickly changed into his best clothes. Then he put on his very best coat of stiff silk, and went back to the party.

'Hello Nasrudin,' called Rashid as soon as he saw him coming. 'I'm so glad you could come. Come in, come in, and sit over here. You're just in time for dinner. Come and sit down next to me!' and Rashid ushered him to the table.

'Hello Nasrudin!'

'Glad you could come!'

'Nice to see you!' called the other guests, as Nasrudin walked past them to his place at the table.

'Now, come and sit here, my friend,' said Rashid, as he pulled out a chair next to his own.

But Nasrudin did not sit down. He stood behind the chair and took off his coat. Then to the astonishment of the guests, who all stopped what they were doing to watch, he spent several minutes arranging the coat on the chair, as though it were sitting at the table. He propped it up straight and tall and placed one sleeve on the edge of the table, the other on the coat's lap. He checked that it was firmly seated, and then he gently pushed the chair up to the table. Then he spoke to his coat.

'There!' he said. 'You sit in this chair next to Rashid and enjoy your meal. There'll be entertainment soon, so you have a lovely time. I'm going home now, but I'll be back to collect you at the end of the evening and you can tell me all about it. I'll see you soon. Bye for now,' and Nasrudin turned to leave.

The guests stared.

'Nasrudin?' said Rashid. 'Are you all right? Are you ill? What's the matter? Why are you talking to your coat? Why have you left your best coat sitting at my dining table as though it's going to have its dinner? Have you gone mad?'

'No!' said Nasrudin. 'There's nothing the matter with *me*! But it's quite clear that you value my coat more highly than you value me! It's obvious that it's my coat you want at your party! When I was in my old working clothes, no one wanted to speak to me, not even you, but now that I am wearing my best clothes, it seems that everyone wants to be friends. Clearly, it is my coat that has made the difference. In that case, my coat can come to your party and I hope you enjoy its company!'

And with that, Nasrudin turned on his heels and left Rashid's house.

I wonder what happened next. Do you think Rashid tried to stop Nasrudin from leaving the party? Do you think Nasrudin was right to be so upset about the clothes he was wearing? Do you think we should *judge people by their clothes? I wonder if you can think of any examples when we do judge people by what they wear.*

It's a tricky question, isn't it. We all like to feel we're wearing the right clothes for the occasion, but we need to make sure we don't judge people simply on what they look like. There's an old saying that goes: 'Don't judge a book by its cover.' Do you think it would be fair to change that to: 'Don't judge a person by their clothes'?

~

Let's think for a few moments about times when perhaps we have formed an opinion about someone based only on what they look like. Let's try to remember that it's the person inside that counts, and not whether they're wearing expensive designer clothes. Let's try to be tolerant towards other people, and not form opinions until we've had the chance to find out more about them, or the chance to get to know them.

Apples at the fête

I have some neighbours who are deaf. When I first went to live at my house, I found it very difficult to have a conversation with them because I didn't know sign language and that was the language they used. We used to have to write things down when we wanted to be sure that we'd understood each other. Over the years we have become friends, and although I am still not very good at British Sign Language, we can now talk to each other.

Perhaps you've been in a situation where you've met someone but not been able to talk to them? Maybe you've met someone on holiday who doesn't speak the same language as you? I wonder how you managed to make friends?

In today's story, some children from several different countries were all on holiday with their parents at a campsite in France. Let's see what happened to them.

The campsite was busy. It was the middle of the summer holidays and it was hot. Scott wanted to go to the camp swimming pool, but his sister wanted to go to the shop. Scott's dad wanted to sit on the terrace with a cold drink, and his mum wanted to go to the beach.

'I know,' said Scott, suddenly appearing to have a bright idea, although in fact he'd been wondering since he arrived at the camp how he could arrange this. 'I know! Why don't you take me to the Kids' Club, then I can join in all the activities, Dad can go and have his drink, and Mum and Kate can go to the shop then onto the beach.'

'Kids' Club?' said his dad. 'What's that?'

'It's great!' said Scott. 'They have leaders who look after you, a bit like teachers, and they do all kinds of interesting things, you know, activities and stuff, and it's really good because the kids like it and the mums and dads and pesky older sisters can go off and do their own thing without worrying about the kids! Can I go, Dad? Please? Mum, can I go?'

'It sounds like a good idea,' said his mum, and she went off to get more information.

Half an hour later, Scott was enrolled in the 7–12 Kids' Club and met his group leader for the week. She was called Danielle, and she was French.

'We are going to 'ave a wonderful time,' she said to Scott. 'We 'ave a big programme of activity for you to do.' Then to Scott's amazement, she spoke to all the other children in the group, but she spoke to each child in his or her own language.

'Wow!' said Scott, as he realised there was a German girl, a Spanish boy, two Italians, a boy from India, another boy from Holland and a girl from Sweden, as well as several French children in the group. 'How do you do that?'

'What?' laughed Danielle.

'Speak all those languages!'

'I went to university to study languages, and I 'ave worked very hard, Scott,' she laughed.

Later that morning, after a talk about safety and doing what they were told, the children were taken to the swimming pool. It was brilliant! The children soon began to get to know each other and to make friends, even though they couldn't understand each other because they all spoke a different language. However, it was surprising how quickly they learned to communicate using a mixture of signs and gestures, and Danielle, of course, was there to translate for them.

Scott and the others went to the Kids' Club each morning, and some afternoons, leaving the rest of the time free to spend with their families. The children in the Kids' Club took part in many different activities. They played football and basketball, they played Frisbee and volleyball. They went on a trampoline, swam in the sea, went in the pool and played on the bouncy castle which was actually a bouncy sinking ship! They went kite-flying, they made a huge model scarecrow, and they painted a massive outdoor frieze on paper fastened to the wall of the shower block. Throughout all the activities, Danielle translated for all the children so that they could understand each other. All too soon the week flew by and it was almost time for the holiday to end.

'We 'ave one last activity for tomorrow,' said Danielle. 'I will take you to the village fête.'

'What's that?' asked Scott, and the others looked on, questioningly.

'It is the festival 'eld every year, it's just next door to the campsite in the local village. You will 'ave a real feel of a French village. And it will be fun! There are games and stalls to try. Dodgems to drive and things to buy. Shall we go tomorrow?' And the children all said yes! Everyone could understand everyone else this time!

The following day was sunny and hot just like all the other days that week. Danielle and the children set off for the village fête and several of the parents went too.

They had a wonderful time. The children went on every stall and game there was. Scott won a coconut, Tanja won a teddy bear. Marisa bought candyfloss, and Kulvir spent his last euro coin on a donkey ride. Everyone laughed when he fell off at the end, but luckily he wasn't hurt.

At last the day was almost over and the pocket money almost spent. Scott held out his hand showing that he had just a few cents left. The other children held out their remaining money as well. Between them they had just over one euro.

'What shall we do with it?' asked Scott, and although no one understood his words, they knew what he meant. They all pooled their cash and put it into one small pile on the grass. The German girl held out her hands, palms upwards, and shrugged her shoulders as if to say, 'What shall we do with it?' The Indian boy pointed to the fruit stall. The Italian girl nodded, then the Spanish boy shook his head and said 'Manzanas!'

'Nein. Äpfel!' shouted Tanja, the German girl.

'Je veux des pommes,' said a French girl.

'Nein, nein, Äpfel!' insisted Tanya.

Then Marisa, the Italian girl joined in, 'Dieci mele!' she called.

'Kuch sabe,' yelled Kulvir.

'Well, I don't know what you're all shouting about, but I think we should spend it on apples!' bellowed Scott.

There was a sudden silence, as they all looked at Scott, then the shouting started again, and a fight broke out.

'Äpfel!'

'Manzanas!'

'Mele!'

'Sabe!'

'Pommes!'

The children made such a din and racket and such a spectacle of themselves, that their parents came running to see what was happening. The French villagers looked on, appalled. Danielle came rushing over from the pancake stall where she'd been just about to buy everyone a chocolate crêpe.

'What on this earth are you all fighting and arguing about?' she said. 'I just don't believe it! You children 'ave been the best of friends all the week and now you are like the enemies. What is the matter?'

'Manzanas! Mele! Pommes! Sabe! Äpfel!' shouted the children, and suddenly Danielle burst out laughing.

'I don't see what's so funny,' grumbled Scott who was rubbing his shin where someone had kicked him.

'But you are all so ridiculous!' laughed Danielle. 'Don't you realise what you are all fighting about?'

'It's to decide what to spend the last of our money on,' said Scott.

'I know,' said Danielle. 'But you are all asking for the same thing. You all want to spend the last cents on apples to share. You think you all want something different, but you all want exactly the same thing. Apples!'

'But that's what I said!' sighed Scott.

'Exactly! You all want the same thing. Now, why don't you pick up the cash, go to the fruit stall, choose your apples, and share them out, which is, I think, what you all wanted to do in the first place!' And Danielle went back to buy pancakes.

The children couldn't be blamed for not knowing each other's word for 'apple', but I'm sure they could have sorted it out without having an argument and a fight. Each child was different from the others, but they all wanted the same thing in the end.

It's just like that in real life. We are all different, but basically we all want the same thing. In our families at home and our school family here, we are all individuals but we all want to be loved and cared for, to fit in, to make friends and to do well. And it's exactly the same for our world family. Everyone is different, yet everyone wants the same thing. We all want to have somewhere to live and something to eat. We all want to be accepted for who we are. We all want to live our lives in peace and freedom.

We all need to work towards that for everyone.

Let's think about ways in which we are different from the people we know. Then let's think about ways in which we are all the same. We all belong to our family at home, our school family and our global family in the world. And, just as we look after each other at home and school, we must look after everyone in our world family. We remember that although we are all different, we are also all the same. We belong to the family of people in our world.

Vegetable samosas for a guru

I wonder if you have ever met someone for the first time, or maybe seen someone in the street and decided, there and then, without any facts, what they are like? We all do that from time to time, but it's really not a very fair way of judging someone.

Maybe you've been in town with your mum or carer, and seen a homeless person, or perhaps you've seen someone from another country dressed very differently from you. It can be easy to jump to conclusions about what they're like, without any facts. Now, I'm not suggesting that you go up to complete strangers and start talking to them, that would be a foolish and possibly dangerous thing to do. What I am saying is that we should be open-minded and tolerant and ready to respect other people, even if they seem very different from us.

In today's story, someone seemed very different from the rest of the people in her village. Let's see what happened.

There was once an old woman who lived in a small village in India. She had no family and lived alone with her animals. She had two goats, a few hens and a small garden in which she grew vegetables and fruit. She had little in the way of money or possessions but she considered herself lucky because she had enough to live on; enough to eat.

She was, however, lonely. Few people in the village had much to do with her for she was a rather strange old woman. She had once been pretty but was now grey-haired and wrinkled. She would often talk to herself. She was always forgetting things. She used to make mistakes and do things in the wrong order. For example, one day she hung her washing out to dry before she'd washed it. Another day she sat down to eat her midday meal before she'd cooked it. She often forgot to wash her hair or clean her teeth.

But instead of looking after her and helping her, as they should have done, the villagers laughed at her; were unkind to her; ignored her. They simply took no notice of her. They left her alone to fend for herself. They felt that she was different from them; that she didn't quite fit in; that she didn't belong.

One day, news reached the village that a wise man – a guru, a holy teacher – was to call in and visit the village on his journey from a town in the south to the city in the north. There was great excitement.

'I can't believe he's coming here! To our village!' the people said.

'We need to give him the best possible welcome,' said the village head-man. 'We must show him what good people we are. We must make a good impression.'

'We could make a banquet for him,' someone said.

'The best meal he's ever had.'

'We must give him the place of honour at the head of the table.'

'Serve him the very best food,' people added.

'We must give him the chance to rest on his journey,' said someone else.

'Prepare a special sofa for him to lie on.'

'Cover it with silken rugs,' they added.

'We must give him gifts,' said another.

'He'll not accept them for himself!'

'He can give them to the poor,' they all agreed.

'He will know, by all this, that we are good and caring people,' said the village headman.

So the preparations began.

Special food was cooked and the best tablecloths were spread under the shade of the trees. People brought gifts and piled them by the side of the road where the holy teacher would see them. Then they waited for him to arrive.

It was a small boy who saw him first.

'He's coming, he's here,' the boy shouted, and a great cheer went up from the assembled crowd.

They helped the holy teacher down from his donkey and led him to his place of honour at the head of the banquet. They pointed to the pile of gifts they had for him, and to the women who were just then bringing dishes of delicious food to the seated villagers. When everyone had been served with food and cool drinks, and they were just about to eat, the guru suddenly noticed the old woman, standing a little way off, separate from everyone else, and with something in her hands.

'Who is she?' he asked the village headman.

'The old woman? She is nobody!' said the headman.

'Nobody?' answered the guru. 'But she must be somebody. Everyone is somebody! Come here, old woman,' he said, waving to the woman to come forward.

She came slowly towards the guru, and she held out a dish in her hands.

'I made these for you,' she said, holding out a steaming dish of vegetable samosas.

The guru took the dish of samosas and looked closely at the old woman. He realised how hard she must have worked to make them. He knew how much she must have concentrated to get the recipe exactly right.

'I grew the vegetables myself,' she added. 'And I made the batter just this morning. They're fresh, and hot,' she said.

'I can see that,' said the guru. 'And they look delicious. Thank you. It was very kind of you to make them for me.'

The woman delved into a pocket in her sari. 'And this is for you. A gift,' she said and she held out a beautiful ripe pomegranate.

'Did you grow this, too,' asked the guru.

'Yes,' laughed the woman. 'My poor old pomegranate tree only gave me one fruit this year, and that is it! It's for you.'

'Thank you,' said the guru. Then he turned to the village headman. 'Do you have a place at the banquet for this good woman?' he asked.

The headman leaned towards the guru and whispered to him. 'You don't want *her* here. Just look at her! She's unwashed and dirty. She's a bit simple, and I certainly wouldn't eat any of her samosas, you've no idea what could be in them!'

'I would like her to sit here in my place,' said the guru, to the astonishment of the headman. 'Her hard work in making that food is as valuable as yours, if not more so. She has put every effort into the task. And as for her gift, she has given more than any of you, for she has given the only pomegranate she has. She may be a little different from the rest of you, but she has proved today that she is a good person. Maybe you can learn to be good to her!' And the guru sat on the ground at the old woman's feet and ate the samosas she had cooked for him.

I hope the villagers treated the old woman with more respect after that. It's easy to turn away from people because they are a bit different from us; maybe they look a bit different or behave differently, but everyone deserves tolerance and respect. Everyone deserves to be cared for.

~

Dear God, help us to show respect and tolerance to other people. Help us to try to understand another person's point of view. Help us to respect other people's opinions. Help us to remember that everyone is 'someone', that everyone is important and that everyone matters. Amen

Theme 3

Friendship

Boris and Mallory

Everyone here knows that to have a friend you have to be a friend. Part of being a friend is being loyal, and not doing or saying anything to hurt your friend. Being loyal to your friend means standing by them if they need you; it means not going behind their back; it means 'sticking up' for them. If we are disloyal to our friends, they're not likely to want to be friends with us much longer.

Today's story is about two people who started off being friends and being loyal to each other, but then something got in the way. Let's see what happened.

Once upon a time there were two good friends called Boris and Mallory. One day, quite by chance, they found a bag with 100 silver coins in it.

'What shall we do with it? Shall we keep it?' said Mallory.

'No, we can't keep it; it's not ours,' answered Boris. 'We should hand it in to the police, they'll be able to find out whose it is.'

Mallory was not so sure about this. He'd seen the sparkle of the silver coins and he wanted to keep them, but in the end Boris persuaded him to do the right thing and hand in the bag.

Much later, Boris and Mallory were again in the place where they'd found the coins, so they called in to see if the money had been claimed by its rightful owner, but to their surprise the police said they couldn't find who it belonged to, and therefore the two friends could keep the bag of silver.

Mallory and Boris were delighted. One hundred silver coins! All for them! To keep!

'What shall we do with it?' asked Mallory.

'Let's just share it between us, half each,' said Boris.

'No!' said Mallory, who in fact didn't just want half the money, he wanted all of it! The glint of silver had made him greedy. 'No! Let's just have ten pieces each and let's bury the rest in a secret place for later.'

'All right,' said Boris, so the two friends took ten silver coins each, then went home and buried the remaining 80 coins in a deep hole under a tree near where they lived.

That night, when everyone else was asleep, Mallory thought up a plan that would give him more than his share. He went to the tree, dug up the bag of silver and stuffed it in his pocket, put the soil back and went home. In the morning he went to see Boris.

'I need some more money,' he said. 'How about if we have another ten coins each? Will you come with me and dig them up? We both need to be there so that we know it's fair. We wouldn't want to cheat, would we?'

'No chance of that,' said Boris. 'We're too loyal to each other to cheat. Come on!' and off they went to dig up the money under the tree.

But of course, the coins were not there.

'OH NO! Someone's stolen our money!' cried Mallory. 'Still, there's nothing we can do about it. We'll never find out who did it, so we'd better just be glad that we each already have ten silver coins. What do you say, Boris?' Mallory expected that Boris would agree with him, and Mallory would pretend to be heartbroken about the missing coins, whilst secretly planning how to spend them.

'Boris will never know that it was me who took the coins,' he thought.

But Mallory's scheme didn't quite go as he planned.

'I don't understand how someone could have stolen our money,' reasoned Boris. 'I mean, it was so well hidden. No one was around when we buried it, so no one can possibly have known it was there. Only we knew where it was.'

Suddenly Boris looked at Mallory. 'Did *you* take the coins, Mallory?' he asked.

'Me?' said Mallory, pretending to be outraged. 'How can you accuse me, your best friend, of stealing our money?'

'Well, you're the only person apart from me who knew where it was,' said Boris.

'You could have stolen it,' said Mallory.

'But I didn't!' said Boris.

'Well, it wasn't me,' lied Mallory.

'It must have been you,' shouted Boris.

'I know what we'll do,' said Mallory, suddenly having an idea that might save his plan. 'We'll ask the tree! The tree must have seen who stole the coins. We'll ask the tree!'

'The tree?' said Boris in amazement.

'Yes,' said Mallory. 'Let's come back this afternoon and ask it.'

'Ask it now!' said Boris.

'No, no . . . we . . . we need to give it time to think,' said Mallory, who needed Boris out of the way until the afternoon. 'Anyway, we need to ask all our other friends to come along and hear what the tree says,' he added.

'Whatever for?' asked Boris.

'So that they all know it wasn't me who cheated on you,' said Mallory.

And so both friends went home, but as soon as Mallory saw that Boris was safely indoors, he ran as fast as he could to his cousin's house. Mallory told his young cousin all about the money and said that the boy must hide himself inside the tree until the afternoon, then pretend to be the voice of the tree and say that it was a stranger who had stolen the money.

'I can't do that!' said his cousin. But Mallory forced the boy to go to the tree and to stand inside it, without making a sound, until the afternoon. Then he went round to all their friends and told them all to come to the tree at exactly two o'clock.

By early afternoon a large crowd had gathered by the tree. Mallory looked at them all, confident that his plan would work and that no one would suspect him of stealing the money.

He stood directly in front of the tree. 'Tell us who stole the money,' demanded Mallory.

'It was a stranger,' answered the tree in a squeaky voice.

'I can't hear you, tree,' said Boris. 'Speak up!'

'It was a stranger,' said the tree, in a stronger voice. Then, becoming braver, the tree added, 'It was a highwayman, dressed in a fine leather coat. He rode a black horse and carried a huge silver sword.' The tree became even more confident as he elaborated on his story. 'And he twirled the sword around his head and nearly chopped my branches off, then he danced on the ground and the vibrations of his dancing set the silver coins jangling deep under the earth, so he knew they were there, and he dug them up and put them in . . .'

'What rubbish!' interrupted Boris. 'I've never heard such nonsense!' and he ran across to the tree before Mallory could stop him, and climbed up into its branches.

'Aha!' he said. 'Here is the voice of the tree,' and he dragged Mallory's poor young cousin out of the tree by the scruff of his neck.

'Owww!' howled the voice of the tree. 'It's not my fault. I didn't want to do it but he forced me,' and the boy told Boris everything that Mallory had told him that morning.

The people were outraged. 'How could he do that to his best friend?' they said. 'How could he cheat and lie and steal from his friend? He doesn't deserve to have a friend!' and they made Mallory give all the money back to Boris. 'You don't even get your own share,' they said to him. 'Boris deserves it all as compensation for your dishonesty.'

I wonder if Boris and Mallory stayed friends after that? I wonder what you would have done if your friend had been as dishonest and disloyal to you, as Mallory was to Boris? Do you think Boris should have forgiven Mallory and stayed friends?

Let's remember that to have a friend we need to be a friend. Let's remember that friends are valuable people who need looking after. Let's think about being loyal to our friends, standing by them when they need us, and doing and saying nothing to hurt them. Let's remember always to be honest to our friends.

Damon and Pythias

One of the most famous stories in the world, about friendship, is from the time of the Ancient Greeks. The story became so famous that poetry and plays have been written about it. The two friends in the story were so loyal to each other that they were prepared to do anything for each other, even if that meant dying.
Here's what happened.

The two friends were called Damon and Pythias and they had known each other since they were small children. They grew up together in Sicily, spent all their spare time together and became the best of friends.

One day, they decided to visit the nearby city but whilst they were there, Pythias said something not very complimentary about the king. Some of the king's guards overheard the remarks and arrested Pythias and dragged him off to the palace.

The king was furious. 'How dare you criticise me?' he thundered. 'No one speaks against the king! I order you to be killed!' and he commanded the guards to throw Pythias in prison to await execution.

Damon was distraught and begged the king to let Pythias go, but the king refused. Damon went to see Pythias in his prison cell.

'I never meant this to happen,' wept Pythias. 'I didn't even really mean those things I said against the king. And now they're going to kill me. But the worst thing is that my mother and sister won't know what's happened to me. I just wish I could go and see them and explain. I wish I could go and make arrangements for them so that I know they'll be cared for after my death. Damon, will you go and ask the king if I can go and visit my family? Tell him I promise to come back again.'

So Damon went to ask the king, but of course the king said no.

'He must think I am stupid!' added the king. 'Does he really think I'm going to release him from prison? If I set him free, that'll be the last I see of him! He's not going to visit his family then come back to be killed, is he! No! He can't go!' and the king began to walk away.

'Sir?' said Damon. 'Will you let Pythias go to visit his family, if I go to prison in his place?'

The king turned back, astonished to hear what Damon was saying. 'You?' he said. 'You will go to prison instead of Pythias, so that he can go free?'

'Yes, sir,' answered Damon. 'I will go to prison in his place. You see, I know Pythias, I know how loyal he is. I know that if he gives his word to come back he will do so. And you, Sir, you have nothing to lose, because if Pythias doesn't come back after visiting his family, you can kill me instead.'

'You would be killed in place of Pythias?' said the king, astounded to hear this. 'You, who are free, will go to prison to be killed; so that your friend, who is condemned to death, can go free?'

'Yes sir,' said Damon.

'I am so amazed by your loyalty, or your foolishness, that I agree,' said the king, and he sent Damon to prison and told the guards to release Pythias.

Pythias, on hearing what was to happen, started to argue. 'You can't do this for me,' he said to Damon, but Damon insisted that it was all decided.

'Then I won't let you down,' said Pythias. 'I will visit my family and make arrangements for them to be cared for. Then I will return to free you and to face my death. I will be back in a few days.' So Damon went to prison to await the execution date, and Pythias set off to visit his mother and sister.

He told them everything that had happened and explained that he had to go back. He made arrangements for his mother and sister to be cared for in the future when he would no longer be there to look after them. Then the time came for him to leave and return to the prison. His mother and sister, although distressed at what was going to happen, understood that he must go; that he had given his word to Damon and to the king, and that he must keep his word.

Pythias set off on the journey.

He had travelled no more than a few hours when he came to the river. A few days ago he had crossed this river at the bridge, but now the water level had risen, the river had burst its banks and destroyed the bridge. There was no way across. Pythias decided he had no choice but to swim to the other side. He waded into the deep water but the current was strong and dangerous. Before he knew what had happened, the water swept him away, dashing him against stones and logs and debris, half drowning him. The river carried Pythias miles downstream. Then, suddenly, he felt his feet against the river bed and he struggled to stand. He staggered to the river bank and collapsed on to the wet grass. He lay there, almost dead, for a day and a half, until a farmer found him and took him home to his wife, who tried to care for him until he was stronger.

But Pythias refused to stay. 'I have to go. I must get back to Damon before it is too late,' was all he would say.

He travelled on, by foot, still weak from his experience in the river, and it was because of his weakness that he didn't see the robbers following him. They attacked him from behind. They hit him over the head, stole his pack, then tied him to a tree and left him to die.

In the prison, Damon waited. Days went by, and then weeks, and Pythias did not return.

'You've been a fool, Damon!' said the king. 'Your so-called friend has abandoned you. I knew from the start that he would never come back. I'm wasting no more time. You'll be killed at sunset today.'

But Damon continued to believe in Pythias. He was absolutely sure that his friend would keep his word and come back.

Pythias, tied to the tree, regained consciousness. He tore at the ropes binding his hands and feet. He managed to free himself, and eventually found the road and continued his journey, arriving at the prison just as Damon was being led out to be killed.

'I am sorry I couldn't return earlier,' said Pythias, and in a few words he explained what had happened.

'I knew you would come,' said Damon. 'I never doubted you.'

'And I cannot believe that there could be such friendship as this,' said the king. 'Two friends who are both prepared to die so the other can be saved. Well, neither of you will die. You both deserve to live.' And the king commanded his guards to set Damon and Pythias free.

What a story! The king, who was called Dionysius, was so impressed by Pythias and Damon's trust and loyalty and friendship, that he later asked both of them to work for him as his advisors and counsellors.

Nowadays, when friends are truly loyal to each other, they are sometimes compared to Damon and Pythias.

~

Let's think for a few moments about the story. I don't suppose we would ever find ourselves in a situation where we would expect to die for our friends, but there will be many times when we can be loyal to them; when we can stand up for our friends; when we can keep our word to our friends. Let's think about being the kind of people that our friends know can be trusted and honest.

Gladys and Ethel

Sometimes friends do things for each other just because they want to, and not because they might get something back in return.

Perhaps you've sometimes given your friend a small gift, not because it's their birthday or it's Christmas, but simply because you wanted to be kind to them. Gifts like that don't have to be large or expensive, and often it's the smallest gifts that show the most thoughtfulness, that are the best.

Or maybe at some time you've done your friend a good turn; not so that they will do something for you, but simply to make them feel happy.

Sometimes, people even give gifts to their friends in secret, so that their friend has no idea who it is from. That happened in today's story. Let's see how it came about.

Gladys and Ethel are farmers who live in North Yorkshire. They've known each other for years and they live on neighbouring farms. Gladys and Ethel are good friends even though they don't actually spend much time together because they are both so busy working. They are good friends in that they know they can trust each other; they know that if either of them needs any help, the other will always be there; they know that neither would ever do or say anything to hurt the other.

One night, Ethel was lying in bed thinking about things in general.

'I'm a very lucky woman,' she thought. 'I have my own farm, I live on my own, I can do as I like. I think I am more fortunate than Gladys, who has a husband and children and grandchildren to look after. She's responsible for all those people in her family, and she works so hard to earn enough money for them all. Whereas I, I am only responsible for myself. I only have to work to support one person. I think I should help her! But what could I do?' And she thought of all kinds of different ways she could help her friend and neighbour. Eventually, just as she was dropping off to sleep, her eyes popped open.

'I know!' she said. 'I'll plough her 10-acre field for her. She'll find *that* useful. But, I don't want her to know it was me!' So Ethel got up and dressed, and went out in the middle of the night to plough Gladys's 10-acre field.

Now quite by chance, at exactly the same time, Gladys was lying awake, thinking about things in general, and her thoughts came round to her friend Ethel.

'I'm a very lucky woman,' thought Gladys. 'I have my own farm, I have my husband and children and grandchildren. I think I am more fortunate than Ethel, who is all alone in the world. She has to do all the work on her farm and there's only one of her, whereas I have all my family to help if needs be. I think I should do something to help Ethel; but what? I know, I'll plough her 12-acre field for her. She'll find *that* useful. But, I don't want her to know it was me!' And Gladys got up and dressed, and went out in the middle of the night to plough Ethel's 12-acre field.

In the morning, both women went out to work on their farms as usual, and both were astonished to find their large fields had already been ploughed.

'Well I never!' exclaimed Ethel, scratching her head.

'Well, fancy that!' said Gladys, wondering who on earth could have ploughed her field in the middle of the night. But neither said anything to the other about the mysterious midnight ploughing.

A few weeks later, Ethel was again thinking of her friend and wondering what else she could do to help her; and, completely coincidentally, Gladys was thinking exactly the same thing.

'I could gather all her apples from her orchard,' thought Ethel. 'It's a terrible job for Gladys, is that. Up and down those ladders all day long. I'll do it for her.' So, once again Ethel set out in the middle of the night to harvest all Gladys's apples.

'I know! I'll pick her turnips for her!' thought Gladys. 'It's a terrible job for Ethel, that is. Bending down in a field all day long. I'll do it for her.' And Gladys set out in the middle of the night to harvest all Ethel's turnips.

In the morning, both women went out to work on their farms as usual, and Gladys and Ethel were astonished to find their apples and turnips all gathered in and heaped in tidy piles at the edge of their fields.

'Goodness me! Whatever next!' said Ethel, scratching her head.

'Well, I'll go to Ossett!' exclaimed Gladys, wondering how on earth her apples could have been picked without her seeing anyone.

A few weeks later, Gladys was thinking again of how she could help her friend; and totally simultaneously, Ethel was thinking the same thing.

'My sheep have produced a good number of lambs this year,' Gladys thought. 'I could give a dozen new lambs to Ethel. I could add them to her flock and she'll never know it's me who's put them there.' And without any further ado, Gladys went out to her field with her sheepdog, gathered up twelve new lambs, and took them to Ethel's field of sheep.

'My sheep have produced a lot of lambs, this year,' thought Ethel. 'I could give a dozen of them to Gladys. I could add them to her flock and she'll never know it's me who's put them there.' And without any further ado, Ethel went out to her field with her sheepdog, gathered up twelve new lambs, and took them to Gladys's field of sheep.

In the morning, both women went out to work on their farms as usual, and Gladys and Ethel were astonished to find that even though they'd both given away twelve of their new lambs, they each had exactly the same number they'd had to begin with.

Ethel went round to see Gladys.

'Have you noticed anything strange going on recently, Gladys?' she asked.

'I most certainly have!' said Gladys. 'It's most odd. My 10-acre field was ploughed, my apples were all picked, and now someone has given me a dozen new lambs!'

'Well, it's the same for me!' said Ethel. 'First someone ploughed my 12-acre field for me, then they picked all my turnips, and now, I too have been given a dozen new lambs. It's quite amazing!'

'It certainly is!' said Gladys. 'And I know who's at the bottom of it all!'

'You do?' said Ethel.

'I do!' said Gladys. 'We are the luckiest people alive, you and me, Ethel. We've got a Yorkshire hobgoblin working for us both! You know the Yorkshire hobgoblins, don't you? They're the invisible little-people of the north. They go around doing good deeds for people who are in their good books. And we've got one!'

'You're right! We've got a Yorkshire hobgoblin all right! All we've got to do now, is to keep him!' said Ethel.

And do you know, they did!

The Yorkshire hobgoblin stayed with Gladys and Ethel for the rest of their days. Every now and then, it did a kind deed for one or the other of them.

Do you think the Yorkshire hobgoblin really existed? Or do you think it was Gladys and Ethel who did the good deeds for each other?

They were both quite happy to do something kind, or to give a gift, without the other knowing it was them. Friends are people who do kind and thoughtful things without needing anything in return; without even wanting to be thanked.

~

Let's think about being kind and thoughtful to our friends. Let's think of ways we can help them, or ways we can show our friendship. Let's remember that we can get as much pleasure from giving friendship as from receiving friendship. Let's make sure we do nothing to hurt our friends.

Theme 4

Sharing

The toy kangaroo

Everyone here is good at sharing. We all know how to share our toys, our time, the things we have to eat. And we know how to involve other people, in our class for example, in our activities, so that we are sharing ourselves.

But how about people we don't know? Is it possible to share with them? Yes, we can give to charities, we can support organisations that help those who have less than us; charities like Oxfam, or Christian Aid, or Cafod, or the NSPCC.

In today's story, someone managed to share something with a child he'd never seen or met. He involved other people and asked them to help. The story is true, and was in the newspaper not long ago.

Here's what happened.

The man was a lorry driver and he lived in Adelaide in Australia. One day he was going to buy a newspaper and he passed the window of a toy shop. There, in the middle of the window, was a beautiful toy kangaroo. It was made of brown furry fabric, it was standing on its hind legs and it had a pair of red leather boxing gloves on its front paws. The kangaroo made the man smile.

'I wish I had someone to buy that for,' he thought to himself, but he had no children of his own. He had no nephews or nieces, no children living next door to him, in fact he didn't really know any children at all.

'Well, if I can't buy that kangaroo for someone I know, then I'll buy it for someone I *don't* know,' he said, and he went into the shop.

A few minutes later he was back in the cab of his lorry, with the toy kangaroo standing up in its box beside him. The man made a label and attached it to the box:

This kangaroo is to be given to the nearest child on Christmas Day.

Then the man set off for the sea port with his lorry load of goods. When he arrived at the port his goods were transferred to a ship, and the toy kangaroo went too.

'Bye Roo,' said the man as he turned his cab round for the drive home. 'I wonder where you'll end up!'

The kangaroo stood up in its box and started its long journey. It travelled over the sea to India, then overland into Pakistan. It went through Turkey and over the sea to Greece. It travelled through Serbia, Croatia and Switzerland, on to France, and into England. And everywhere it went, lorry drivers asked what it was for. Then they read the label round its neck and they knew it was a present. For someone. Somewhere. On Christmas Day. A present given because a lorry driver in Australia wanted to be kind and share a gift with someone.

On Christmas Eve, the toy kangaroo was in the cab of a lorry driving north up the M1 motorway. The driver had been given the kangaroo that morning in Portsmouth.

'You'll probably be the one to deliver it to where it's going,' the loader in Portsmouth had said.

'But where *is* it going?' asked the driver.

'To whichever child it happens to be near on Christmas Day!'

'But how will I know?'

'Just take it!'

And so this lorry driver had the toy in its box in his cab. It was getting late now. The driver wanted to be home for the start of Christmas, but it didn't look as though he was going to make it in time. There were still many miles to go. Perhaps he could just forget about the toy. After all, he didn't have to deliver it! It wasn't his responsibility. He hadn't bought the toy. Anyway, he didn't know where to take it.

He turned off the M1 into Leeds. Another hour and he should be home. It was ten minutes to midnight now. Nearly Christmas morning. Nearly home. He drove along the dark shining streets. In front of him was the clock tower of Seacroft Hospital. He glanced at the clock to check the time, and as he did so, the clock struck twelve, and at the same time hundreds of church bells began to ring out to herald the start of Christmas.

The driver looked again at the clock, then at the toy kangaroo sitting beside him on the empty seat. He stopped his lorry and parked it at the edge of the road. He picked up the toy kangaroo and walked to the security man at the hospital gate.

'Do you have any children in this hospital?' he asked. The security guard was suspicious. 'Who wants to know?' he replied. The driver began to explain the entire story, starting with the driver in Australia and the kangaroo's incredible journey half way round the world, ending up with it arriving here outside the hospital at midnight on Christmas morning.

'Just a minute,' said the security man, and he spoke to someone on his mobile phone. Then, 'OK!' he said. 'You can come in,' and he opened the gate and took the driver to the main door of the hospital. A doctor met them and the driver explained the whole story again. He was then taken to one of the wards and met by a nurse at the desk. Once again he told the incredible story of the kangaroo's journey from Australia.

The doctor and nurse took the driver to the first bed in the ward. In it lay a small girl.

'This is Adelaide,' said the nurse. 'She's not very well and has just come into hospital today. But we'll soon have her well again, won't we Adelaide,' and she smiled at the girl.

'Hello Adelaide,' said the driver. 'Look what I've brought for you! This toy kangaroo has come all the way from Australia to say Happy Christmas and Get Well Soon. And what an amazing coincidence that your name is Adelaide, because there's a town in Australia with the same name and that's where the kangaroo set off from. So you see, he must have been for you all along.'

And that's how Adelaide, in Leeds, had an extra Christmas present, all because a lorry driver had a kind thought and wanted to share some happiness, and a great many other people helped his idea to work.

It's quite an amazing story, isn't it? Now I know we can't all go around buying toys and sending them off around the world, but we can be aware of just how lucky we are, and just how much we all have. And we can try to think of ways to share what we have with others so that the world becomes a fairer place.

~

Let's think of ways we can share what we have with other people. We can share with our friends and family. We can play fairly when we share games and toys. We can share our sweets and treats with those around us and make sure we are not greedy and selfish. We can share our time with people.

And we can be aware of people in other parts of the world who perhaps do not have as much as we do. We can each play our part in trying to make the world a fairer place, and trying to ensure that all the world's people share food and medicines and opportunities so that we are fair to everyone.

Two of everything

I already know that everyone in our school is good at sharing. I know that, because I see people sharing things every day. I see grown-ups sharing their skills and expertise, I see children sharing their abilities and their knowledge, and I see everyone sharing their time and often their possessions.

But I wonder if our attitude to sharing would change if, for example, we had nothing. Or, on the other hand, if we were all suddenly to become exceptionally wealthy, I wonder if our attitude to sharing would change then.

Something changed for the people in today's story; let's see how it affected their attitude to sharing.

There was once a Chinese man called Mr Wong Chong who found an enormous brass pot whilst he was digging in his garden. Mr Wong Chong had never seen anything like it. The pot was old and dirty, but it looked as though it had once been magnificent. It was as big as a laundry basket, as round as a barrel, and had small squat handles that looked like the ears of a bear.

'What on earth can it be?' said Mr Wong Chong to himself as he pulled the enormous pot out of the earth. He brushed as much loose soil from the pot as was possible, buffed it up a bit with the sleeve of his jacket, hoisted it onto his back and took it home to show his wife.

'But whatever is it?' she asked.

'I don't know,' said Mr Wong Chong.

'Is there anything in it?' asked his wife, and she leaned into the pot as far as she could and ran her hand around the base and sides. 'No! Empty, except for a bit of dust and two pebbles. Look!' and she held the smooth round pebbles in her hand for Mr Wong Chong to see. 'I'll clean it up,' she said. 'It'll come in useful for something, I'm sure,' and she set to work with salt, lemon juice and elbow grease to clean the pot. Soon the outside of the huge brass pot was restored to its lovely golden-yellow colour and Mrs Wong Chong leaned in to clean the inside. As she did so, one of her hairpins fell, with a ping, to the bottom of the pot. Mrs Wong Chong leaned in further to reach it, and was surprised to find not one, but two hairpins lying there.

'That's funny,' she said to herself. 'I'm sure I only dropped one pin,' but she picked them both up, pushed them back in her hair, and thought little more of it.

A few minutes later, she accidentally dropped her cleaning cloth into the pot and leaned in to get it out. To her amazement, there were two cloths there.

'That's odd,' she said. 'Now this time I *know* I only dropped one cloth into the pot.' And Mrs Wong Chong began to experiment by dropping more things into the pot to see what would happen. She dropped in a comb, a pair of scissors, a pencil, a saucepan and a sweeping brush. Out came two of everything. She put in a dish of rabbit stew. Out came two. She placed a loaf of bread and a cherry cake in the bottom of the pot. Out came two loaves and two cakes.

She called Mr Wong Chong over to come and see the incredible pot. And she demonstrated the magic of the pot by dropping her husband's straw hat into it and immediately pulling out two identical hats.

'Well I never!' exclaimed Mr Wong Chong. 'Whatever shall we do?'

'We need to think,' said his wife. 'We need to be wise and sensible. This magic pot could make us greedy, or it could help us and all our neighbours. Let's not tell anyone about it, but let's share what it gives us with everyone we know.'

'That's a good idea,' said Mr Wong Chong, and so that's what they did. Every morning they put something into the pot that they knew would be helpful to their neighbours, and as soon as the pot had made two of everything, they shared what it had given.

On Monday they put in two chickens and a piglet. When the pot gave them two of everything, they gave the two extra chickens and the second piglet to Mr Chang who lived next door.

On Tuesday they dropped in a packet of pencils and a box of paints, then gave the additional pencils and paint to the little boy next door.

On Wednesday they put a bag of rice, some apples and four cabbages into the pot, and shared the extra food with old Mrs Lin who lived down the lane.

On Thursday they put in a pair of trousers, some warm boots and a thick padded jacket. When the pot had delivered two of everything, they put the clothes back in, and out, then back in again. In no time at all they had eight sets of jackets, trousers and boots. They kept a set each and gave the rest to six of their neighbours.

On Friday they noticed that Mrs Yan's bicycle had broken. So they got Mrs Wong Chong's bicycle out of the shed and put it in the pot. Sure enough, in just the time it took for a wheel to turn, there were two bikes. Mrs Yan was delighted.

On Saturday they put the shed in the pot. Of course they had to dismantle it first, then when the two sheds came out, Mr Wong Chong had to rebuild their shed and also one for Mrs Yan to keep her new bicycle in.

By Saturday evening the neighbours were agog.

'Where are they getting everything from?' they asked each other. 'We're not wealthy in our neighbourhood, and the Wong Chongs are certainly not rich, so where are all these things coming from?'

'I've noticed that all is very quiet at their house first thing in a morning, then they come out with something to give away,' someone said. 'Why don't we all go and watch, tomorrow morning, and see what happens.'

'Good idea,' they all agreed. And so it was that early on Sunday morning, all the neighbours crept along under the window of the Wong Chongs' house, and listened.

'What shall we have today, Mr Wong Chong?' asked his wife.

'Well, I think Mr Ting could do with a new fishing rod,' he said, and he put his own rod into the pot.

Mrs Wong Chong leaned into the pot to pull out the second fishing rod, but just as she did so, she became aware of someone watching her. She turned round and suddenly saw a row of faces peering at her through the window.

'My goodness me!' she started . . . and she fell into the pot.

The neighbours all rushed into the house to help but were amazed to see two Mrs Wong Chongs sitting in the bottom of the pot. They pulled them both out.

'Oh no! Now what are we going to do?' they said, realising straight away that here was a magic pot that clearly made two of everything. They all turned to Mr Wong Chong.

'Well, there's only one thing for it!' he said. And he jumped into the pot himself.

'What a clever idea!' laughed the neighbours, as they pulled out the two Mr Wong Chongs. 'Now we have two Wong Chong families we'll have to build a second house.' And that's exactly what they did.

The Wong Chongs lived next door to each other for the rest of their lives, and the whole neighbourhood used the two-of-everything pot for all those things that they needed.

And the best thing was, no one became greedy.

It's a good story, isn't it? Many folk tales, like this one from China, are amusing. They were told to make people laugh, to entertain them. But they also had another purpose. They were stories told as a way of teaching people how to live together in their communities; how to get along together; how to look after and care for each other. Many of these folk stories are hundreds of years old, but I think their messages are just as relevant to us today, as they were to the first people who heard them. What do you think?

~

Let us try not to be greedy, but to share what we have with others. Let's remember to try to share our time as well as our possessions, with others. Let's spend a few moments thinking of ways we can share what we have today, with the people we shall be with today.

One-third of the world is hungry

Assembly preparation: you will need:

- Two large tables at the front of the hall, one preferably with flowers, tablecloth, etc., the other left empty.
- A bowl of cooked rice.
- A shopping bag filled with plenty of normal groceries (with appeal to children!).
- Two bowls and two spoons.
- Eight children to help.

We are all very lucky because we have plenty to eat. Every day we have breakfast and lunch and tea and supper, and I expect you, like me, have fruit or sweets, and drinks in between your meals as well sometimes.

I suppose someone in your family goes to the supermarket regularly; maybe you go with them, to buy the food you'll need for the coming week. I've brought some of my supermarket shopping with me into assembly today, and I'm going to ask these two children here to unpack these bags and put all my shopping on this table.

(**If this assembly should coincide with a harvest festival, the contents of the bags could be added to the harvest table.**)

Well, that's quite a pile of things, isn't it? And it's quite a contrast to this empty table here, where I'm going to put this bowl of rice.

And now, I need six more children to help me. They each have a plate and I'm going to ask them to stand in a line between the two tables.

I am going to ask the first child to go and take a spoonful of rice from the bowl, and put it on their plate. I am not going to invite the second child to have any rice, nor the third child. Their plates will stay empty. I am going to ask the fourth child to have a plate of rice, but I am not going to ask the fifth or sixth child to have any.

Now, is that fair? No, of course it's not fair because two children have a plate of rice each, but four children have nothing at all. So, let's see if I can put that right.

I know, the four children who have nothing can go to the table with all my shopping on it, and they can choose anything at all they want. Go on, you can choose plenty, and anything you want.

Is it fair now? No of course it's not because now, four children have lots of food, but these two children have only a small amount of rice each. Four children could choose what they wanted but these two children couldn't; they were only offered rice. Four children have full plates, but these two children have plates that are nearly empty.

I can see very clearly that this is unfair, but I am now going to ask two of the children who have plates *full* of food to go and choose some more! Yes, I can see that you are unsure of this, but you can have some more. You may need to put some of the food into a bag if you have chosen more than you can carry.

It becomes more and more unfair, doesn't it? And yet this is exactly what our world is like at the moment. Some of us have lots to eat; some of us actually have too much! But some people in the world do not have enough. Two out of every three people have plenty, and some have more than plenty, but one out of every three people does not have enough. Two-thirds of the world have plenty of food; one-third of the world is hungry.

This week we've been thinking about sharing, and at the moment sharing food and sharing the earth's resources is something that most people in the world are not very good at.

Of course, we can't just send food off to other countries. We can't pack up our breakfast cereal or our lunchbox and post it off to someone who doesn't have enough. But we can be aware of the unfairness in the world. We can be aware that people in many other countries need help and support from people like us who live where there is plenty. And we can perhaps support organisations like Christian Aid and Oxfam and Cafod, who work at trying to share more fairly, what we have.

～

Dear God, help us to be aware that many people in the world do not have the things we take for granted, like enough food, or clean water, or access to medicine, or homes to live in. Help us to do what we can to make sure that the world becomes a fairer place, so that everyone has fair shares. Help us to know that each one of us is part of our global, our world, family, and that we each have a responsibility to help one another. Help us all to be thoughtful, generous people. Amen

Theme 5

Differences

Iyadola's babies

Everyone in the world is different . . . and everyone in the world is the same!
What on earth can I mean by that?

Well, we are all different. We have different ideas, we like different things.
We have different backgrounds, different beliefs; we might come from a
different country or a different culture from other people. We all look different:
some people are black, others are white, but even people from the same ances-
tors are not identical. Brothers or sisters don't look completely alike, and even
twins are rarely exactly the same. Yet, we are all the same because we all belong
to the same human family – the world family. We all need to be cared for, we
all want to be loved and looked after.

So, why are we all so different when we are all so much the same? The people
in West Africa have a lovely old traditional story – a myth – which explains it.

Nyame was the great sky god who lived high above the clouds. One day, to
amuse himself, he made an enormous round basket. He put soil and water
in the basket and planted trees and flowers in the soil. He made animals,
birds and insects and put them in the basket too. Then he made a hole in
the sky and pushed the basket through. It hung there like a beautiful round
ball.

Nyame spent so much time watching his beautiful basket, which he called
his Earth, that the two spirit people who lived inside him wondered what all
the fuss was about.

'We need to see this basket for ourselves,' said the spirit woman, and she
led the spirit man to the very edge of Nyame's mouth so that they could look
out and see the Earth. But, just at that moment, Nyame gave a tremendous

sneeze and the two spirit people fell right out of his mouth; down, down, they fell, until they landed on the Earth.

'What are we going to do?' said the spirit man.

'We must have a look around, of course,' said the spirit woman. So they looked all around at what they could see. They saw the wonderful animals and birds and insects, they marvelled at the beautiful plants and flowers, and they felt the strange effects of the wind and rain and sun on their faces. They spent such a lot of time looking about them that they soon grew hungry.

'I'll catch something,' said the spirit man, and he caught a fish for them to eat.

Soon, the spirit man discovered that he could catch other animals to eat, especially if he sharpened a stick and used it as a spear. The man had become a hunter. He went out early every morning and came back late every evening, leaving the spirit woman all alone during the day.

'I'm lonely,' she said to him one night. 'But I've had an idea! Suppose we get some clay from the edge of the river, and make some little clay people just like us! We could bake them in the fire and when they're done we could breathe life into them and they could be our children. Then, when you're out hunting all day I won't be lonely.'

'I'm not sure,' said the spirit man. 'The last time you had an idea it landed us here! This new idea might get us into trouble.'

'No it won't,' said the spirit woman. 'It's a good idea!'

So the very next day they made a whole batch of little clay babies and put them into the embers of the fire to bake.

'We mustn't let them burn!' warned the spirit woman.

But no sooner had they put the clay babies into the embers than Nyame poked his head through the sky and called to them.

'Where are you both?' he shouted. 'Come out and talk to me!'

The spirit woman snatched the clay babies out of the fire and hid them in some leaves. She didn't want Nyame to see what they'd been doing, in case he was angry with them. Then they walked into a clearing where Nyame could see them and talked with him for a long, long time. At last Nyame left to go back to the sky.

'I thought he would never leave!' said the spirit woman. 'Quick! Put the clay babies back in the fire, they need to cook some more.'

But no sooner had the spirit people put a few of the clay babies back into the fire, than Nyame came thundering by again.

'I forget to ask you,' he said. 'Why have you got such a big fire on a hot day like today?'

'Ummm, we were cold,' said the spirit woman, feeling rather foolish, as the day *was* hot.

'Are you ill?' asked Nyame, sounding concerned.

'No, we're fine,' they answered.

But Nyame stayed talking for so long that when the spirit woman was at last able to take the clay babies out of the fire, they had all burned black.

The spirit people made another batch of babies, then another and another, but every time they were in the middle of baking them in the embers, Nyame came and interrupted them.

At last he became hungry and went home to the sky for his tea, and the spirit man and woman were able to take the last of the clay babies out of the fire and unwrap from the leaves the ones they had made earlier. They spread all the clay babies out on the grass in a long line.

But, what a sight!

Some of the clay babies were still white as bone and hardly cooked at all. Others, like the first ones they made, were cooked so long they were black as night. And in between were clay babies of all colours: beige and ecru, sienna and pink, terra-cotta and ochre and umber. Nutmeg and cinnamon, ginger and walnut, hazel and chestnut and fawn.

'But they're all different,' wailed the spirit man.

'No they're not!' laughed the spirit woman. 'They're all the same! They are all my babies!' and she swept them up into her arms and breathed life into each and every one of them, so that they wriggled their little arms and legs and ran about at her feet.

After that, the spirit woman was never lonely again when her man went hunting. She cared for her babies, loved them and looked after them, and ever since then has been called Iyadola, which means Earth Mother.

That West African story was told thousands of years ago, to explain why and how there are people on our earth who look different from each other. Iyadola, the Earth Mother, knew that her babies all looked different, yet she knew they were all the same, they were all made in the same way and they all needed to be loved and looked after.

Although that story is old, and we now know that all the people on our earth didn't really come from clay babies, it still teaches us that we are all from the same family: our world family, and we all have the same needs as human beings.

Let's think about our world family. We come from different countries, from different parts of the world. We all have skin and hair colour that is different from each other. We have different backgrounds and beliefs. We have different traditions and customs. But we all belong to our world family, we are all neighbours. We all need to be loved and cared for. We all need to play our part in looking after everyone in our world family, and making sure life is fair for everyone.

Foolish John

We all like to be the same as our friends, don't we? We like to feel we have lots in common with them. We like to fit it.

From time to time new people join our class or our school or our neighbourhood, or even our family, and at first it can sometimes be difficult for them to fit in. Sometimes, if the new person feels different in any way from the rest of us, they can find it hard to make friends. And that's when it's our job to be especially welcoming. Fitting in, if you feel a bit different, is quite hard to do. But it shouldn't be, because we are all different from each other in some way or other. The main thing to remember is that everyone is important, and that everyone is good at something.

In today's story, someone was cruel and unkind to a person they thought was different, but things didn't turn out quite as he expected!

There was once a young man who did everything so differently from everyone else that all the people who knew him called him Foolish John, and forgot what his real name was. Foolish John used to do most things backwards, or at the wrong time, or in a different order from what was usual.

For example, Foolish John always took out his umbrella when the sun shone, but when it rained he would take off his hat and coat and sit outside his house in a deck chair. Everyone used to laugh at him.

In winter when the weather was cold and frosty, Foolish John used to wear his shorts and tee-shirts, and everyone used to laugh at him. In summer, especially when there was a heatwave, he would wear a pullover and a jumper, three pairs of trousers, four pairs of socks, two scarves, a woolly hat and his overcoat. And everyone used to laugh at him.

Foolish John always went to bed as daylight began and got up as it began to get dark. He walked backwards wherever he went and he carried a mirror so that he could see where he was going. Everyone used to laugh at him.

One day the king heard about Foolish John.

'Send him here to the palace,' ordered the king. 'He can come and amuse me and my court. I like something I can laugh at.'

So Foolish John was taken to the palace and told to stand before the king. The king and the courtiers teased him and poked fun at him. They bullied him and called him unkind names. And they laughed even louder.

'Oh, ho, ho!' guffawed the king. 'This is such *fun*! It's so easy to laugh at you, Foolish John, because you are just so *stupid*!' and he laughed until tears rolled down his cheeks. But some people in the king's palace began to feel uncomfortable about the king's behaviour towards Foolish John. They thought the king was being too cruel, too unkind. They thought the king, of all people, should know better than to behave in that way to one of his own people. But no one dared say anything in case they angered the king.

The king, however, knew nothing of how some of his people felt, and he carried on teasing Foolish John, thinking that everyone was enjoying poking fun as much as he was.

'Have you always been so stupid?' he asked. 'Do you always look so silly or have you had to practise for a long time?' and he roared at his own joke. 'Why are you so tall and thin? You look like a beanpole, or a piece of spaghetti, or a length of string. How long is a piece of string anyway? Is it as long as you?' and he roared with laughter again.

Foolish John said not a word, and hung his head in shame.

'Come on, boy. Speak!' shouted the king. 'You *can* speak, I suppose? Well? Cat got your tongue? Have you left your voice behind?' and he prodded Foolish John with a silver stick as though that would make him speak.

But Foolish John felt too miserable to speak. He had no idea what to say to the king, so he stared at the marble floor and tried hard not to cry.

The king poked him again and said, 'Well! If you won't *answer* my questions, maybe you'd like to *ask* me one. Now that *would* be good!' he chortled. 'Yes, that *would* be amusing! *You*, asking *me* a question. Listen up everyone!' he announced to the crowd in the room. 'This stupid boy here is going to ask me a question. I'll wager he won't be able to think of one to ask! But if he does, and if I can't answer it, I'll eat my hat! No! Better than that! If he asks me a question I can't answer I'll give him half my kingdom! There! How about that!' and the king laughed so much at his own cleverness that he almost fell off his throne.

Most of the crowd joined in the laughter at the thought of Foolish John being able to ask the king a question he couldn't answer. After all, it was impossible . . . wasn't it . . .?

Slowly, Foolish John lifted his head and looked the king in the eye.

'I have not one question, but three,' he said. 'Three questions you will be unable to answer.'

The king turned purple with rage at the impudence of the boy. The rest of the courtiers grew silent.

'What gets wetter as it dries?' Foolish John asked in a clear voice.

'What has no top and no bottom, no left and no right?' he asked.

'And what is at the end of your kingdom?'

The crowd stood immobile, awaiting the king's answer. The king said nothing for a long time. Then he grew red and began to shout.

'What kind of stupid questions are those?' he demanded. 'They're not proper questions! They don't have proper answers! They're trick questions! You're cheating! I take back my challenge.'

'But Sir,' said one of the king's ministers. 'The boy has done as you asked. A riddle question is a question nevertheless. Can you answer his questions? Or not?'

'No, of course I can't answer his questions,' yelled the king. 'Because they don't *have* answers!'

'They do,' said Foolish John, quietly. 'A towel gets wetter as it dries. A ball has no top and no bottom, no left and no right. And, at the end of your kingdom is . . . the letter M.'

'He's right!' shouted the people. 'He's right. He's asked questions that our king cannot answer. Foolish John is not as silly as he seems. In fact, he's very clever. Very clever indeed! Give him half the kingdom as promised!'

And so it was that Foolish John was given half the king's kingdom. He was also given his old name back, as people suddenly remembered what it was. They also suddenly remembered that it's cruel and unnecessary to laugh at other people, and that people who seem silly are often not as silly as they seem!

What do you think about the way the king treated Foolish John? I'm sure you were as horrified as I was at his behaviour. I'm pleased to say we have no one in our school who would behave in such a way towards John, if he came here. The king, of course, forgot what we all know: that everyone is good at something, we just have to discover what it is.

～

Let's spend a few minutes thinking whether we have ever laughed unkindly at someone else. Perhaps they've been new to our group of friends, or to our neighbourhood. Perhaps we were unkind because we didn't know them at that point. Let's try to make sure we never laugh unkindly at someone else. Let's remember that although we are all different from each other, we are all the same inside and we all have the same feelings.

Mr Chang and the yellow suit

I'd like you to think of someone famous, someone whom you admire. No, don't tell me who it is, just think of them. Now think of the person sitting next to you. They're probably not famous at all, but think of something about them that makes them special. It could be that you don't know the person sitting next to you very well, but you'll know something about them; something that makes them unique and different from anyone else you know.

Sometimes we think that only famous people can be special, but that's just not true. Everyone is special in their own way. Listen to this Chinese story about a man who thought he was very ordinary.

Mr Chang was a very ordinary man. He lived in a conventional house, with commonplace things in it; he had an average sort of job and every day he went to his regular work wearing his usual black suit, just like all the other ordinary people in China at that time.

But Mr Chang wanted to be different.

Each day, on his way to work, he would see Mr Mo, the Chinese emperor, in the palace gardens, eating his breakfast, or pruning his roses, or walking his dog, and Mr Chang would wish he could be special, just like Mr Mo. Mr Chang began to wonder just what it was that made Mr Mo so special, apart from the fact that he was the emperor, of course, and that he lived in a palace, and had hundreds of servants and was in charge of the whole country, and wore a golden yellow suit.

'That's it!' said Mr Chang, suddenly to himself. 'That's it! That's what makes him so special – he wears a yellow suit!' and Mr Chang imagined what it must be like to wear a golden yellow suit every day instead of the boringly ordinary black one *he* wore every day.

'I'd like to have a yellow suit,' he decided, and he went straightaway to visit his tailor.

'You can't wear a yellow suit!' said the tailor, horrified at the very idea. 'Only the emperor is allowed to wear yellow. You'll get into serious trouble if you are seen in a yellow suit!'

'But I'd really like to have one,' said Mr Chang. 'If I had a yellow suit I'd feel so special; I wouldn't feel ordinary any more.'

'You'd feel special all right!' warned the tailor. 'You'd end up in prison! That'd make you feel special!'

'But I really do want to wear a yellow suit. Have you got one?'

'Well, as a matter of fact I have,' said the tailor. 'But if I sell it to you, you must promise never to wear it outside, and never let anyone else see you in it.'

'All right, I promise,' said Mr Chang, and he bought the beautiful golden yellow suit from the tailor, took it home, and put it on. Immediately Mr Chang felt different. He felt important and special in his yellow suit. In fact he felt so different that he wanted to wear it all the time, but he knew he must not.

'But, if I wore my new yellow suit *under* my ordinary black clothes, no one would know, so that would be all right,' he reasoned to himself, and he put on his old black suit over the new golden yellow one, and went out.

The deliciously important, special, different feeling that Mr Chang felt wearing his new suit continued, and he strode around the town, looking and feeling every inch an emperor. He was so busy feeling different and important that he completely ignored several of his friends and neighbours, who said to each other, 'Whatever is the matter with Mr Chang? He's very snooty today!'

After several hours of walking about feeling important, Mr Chang felt tired, and sat down by the pond in the park to rest. Two little girls were playing badminton nearby and one of them hit the shuttlecock so hard it fell into the pond with a splash and the girls began to cry.

'Don't worry about it,' said Mr Chang, jumping to his feet. 'I'll get it for you,' and he rolled up his trouser legs and his jacket sleeves and waded into the water. But, at the sight of the golden trouser legs and the yellow sleeves under the black ones, the girls sprang back.

'Oh no!' they said. 'You are much too important to go wading into the water. It's only a shuttlecock, it need not concern you.'

'I'll get it,' insisted Mr Chang, and he fished it out of the water for them.

But just as he was giving the shuttlecock back to the girls their nanny came hurrying over, and she too saw the golden yellow suit underneath Mr Chang's black one.

'Why are you wearing that yellow suit, Mr Chang,' she said.

But before Mr Chang had time to answer, several more people in the park began to crowd round to see what was going on.

'He's wearing a yellow suit!' they whispered. 'He shouldn't do that! Only the emperor can do that! He'll get arrested!' And sure enough, Mr Chang was apprehended for daring to wear a golden yellow suit, and he was taken before the emperor, Mr Mo.

The emperor was furious.

'How dare you,' he shouted. 'Only I, The Emperor Mo, can wear a suit of golden yellow. How dare you impersonate me!'

'I didn't mean to be rude to you, Sir,' said Mr Chang. 'And I wasn't trying to *be* you, I only wanted to know what it would feel like to wear a yellow suit. To see if it would make me feel important.'

'And did it?' thundered Mr Mo.

'He wasn't too important to help us get our shuttlecock out of the pond, Daddy,' said the two little girls as they ran into the emperor's room.

'Daddy?' thought Mr Chang. 'They are the daughters of Mr Mo? Oh no! Of all the people to try to help, and I chose the emperor's children!'

'So, Mr Chang,' boomed the emperor. 'You helped my children?'

'I simply fished their toy out of the pond, Sir,' replied Mr Chang.

'Then I forgive you,' said the emperor. 'And I will reward you. Tonight we are having a fireworks party. You can come, and for tonight only, I shall allow you to wear your golden yellow suit to the party.'

Mr Chang went to the party, but he didn't wear his yellow suit; in fact he never wore the golden yellow suit again. He wore his best black suit to the party, and he enjoyed being himself.

When the fireworks were finished and the party was over, Mr Chang went home to his ordinary house. He looked out of his window at the stars sparkling in the night sky, and decided he was just like them.

'I'm not as bright or important as the sun or the moon, but I'm special just like each one of the stars,' he said.

Mr Chang in the story had discovered what we all know already: that everyone is special in his or her own way. Nobody is 'ordinary', and although we are all basically the same, we are all different with our own strengths and our own personalities. Everyone is special.

～

Dear God, help us to remember that each one of us is special; each one of us is good at something, and each one of us is unique. Help us to discover what is special about each other, help us to find out what it is we each do well. Help us to learn about each other so that we can better understand everyone in our world. Help us to celebrate our differences as well as our similarities. Amen

Theme 6

Inclusion

Sammy and the Town Hall Concert

Do you like music? I think almost everyone does. Everyone has their favourite kind of music, whether it's pop or jazz or classical. Lots of people like to play an instrument, and I know many of you can play the piano or violin, trumpet or recorder. I wonder if you think that everyone should have the right to be able to enjoy music. I know I do. The headteacher in today's true story feels very strongly that music is for everyone. She believes there should be total musical inclusion. That's an important sounding belief, perhaps you can tell me at the end of the story what you think it means.

Sammy loved to sing. And he was good at it!

There were many other things that Sammy wasn't so good at, like reading and writing, PE and sums, but he was good at singing. He would come in to school singing in the morning, and sing to himself most of the day.

'You always cheer me up, Sammy,' his headteacher, Mrs Peace, used to say whenever she saw him, and Sammy would laugh and sing her another song whilst she listened.

Sammy went to a special school. It was for children like him who had special needs; children who had difficulties or disabilities of one sort or another. Many of the children found it difficult to learn, but of course, everyone was good at something, and many of the children, just like Sammy, were good at singing.

This may have had something to do with Mrs Peace, and Mrs West, one of the other teachers, because both of them were very keen on music. In fact, Mrs West used to have music workshops in her classroom and teachers from other schools would come and see how she taught music to the children at Armley Grange.

One day an inspector called to see the school.

'Welcome to Armley Grange,' smiled Mrs Peace, showing him in. 'Come and see the children in Mrs West's music workshop,' she added proudly. But, much to her surprise, the inspector was not impressed.

'Most of these children cannot read or write,' he said. 'So what is the point of trying to teach them music?'

Mrs Peace was furious. 'Music is for everyone,' she said. 'These children have as much right as anyone else to be taught music. These children love music. Most of them are very good at it! Have you heard them sing?'

'I haven't time to listen to them sing!' said the inspector, impatiently, and he went off to do things he considered more important.

Mrs Peace remained extremely angry about the attitude of the inspector.

'How dare he suggest that our children should not be taught music!' she said to Mrs West. 'I've a good mind to put on a concert and make him come and see it!' she added.

'That's a very good idea,' said Mrs West. 'Let's do it! Let's put on a concert, but let's make it a huge one. Let's make special needs music worth celebrating!'

'We could invite other schools to join us,' said Mrs Peace, as the idea began to grow in her mind.'

'If we invite other schools, then our school hall might not be big enough,' said Mrs West.

'Then we'll find somewhere bigger!' said Mrs Peace.

'But where could we go that would fit hundreds of children and an audience?'

'I know!' said Mrs Peace. 'We could hire Leeds Town Hall. *That* would be big enough!'

'But it's enormous!' said Mrs West.

'Then we'll just have to have an enormous concert, won't we?' laughed Mrs Peace.

By now, the two teachers were beginning to feel really excited about their idea. But the task, like Leeds Town Hall, was huge. They would need permission to put on the concert. They would have to invite special needs children from all over Yorkshire if they were to fill the Town Hall. They would have to plan a programme, learn songs, have enough time for the children to practise.

'And what about someone to play the music?' asked Mrs West. 'Who's going to do that?'

'We have to think BIG,' said Mrs Peace. 'It's to be a big concert, in a big hall, so we need big music!'

'Got it!' shouted Mrs West. 'The Yorkshire Post Brass Band! You can't get much bigger than that!'

'Perfect!' said Mrs Peace. 'Now all we have to do is persuade them to do it.'

'And how about if we ask someone famous to conduct the concert,' said Mrs West. 'What about Simon Lindley, and he can bring the whole of the Leeds Parish Church Choir with him!'

'Brilliant idea!' said Mrs Peace. 'And we'll need someone important to open the concert . . . what about . . . the Lord Mayor!'

'Yes!' shouted Mrs West.

So Mrs Peace and Mrs West began the mammoth task of organising the concert. They invited other teachers involved in music for special needs children to help. They asked Mrs Holstock, a lecturer at the local college for teachers, to write some special music. They wrote to the Yorkshire Post Brass Band, to the Leeds Parish Church Choir, to Simon Lindley the conductor, and to the Lord Mayor of Leeds, and asked if they would join in. They invited special schools all over Yorkshire to be involved, and they booked the massive Leeds Town Hall for the occasion.

And *everyone* they asked agreed to help.

Rehearsals began. Sammy and the others in his class worked harder than they had ever done before to learn the words and the music to the songs and carols. All over Yorkshire, other children in other schools practised for all they were worth. The choirboys practised in the Parish Church and the brass band practised at the Yorkshire Post.

At last everything and everyone was ready. Mrs Peace and Mrs West had just one more job to do. They sent an invitation to the inspector who had said there was no point in teaching music to children with special needs.

'We are pleased to invite you to the Lord Mayor's Christmas Concert at Leeds Town Hall at 7 pm on Thursday 7 December', the invitation read.

The inspector arrived at quarter to seven and was amazed to see the huge Town Hall absolutely filled with people. There was not a spare seat to be found. At ten to seven hundreds of children walked to their places on the stage and at five to seven the Brass Band brought their instruments on to the stage. At seven o'clock the Lord Mayor of Leeds marched on to the stage in all his ceremonial robes, and declared the concert would begin.

The music started and the children sang. Hundreds of beautiful clear voices ringing up to the ceiling of the enormous Town Hall. Sammy's voice sang out with the rest. He had never enjoyed anything quite like this. The audience clapped and cheered. Song after song, carol after carol, the music went on. Then, all too soon, it was over.

'Brilliant! Wonderful! Magical! Tremendous! Superb!' the audience said.

'You were right,' said the inspector to Mrs Peace. 'Music is for everyone and you have proved it. This is the very best concert I have ever been to, and the children with special needs were undoubtedly the stars of the show. Thank you. I have learned something tonight.'

'You have learned,' said Mrs Peace,' what I have always known. That everyone is good at something.'

Well, have you worked out what 'total musical inclusion' means? Yes, it means music for everyone, no matter how good they are at anything else.

When Mrs Peace and Mrs West planned that very first concert, they probably didn't think of it continuing year after year. But those Town Hall Concerts have now been held every Christmas for more than 25 years. The music workshops have grown into an organisation called YAMSEN* which stands for the Yorkshire Association for Music and Special Educational Needs. YAMSEN now involves adults as well as children, but it still aims to make music available to people with special needs, because music is for everyone and everyone can be good at it.

~

Dear God, help us to remember that everyone is good at something. Help us to make sure that we treat everyone equally, and that we do not jump to conclusions about people. Help us to remember that including people is important, even if they may seem different from us. Help us to remember that everyone has something to offer and that everyone matters. Amen

Lisa goes to school

I wonder if you know what Braille is. Yes, it's a special alphabet of tiny raised dots, that people who can't see, can feel in order to read.** I wonder if you've ever seen anything written in Braille. Next time you're in the supermarket, ask the grown-up you're with to show you some of the cleaning products; they nearly all have some Braille written on them. Braille is on these products as a warning because, of course, cleaning fluids can be dangerous.

---

* Further information about YAMSEN can be found at www.yamsen.org.uk.

** An image of a finger 'reading' Braille can be found at www.accesscommunication. co.uk/images/braille.jpg.

I wonder if you think that people who can't see should have the same rights as everyone else. For example, should blind people go out to work? Can blind people take part in sports? I have a friend who is a keen cyclist. She rides a tandem and every week she does a training ride with a man who is blind. She rides at the front and does the seeing; he rides behind and does the powerful pedalling. They are a good team and neither can do the ride without the other.

And what do you think about blind children going to school with children who are not blind? Should they do this? Listen to today's story and see what you think.

Lisa started nursery when she was three, just like her older brother had done, and just like all her friends in the street where she lived. Lisa loved nursery. Her mum used to take her every morning and hand her over to the teacher, and there was usually some funny story to tell about something Lisa had done, or said, since she'd been at nursery the day before, because Lisa was always full of life, and mischief, and laughter.

'Hello Mrs Matthews,' Lisa would say, smiling up at her teacher.

'Hello Lisa. And what are you going to play with this morning?' Mrs Matthews would ask.

'Bricks!' Lisa would laugh. She liked to play with the big bricks. She liked the cool feel of the tough plastic and the big square shape of them. She liked to pile them up as tall as herself, and to feel how high they were. But there were other things she liked about nursery, too. She enjoyed listening to stories, and singing. She liked playing in the sand and water. She enjoyed running about outside and playing on the tricycles; but for this, she needed help, because Lisa was blind.

She was blind when she was born and the doctors told her parents, very gently, that there would be all kinds of things she would be unable to do.

'But there'll be lots of things she *can* do,' said her mother, and she took Lisa home, determined that she would be just like any other child, despite being blind.

At nursery, Lisa had a special helper called Mrs Ibbetson whose job it was to make sure she was safe, and to help her with things she found difficult. But Mrs Ibbetson was very clever, because she didn't do things *for* Lisa, she helped her to do things for herself.

Lisa learned quickly. She was a bright girl and was soon able to do many things as well as her friends who were able to see. And whatever she did, she was always cheerful, always laughing and smiling. Everyone liked her.

But when Lisa was five, and it was time to go to primary school, the people in charge of schools at the education office said to her parents, 'We're sorry, but it's out of the question! Lisa cannot possibly go to her local school. She's blind! She must go to a special school where the teachers are trained to deal with children like her!'

'Children like her!' said Lisa's mum. 'How dare you speak of her like that! She's a child! Just like any other child! She just happens not to be able to see. We want her to go to the local primary school with all her friends.'

'We're sorry, it's not possible,' said the education officers.

'But we want her to come to our school,' said the headteacher.

'And we want her to go to the primary school,' said Mrs Matthews and Mrs Ibbetson.

'And *I* want to go to that school,' said Lisa.

'It'll never work,' said the education officers. 'You'll see! You can try it for a year, but she'll not be able to cope in an ordinary school.'

So Lisa went to primary school with all her friends, and with Mrs Ibbetson to help her. But, how was she to learn to read and write when she couldn't see? How was she to do maths when she couldn't see the book or the board or the paper? How could she do science or history or art?

'She will learn Braille, like other children who are blind,' said the head-teacher. 'But you will have to learn it first,' she said to Mrs Ibbetson.

So Mrs Ibbetson went to college in her spare time to learn Braille, and then passed an exam in it. The school bought a Braille machine for Lisa to use so that she could write, and lots of books in Braille for her to read. Mrs Ibbetson began to teach Braille to Lisa. It was difficult at first, trying to make sense of all those tiny raised dots, but Lisa was determined to learn to read and write, just like everyone else in her class. It didn't seem to matter that she was learning the same thing in a slightly different way from everyone else.

The time flew by and soon the children were ready to move into Year 1. The education officers came back to see Lisa.

'We have a special school ready to take your daughter,' they said to Lisa's mum. 'She can transfer there right away.'

'But you haven't looked at what Lisa can do!' said her mum, and she put one of Lisa's Braille books in her hand. 'Read this story to the visitors, Lisa,' she said. And Lisa read the whole story without one single mistake.

'And I can write something for you,' added Lisa, and she sat at her Braille machine and wrote, 'My name is Lisa. I go to White Laith School. I want to go into Year 1 with all my friends.' She gave them the piece of paper.

The education officers were astounded. 'This is unbelievable,' they said. 'We would never have believed it possible.'

'I told you, she's just an ordinary child who happens to be unable to see,' said Lisa's mum. 'She just needs the same opportunity as everyone else.'

'You're right,' said the education officers. 'She can stay at White Laith School.'

So Lisa stayed at school with her friends. She continued through to Year 4 and by then she had learned to use a white cane to get around the school and the playground. By the time she was in Year 5, she needed to extend her mobility and needed more space to practise on than the school could provide, so a local factory offered the use of their offices and staircases, corridors and lifts. Lisa, with Mrs Ibbetson to help, walked miles in the factory, becoming more confident with every step she made.

The people at the factory were so impressed with Lisa's hardworking attitude and her cheerful personality, that they collected enough money to buy and train a guide dog for her.

'But I can't have one till I'm eighteen,' said Lisa. 'They don't give guide dogs to children!'

'Then we'll put the money in trust until you *are* eighteen,' they said, and that's exactly what they did.

Lisa is now at college. She never went to a special school for blind children, but continued through primary and secondary school with the same friends she'd been to nursery with, all those years before.

Well, what do you think about Lisa going to her local school? The people from the education office had assumed things about Lisa. They had assumed that because she was blind she would be unable to do most of the things that ordinary children can do. But they assumed this without giving her chance to prove what she could do.

I'm afraid we all do this at times. We all jump to conclusions about people before we know them. We look at people's disabilities and not at the people themselves. We think we know what they can, or can't, do without actually finding out. Let's make sure that we give people with disabilities the same chances and choices as everyone else.

~

Let's make sure that we treat everyone fairly. Let's make sure that we don't jump to conclusions about people with disabilities. Let's remember that everyone has the same rights as everyone else; that everyone needs to be treated equally; that everyone is a valuable person in their own right, no matter what they can, or cannot, do or how different they may seem.

The king's children

What do you think the word 'inclusion' means? Yes, I was sure you would know. It means including people; not leaving them out; not discriminating against them because they seem different or not as clever. It means recognising that everyone has something to offer; everyone is important; everyone is good at something.

In today's story a king is expected to choose which of his children is the most talented. But it's an impossible choice. Let's see what happened.

Once upon a time there was a king of a faraway land who had four fine children; two boys and two girls. When the children were almost grown up, the king's advisors said that he must decide which of his sons or daughters was the most talented.

'You need to know,' they said. 'For it will soon be time to choose your successor. One of your children must lead your country after you, and it must be the most talented of them.'

'But it is impossible to choose!' said the king. 'Each of my children is talented in his or her own way. Each of them is good at something. Nothing can be achieved by trying to compare them!'

'But you must choose the most talented,' insisted the advisors. 'And if you can't decide, then we will decide for you.'

And so it was arranged that the king's four children would compete against each other in order for the advisors to decide which of them should reign over the country after the death of their father.

'But what will they each do?' asked the king.

'They can decide that for themselves,' said the advisors. 'Each of them will ride their horse up to the giant oak tree in the palace grounds, then they can do whatever they like to show us how talented they are. We will then be able to see which of them is the *most* talented.'

The day of the contest arrived. The king, the advisors, and a whole company of onlookers stood by the giant oak tree to watch the contest. Alpha, the king's eldest son, mounted his fine black horse. He rode, strongly and firmly towards the tree. When he was in the shade of its branches he slid from the saddle, then, to the astonishment of the crowd, he hoisted the horse on to his back and began to climb the tree. Higher and higher he climbed until he reached the very topmost branch, which swayed and dipped under the combined weight of the boy and the horse. Alpha waved to the people below, then surely, steadily, he climbed down the far side of the tree.

'Such strength!' exclaimed the crowd. 'What skills he has! Such a strong boy would make a fine king.'

Next, it was the turn of Beta, the king's eldest daughter. She rode up to the tree on her fine white horse. She held long coloured ribbons in her hands. Beta stood up in the saddle, threw the ribbons over a high branch and let the ends flutter in the breeze. Then she went to speak to the people in the crowd.

'Come and help me,' she said, and she persuaded some two dozen people to come up to the tree. She gave them each a ribbon to hold, and explained what she wanted them to do, whilst taking a small accordion out of her saddle bag. Beta began to play the accordion and as soon as they heard the music, the people started to dance. The tree had become a maypole and soon the dancers had woven a beautiful plait with the coloured ribbons. Beta smiled and played on. The dancers unplaited the ribbons and danced with them back to the crowd. The effect was magical.

'What a clever girl,' said everyone. 'What skills she has in organising people. Such a girl would make a wonderful leader for our country.'

Then came the turn of Gamma, the king's second son. He mounted his fine russet horse, and rode twice round the tree so fast that the people hardly had time to catch a glimpse of him before he was gone. Then, suddenly, he was there again, this time wielding a huge golden spear. He rode towards the tree, his horse's hooves just a blur in the loose earth. Gamma hurled his spear towards the trunk of the tree, twisting the spear at the same time so that the gold glinted and sparkled in the sunlight. In a flash the spear pierced the tree, leaving a wide gaping hole in its trunk. Gamma leapt from his horse, squeezed through the hole, jumped back into the saddle and rode off in a cloud of dust.

The people were amazed. 'Such dexterity,' they said. 'Such skill with a spear. And such speed! A boy with such speed would indeed make a fine king.'

Last came Delta, the king's youngest daughter. She quietly trotted up to the oak tree on her piebald pony, climbed down, then led the pony to some fresh green grass. As soon as the pony was grazing, Delta took a small basket from the saddle and began to collect acorns that had fallen from the tree. Then she took them a short distance from the tree and began to plant them, one by one, in the soft brown earth. When she had planted them all, she returned to the pony, smiled at the people and went to sit by her father.

'What a kind and gentle girl,' said the people. 'So thoughtful and caring. And see how she looks to the future with the planting of the acorns! It will be a hundred years before those acorns grow into oaks, yet she has had the vision to see them. A girl who is so caring and with such vision for the future would make a fine leader for our country.'

And the people began to talk amongst themselves about which of the king's children should succeed him after his death. But no one could agree.

The king's advisors started to argue about which child was the most talented, but they too could not agree.

At last the king spoke. 'I told you it would be impossible to choose,' he said. 'Each of my children is talented in his or her own way. Each of them is good at something. Nothing can be achieved by trying to compare them! The trouble with trying to compare people is that you can make someone look as though they're no good at one thing, when in fact, they are really good at something else. Everyone is good at something and everyone must be given the chance to find out what it is.'

And with that, the king walked back to the palace and his children went with him. The advisors were left scratching their heads, still wondering what to do about choosing a successor to the king when the time came.

I wonder what you would have done. I wonder what you think of the skills and talents of the king's four children. How would you solve the problem of finding a successor to the king?

Everyone in our school knows that although we are all different, we are all the same, and that every one of us has our own skills and talents. Sometimes those skills and talents are well hidden, but they are there; and we must all give everyone the chance to find them.

~

Let's spend a few moments remembering that everyone is special, everyone is important, everyone has something to offer, and everyone is good at something. Let's make sure we don't leave people out of our games or our plans because we think they might not be able to join in. Let's remember to give everyone the chance to be included, even though they might have different skills or talents from those we have.

Theme 7

Communication

Joey Deacon

If I asked you to think of 'communication' I wonder what would come into your mind. I'm sure you would think of all sorts of things to do with technology: mobile phones and satellites, radar and television. Or you might think of speaking and listening; communicating with each other face to face.

But what of communication if you couldn't speak, and if it was in the days before computers and modern technology? How would you communicate then? I have a true story for you today, of something that really happened not all that long ago, but in the days before computers had been invented to help people who had disabilities. Here's what happened.

It all started when Mrs Deacon had another baby boy. She was delighted to have another boy and she decided to call him Joey.

One day, when the baby was still very small, Mrs Deacon noticed that his arms and legs, and his fingers, didn't seem to be moving properly. She also noticed that he wasn't feeding as easily as her other children had done. As time passed she became more and more convinced that something was wrong.

She took Joey to see the doctor who said he must go to hospital to have some tests. By now, Mrs Deacon was extremely worried. In hospital, the specialist doctor told Mrs Deacon that there was indeed something seriously wrong with her baby. He had cerebral palsy. The part of Joey's brain that controlled movement and muscles wasn't working as it should. The specialist said he was sorry, but that there was very little hope of Joey leading any kind of normal life. He would never be able to walk, or use his hands properly, or even talk, he said. The doctor added that there was no treatment Joey could have, and that there was nothing anyone could do. He even suggested that the best thing Mrs Deacon could do would be to put Joey in a home for children with disabilities, and forget about him.

Although Mrs Deacon was upset to hear what the specialist said, she was also extremely angry.

'There will be something that Joey can do,' she said. 'Just you wait and see, because *everyone* is good at something!' and she took Joey home.

Mrs Deacon looked after Joey, she talked to him and tried to teach him to do things just as she had taught her other children, but Joey made no progress. By the time he was six, he should have started school, but he still couldn't walk or talk so school was impossible.

One day Mrs Deacon was chattering away to Joey as she always did as he sat in his chair whilst she did her housework. She talked about the cars parked outside on the road; there were four cars, and as she looked at Joey she noticed that he made a sound and blinked his eyes four times. No, she thought, he can't count the cars; it must be just a coincidence that he blinked four times. But nevertheless, she turned her whole attention on Joey and said, 'How many cars are there, Joey?' Joey made more sounds and blinked four times.

Mrs Deacon was astonished. 'How many trees are there?' she asked. Joey looked out of the window and blinked six times. There were six trees. Mrs Deacon asked Joey how many chairs, tables, books, toys, cups and saucers he could see, and Joey gave every answer with his eyes. Every answer was right.

'I *knew* it!' said Mrs Deacon. 'I knew you would be able to do something. You can talk to me with your eyes. You can communicate.'

From then on, Mrs Deacon worked hard to understand Joey's strange sounds and movements, and Joey learned to communicate with his mother using his eyes.

Many years later, Mrs Deacon became ill and sadly she died. Joey's aunt and grandma and his dad looked after him, but they couldn't understand what he tried to say to them, and Joey became difficult because he couldn't communicate with them. Joey was now a man and it was decided that he would be better looked after in a special hospital, and so he left the house where he had lived since his childhood and moved to the hospital.

The nurses cared for him but they were very busy and didn't have time to learn how to communicate with him, and so once again there was no one to understand him and Joey became unhappy. But, staying at the same hospital was another man with disabilities called Ernie, and Ernie had something the nurses didn't have: he had spare time. He was very good at watching and listening, and he spent so much time staring at Joey and listening to the sounds he made, that before long he was able to do what Joey's mum had been able to do; he was able to understand Joey.

At last Joey had someone with whom he could communicate and Joey and Ernie became firm friends. They had two more friends in the hospital; Michael, who was the only other person apart from the doctors and nurses who could read and write; and Tom, who had an old typewriter and could copy words although he couldn't read them.

One day, Joey watched one of the rare visitors reading a book to one of the patients as he lay in bed. 'I wish I could write,' thought Joey. 'I wish I could write a book all about me, and tell everyone what it's like to be unable to talk or communicate. I wish I could tell everyone that I'm still me, inside, even though I'm different from everyone else. I wish I could tell them so that they would understand.' But Joey knew it was impossible. He couldn't even hold a pencil and he certainly couldn't use a typewriter. Then, quite suddenly, he had an idea. An idea that was so far-fetched, so crazy, it just might work.

Joey knew he couldn't write a book by himself, but with the help of Ernie, Michael and Tom, they just might be able to do it together.

The next day Joey painstakingly explained to Ernie that he wanted the four friends to write a book. It took some time for Ernie to understand him, but at last he did. Then Ernie spoke to Michael and Tom. They both agreed to help. And so work on writing the book began.

Joey managed to communicate with Ernie and make him understand what he wanted to say. Ernie told Michael what Joey had said, and Michael wrote it down with pencil and paper. The writing was then given to Tom, who copied it down on his typewriter. And in this way a whole book telling the story of Joey and his friends was written.

It took an incredibly long time. It took one whole day just to write four lines. It took fifteen years to write the whole book. But together they did it. Joey had told his story for everyone to read.

The story would be very different nowadays, of course. Nowadays we help people with disabilities to live in the community and be part of our neighbour-hoods. We have computers and technology to help them communicate. You may have heard of Stephen Hawking, a scientist, who like Joey is unable to speak as we do, but he is able to communicate with his computer and he has written many books.

Joey's achievement, all those years ago, was remarkable. He taught us that perseverance and working together made something possible which had seemed impossible. *And by communicating his feeling and thoughts, he helped ordinary people have a better understanding of people with disabilities.*

~

Dear God, help us remember that each and every one of us is good at something. Help us to share our talents and work together. Help us to understand the importance of communication and that by communicating with each other we can get to know each other better, and understand each other better. Amen

The story-telling star

One of the oldest ways of communicating in the world is story telling. Long, long before people could write things down, they passed on stories from one generation to the next. The stories weren't just for children, they were for every-one within a community. They were told as a way of teaching people about the world, or about their culture; about how to get along together, or how to understand each other better.

In fact, when we have stories in assembly, we are following a long and impor-tant tradition of story telling because we too have stories for those same reasons. And, as we know, some of the oldest and best stories still have some-thing to teach us today, even though they were first told thousands of years ago.

Here is a story from North America which tells of the birth of all the stories in the world.

Once, way back near the beginning of time, there was a young man who travelled here and there . . . selling this and that . . . to these people and those. Each evening, when his business of the day was finished, he would look for an inn or a lodge to spend the night. But it was the custom in those days for travellers to pay for their night's lodging with a story. Storytellers could dine well and sleep tight, for they were highly regarded amongst the rest of the people.

This presented the young man with a problem, for he knew no stories, and did not know how to tell them. Often he was turned away from an inn or a lodge.

'A story for payment?' the innkeeper would say.

'I'm sorry,' the young man would reply. 'I have no story to tell.'

'Then be gone,' the answer would be, and the young man would go else-where, only for the same thing to happen again.

On one particular occasion, the young man had just been turned away from an inn. The night was cold and dark and frosty, and there was no time for him to travel to the next village or town. He headed for the shelter of a small wood, found a dry hedgerow and settled down under the trees with earth for his mattress and leaves to cover him.

He was almost on the point of falling asleep when he thought he heard a voice.

'Shall I tell you a story?' it asked.

The young man sat up and looked around, expecting to see someone there, someone playing a trick maybe, or simply another traveller. But there was no one. Then, he heard the voice again. 'Shall I tell you a story?'

The young man looked up, and high above him was a bright silver star, glittering in the dark sky. 'It was you! You spoke!' he said.

'Yes,' laughed the star. 'Well? Do you want to hear a story, or not?'

'What kind of story?' asked the man.

'All the stories there have ever been,' said the star. 'You see, I am the story-telling star and I will share my stories with you if you promise to pass them on to others. That way, all the stories in the world will stay alive.'

'All right,' said the young man, already thinking of all the nights' lodgings he would be able to have if he had stories to tell.

So the star began.

'Stories are like stars,' he said. 'They are countless and they last for all time.'

'But what are they *for*?' asked the man.

'They are for all the reasons you can think of,' said the star. 'They are to teach people how to live; to make people laugh or cry; to make people think. Stories can help people understand the past and reach towards the future. Stories can touch the innermost feelings of men and women and children,' said the star.

'But that doesn't help me to *tell* them,' said the young man. 'Or to remember them,' he added.

'Ah, some stories you will remember forever,' said the star. 'Other stories you will only partly remember, and then there are others you will forget almost as soon as you have been told them.'

'Well, that's no good!' complained the young man. 'How can I retell them if I can't even remember them!'

'Listen,' said the star. And he began to tell the young man the story of how the world began. Of how the first mountains and rivers, insects and fish, animals and people came to live on earth.

'I won't forget *that* story,' said the young man, when the star had finished telling it.

'Exactly!' said the star. 'It's one of those stories you will remember forever. Now, listen again.' And the star began to tell the tale of the man who caught a magic fish, and whose wife became greedy and wanted the fish to give her more and more expensive things.

When the story was finished, the young man wailed, 'But I have already forgotten half of the story!'

'You've proved me right!' laughed the star. 'It's one of those stories you can only *half* remember!'

Well, *half* a story is no use to me,' grumbled the man. 'I can't just tell *half* a story!'

'You have to jog your memory for the rest,' said the star. 'You can do it, you know! Now, listen again.' And the star began to tell the young man a long, complicated story about a fox and an otter who met a wolf and a bear.

But long before the story was finished, the young man interrupted.

'It's no use. I can't remember any of it!'

'Of course you can't,' said the star. 'It's one of those stories you forget even before you've heard it!'

'This is stupid!' said the man. 'Call yourself a story-telling star? You've taught me *nothing*!'

'Nothing, you say?' answered the star. 'We'll see! Tell me the first story.'

So the young man retold the tale of how the world began.

'Good!' said the star. 'Now, tell me the second story.'

The young man began, and each time he forgot what happened next, the star said, 'Go on!' and encouraged him until he remembered.

'Now tell me the third tale,' said the star.

'But I can't remember it,' moaned the man.

'You can!' said the star. 'Use your imagination!'

So the young man used his imagination and made up a story. He amazed himself that he was able to do so, and when he had finished the star said, 'Well done! You see, you *can* tell stories. You now know all the stories that have ever been; the remembered ones and the half-remembered ones, and more importantly, the ones you have made up yourself in your imagination. You *are* a storyteller!' And the star faded away into the night sky.

The young man walked out of the wood and went back to the inn he'd been turned away from earlier. He asked for a night's lodging.

'A story for payment?' asked the innkeeper.

'I have hundreds of stories for you,' replied the young man. And from that night on he was welcomed wherever he went, for he always had a story to tell. It was as though he could tell all the stories that had ever been!

We are lucky because we can read stories for ourselves. We have picture books when we are very small, and more difficult and complicated stories when we are older. And there are stories everywhere, just waiting for us to enjoy. There are traditional stories, true stories, adventure and action stories; there are myths and legends and fables and folk tales. There are dozens of different kinds of stories, far more than the story-telling star could possibly have told during just one night!

And of course, we can use our imaginations and write our own stories about whatever we want. Maybe you could think of something you want to say, and make up a story to say it! You'll be communicating through story just like the storytellers of old, and just like modern professional writers of today.

~

Let's think about how lucky we are to be learning to read and write well. Let's think about all the millions of books there are and of all the information and stories they contain. We can choose to read any one of them whenever we want, and the authors can communicate with us through their written words. Let's make sure we respect books and treat them with care.

RAF Tornado rescue

We are very lucky to live in an age of modern technology. We have computers and satellites and we can communicate with people hundreds and thousands of miles away. I know many of you are able to email members of your family who live in other countries, and some of you have webcams and Skype so that you can see and hear them as well. But sometimes these ways of communicating can break down temporarily. When that happens it's inconvenient, but rarely disastrous; unless of course you're flying an aircraft!

In today's true story, the communications system failed in a small aircraft. Here's what happened.

A pilot was flying his two passengers on a trip over Glasgow and the surrounding countryside in Scotland. They were flying in a small, twin-engine plane called a Beechcraft, and all three of them were enjoying the flight. The weather was quite good when they set out but it became cloudy during the flight and threatened to rain, so the pilot decided to head for home and the airport at Glasgow.

But, just as he began to turn the plane round, the lights on all the instruments in the cockpit went out. The whole communications system, together with all the flight information system, and all the navigational aids, had failed. The pilot had no means of getting in touch with anyone. The radio system was down. He had no way of knowing which direction to fly in, or how high he was flying, or how fast the plane was going. All the flight instruments were down. The only things left working, fortunately, were the two engines.

The pilot knew that under normal circumstances it *is* possible, though difficult, to land a plane without the flight instruments, as long as there is no cloud and the pilot can see clearly. But this pilot looked out of the cockpit and saw huge banks of rolling cloud beneath the plane. Flying through that with no help from the instruments would be absolutely impossible. He would become disorientated and without knowing his speed or height or direction, the plane would surely crash. The three people in the Beechcraft knew that only something very special could save them.

On the ground, in the Glasgow airfield control tower, the air-traffic-controllers on duty quickly realised that something was seriously wrong when they lost radio contact with the tiny Beechcraft. They sent out a radio message to the nearest other aircraft to see if it could help. The nearest plane was an RAF Tornado jet.

The two RAF men were flying the Tornado on a routine training exercise when they heard the message that a Beechcraft was in trouble. They knew that the Beechcraft couldn't fly safely through the thick cloud, and therefore couldn't land. They knew how serious the situation was for the people in the Beechcraft. They knew they somehow had to help.

The Tornado quickly picked up the Beechcraft on its radar, and the RAF men flew towards the little plane, but with no radio signals they couldn't talk directly with the Beechcraft's pilot. They would have to find another way to communicate. They flew alongside and rocked the Tornado's wings so that the Beechcraft pilot would see that they were there to help. The pilot had hoped someone would come to help them, but never dreamt it would be a Tornado fighter jet!

The two pilots looked at each other through their cockpit windows and the Tornado pilot gave hand signals to the Beechcraft pilot, to tell him that they would fly alongside, towards Glasgow – the nearest airport, and try to guide him down to the runway. The Beechcraft pilot signalled that he had understood. But as they neared Glasgow, the Tornado pilot looked down at the rolling banks of cloud and knew that landing there would be impossible. Quick thinking was needed and the Tornado pilot decided to fly on to

Edinburgh, where the weather might be clearer. He hand-signalled to the little plane to say this is what they would do, and its pilot gave the thumbs-up to say he'd understood.

But, flying further wasn't easy. The Beechcraft was a much smaller plane and was travelling much more slowly than the Tornado jet. It took all the Tornado crew's skill to keep their speed down and stay with the Beechcraft. Approaching Edinburgh, they used more hand signals to say it was time to begin the descent. But, when they started to descend there was more cloud and the small plane really struggled to cope with it. Both planes had to pull out of it and ascend into the clear air above.

More quick thinking was needed if they were ever going to land the Beechcraft safely. Both pilots knew they now faced another danger: the Beechcraft's fuel tanks would soon be running low. They *had* to land soon or the fuel would run out and the plane would crash.

The Tornado changed direction again and signalled to the Beechcraft to follow its lead. The jet flew further north to Dundee and the RAF fighter station nearby. The Tornado crew knew this was their last chance to help the Beechcraft and its three people on board. They *had* to land the plane here.

More hand signals told the Beechcraft pilot that they were going to begin the descent. He looked anxiously out of his window. No cloud. The Tornado had led him to the safest landing place possible. But how was he to land the plane with no instruments? How could he do it with no electronic information to help him? The Fighter jet continued to fly alongside for as long as it possibly could, giving hand signals to guide the light aircraft. Then . . . he was on his own. And, just a few minutes later, the small Beechcraft was safely down on the landing strip.

Later, the commanding officer of the RAF fighter station where they landed said, 'I am extremely proud of the Tornado crew. Their courage, professionalism, determination and calmness under pressure in a most testing situation, represents the finest traditions of the Royal Air Force. Their skill undoubtedly saved the lives of the three people in the Beechcraft.'

Even with no communication systems at all, the two pilots managed to make each other understand what they meant. They solved the very serious problem the Beechcraft had by staying cool and calm, by thinking through the problem, and of course by showing courage. It's a story with an example to all of us. We're unlikely to have to solve a problem whilst flying a plane, but we can use those same skills of staying calm and thinking things through, to solve other problems.

And we can remember that even when our electronic communications systems fail, we human beings can find other ways to communicate.

~

Let's think about ways we can communicate with people. Maybe you've been on holiday and met children from other countries who don't speak your language. You'll know that it's still possible to make friends and communicate with them. Communication with other people is important. It's by communicating and sharing our thoughts and ideas that we learn about people. It's by communicating with other people that we can help them.

Theme 8

Fairness

Thirsty work

Assembly preparation: you will need:

- An upturned cardboard box hiding a large jug (or bottle) of water and eight glasses or clear plastic beakers
- Seven children to help.

I have an upside-down cardboard box on our assembly table today, as you can see. Hidden underneath this box, I have the most valuable and important thing in the world. I wonder if you can guess what it is.

Well, all those things you've mentioned are indeed valuable and important, but this is even more fundamental – that means even more essential. It's some-thing that's necessary for life itself. Yes, you've got it! It's water. Here it is! A jug of water. I'm going to pour some out and have a drink. Mmm! It's good; cool, clear, clean and refreshing.

Now, I'd like seven people to come and help me. These seven people can all have a glass (or plastic beaker) but I'm only going to offer one of you a drink. Who is it to be? There you are; you can drink as much or as little as you'd like.

Do you think that's fair to the other six children? No, of course it's not. But if these seven children represented all the people in the whole world, only one of them would have easy access to good, clear, clean water. Only one person in seven in the world has a tap in their home for fresh clean water.

I'm going to ask these six children to stand together, and I'm going to ask the rest of you to use your imagination as I tell you this story, and pretend that these six children are the ones in the story.

These six children live in a small village in Africa. They are all friends; they enjoy playing together and having fun. They live with their parents and their brothers and sisters. There are 250 people altogether, living in their village. But their houses do not have taps. There is no water in the village, no village pump. There is only a tiny amount of rain each year and because of this, the streams and rivers have all dried up. The only water they can use is in a pond several hundred metres beyond the houses. The pond is also used by animals, and the water is muddy and dirty.

This boy lives the furthest from the pond. His mother spends most of every day walking to the pond and home again, to the pond and home again, carrying every bucketful of water the family needs for cooking and washing. The water is heavy to carry and his mum is tired and unwell because of having to do this work. Sometimes she asks this boy to carry the water for her. He doesn't like doing it because it's hard work, and it's difficult not to spill or waste any of the water.

This girl and this boy next to her have just been very ill, together with all the other people in their families. They became ill because of drinking the dirty water.

The mothers of the next two children used to have a garden and grow vegetables, but they can't do that now because there has been so little rain. It's too far to carry water from the pond to water the gardens.

This child's aunt died a few months ago. She became ill because of the dirty water. She used to look after the family's few animals, but now this child has to do that job and take the animals to the pond every day so that they can drink, then make sure they are brought safely home again.

One day a group of people from a charity called UNICEF* come to the village. They talk of the possibility of putting in a well, and a pump, and having a sink with a tap of clean running water in the middle of the village, that everyone can use. They talk to the adults about how to look after the water and keep it clean.

The men are given tools to dig the well. They are shown how to install the pump. After a few days, the well is ready. The women are delighted that they don't have to carry the heavy buckets of water as far as they used to. And the children? Well, they have their first ever 'shower' under the tap in the middle of the village. You can imagine the shouting and laughing and splashing that goes on!

The lives of these six children are enormously improved by just having a tap with clean running water in their village. And there's now talk of extending the pipes so that they could perhaps have a tap in each of their houses.

---

* Further information can be found at www.unicef.org.

Water! In our country we take it for granted! We are lucky because, even though we sometimes have water shortages, we usually have plenty of rain to fill the reservoirs, and we all have taps with running water in our homes. In fact we have so much water, for drinking and cooking, cleaning our teeth and having baths and showers, for washing clothes and cars and for watering plants, that we usually just take it for granted. We are so used to having easy access to water that we don't even think about it. Perhaps we could think a little more about the water we have in our houses, and here in school. Perhaps we can all try a little harder not to waste this precious resource. And maybe we can all do our best to support charities like Unicef, who are trying to bring fresh, clean water to more people on our earth, and make life fairer for all our world neighbours.

∿

Let's thank God for all he has given us and especially for the fresh clean water that we have in our homes. Let's try not to waste this precious resource and try not to take it for granted. Let us remember all those people who do not have enough water. Let's all do our best to make the world a better and a fairer place.

The toolbox

Fairness isn't just about having fair shares, it's also about treating people fairly. I know how upset I feel if I think someone has been unfair to me by, for example, not taking turns, or by not considering my feelings. And I know that you think the same because I sometimes hear you say 'It's not fair' if you think there's been some injustice. We all like to be treated fairly, and that means treating other people fairly too.

And to treat people fairly means thinking fairly, and not being prejudiced. I wonder if you know what the word 'prejudice' means? Yes, it's when people form an opinion, usually a not very good opinion, about someone, without finding out the facts. It's making your mind up about what someone's like, without finding out about them first. It's jumping to conclusions about somebody before you've had a chance to get to know them.

Today's story is about someone who did exactly that.

Mr Jones had been building a new shed in his garden. He was quite keen on DIY and was always building or making something or other. He'd put in a new kitchen and built shelves in the sitting room to house all Mrs Jones' books. He'd made cupboards and mended drawers and even converted the loft into a workroom. Now, he turned his attention to the garden. He built a wall, erected a fence, put up a greenhouse, planted new flower beds, and was half way through building the shed . . . when he lost his toolbox.

You see, Mr Jones was a very good worker, but he was incredibly untidy. He was extremely good at getting all his tools *out*, but not very good at putting them away again.

'I do wish you'd learn to tidy up after yourself,' Mrs Jones would say. But she'd been saying the same thing for years now, and it hadn't made any difference.

On this particular day, Mr Jones had put up the walls of the shed and put the roof on. The door and the glass for the windows, together with all the shelves and fittings for the inside of the shed, were strewn all over the lawn. 'I think I'll just have a tea break before I fit the door,' he said, and he went inside to ask Mrs Jones to make him some tea and biscuits, leaving all his things scattered all over the grass.

When he came out again, he couldn't find his toolbox. His lovely, blue, shiny, metallic toolbox. He looked all over the garden, but it was nowhere to be seen. Just then he noticed his neighbour, Mr Brown, hurrying out of his garage and disappearing into his house through the back door.

'It's *him!*' thought Mr Jones. 'He's stolen my toolbox! It must be him! Why else would he creep about like that and sneak in through his back door without a word to me!' and Mr Jones hurried indoors to tell his wife how Mr Brown had come in to their garden whilst they were having their tea and biscuits, and how he'd stolen Mr Jones' toolbox.

'But are you sure?' asked Mrs Jones. 'It doesn't sound at all like something Mr Brown would do! Did you actually *see* him take the toolbox?'

'I didn't need to *see* him do it!' said Mr Jones. 'It's obvious it was him. Look!' and as they looked, Mr Brown came out of his house again and walked towards the garage. He glanced across at the Jones's half-finished shed as he went.

'There! Did you see that!' exclaimed Mr Jones. 'There's a thief if ever I saw one! Did you see how furtively he looked across here? He was looking to see if I've noticed yet that the toolbox is missing! There's guilt written all over his face! It was him all right! He's stolen my toolbox and put it in his garage. Well, he's not going to get away with it! I'll show him!'

'But it might not have been Mr Brown,' said Mrs Jones, timidly. 'You only *think* it was him. You didn't see him do it and you haven't any proof.'

'I don't need proof!' thundered Mr Jones. 'I know it was him. I can tell, just by looking at him!' and he stormed outside to put away the unused parts of his shed. He couldn't do any more work without his toolbox.

As he was collecting the panes of glass to put them inside the shed to keep them safe, he noticed something shiny and metallic and blue round the back of the shed. Round the back, where he'd not looked when he'd been searching for the toolbox!

There it was!

Exactly where he'd left it!

Round the back of the half-finished shed!

His toolbox!

Oh dear!

Mr Jones went back into his house.

He was just about to tell Mrs Jones that he'd found the toolbox, when Mr Brown came out of his garage again and walked towards his house. Once again, Mr Brown glanced across at the Jones's shed.

Mrs Jones prepared herself for another angry tirade from her husband, but was amazed to hear him say, 'We are lucky to have such a good neighbour as Mr Brown, aren't we?'

She stared at her husband.

'You could never imagine him stealing anything, could you?' went on Mr Jones. 'I mean, you only have to look at him to know he's honest and trustworthy. He's got such an honest face. Such a kind and genuine sort of face. And see how he keeps looking over at our new shed. He's obviously admiring my handiwork. I bet he's green with envy. I bet *he'd* like a shed like that one. Maybe I could offer to build him one when I've finished ours!'

'But I thought you were angry with him. I thought you said he'd stolen your toolbox?' said Mrs Jones.

'Stolen my toolbox? Goodness gracious me no!' said Mr Jones. 'He'd never do anything like that. You only have to look at him to know that he's as honest as can be!'

'You've found your toolbox, then!' said Mrs Jones.

'Oh yes. It was never really lost,' said Mr Jones.

'I thought not!' she said.

Mr Jones was very quick to jump to the wrong conclusion about Mr Brown. And it's interesting to see how guilty he thought Mr Brown looked, when he thought he'd stolen his toolbox; yet when he realised he hadn't stolen the toolbox, he couldn't see any guilt at all.

Sometimes we all do what Mr Jones did. Sometimes we jump to conclusions about people. Sometimes we see what we want *to see in people. Sometimes we have preconceived ideas about people; we* think *we know what they're like, but we don't give them the chance to prove what they are* really *like.*

Jumping to conclusions about people, having preconceived ideas about people and being prejudiced about people isn't fair. We need to get to know them, and understand them, before we form our opinions.

~

Dear God, help us to treat people fairly. Help us not to jump to conclusions about the people we meet. Help us not to be prejudiced, but to form our opinions on facts and understanding. Help us to make the world a better and fairer place by trying to understand the points of view of other people. Amen

Fair pay

I know that everyone here likes to be treated fairly. I know that we all get upset if we think things are not fair. I know that everyone in our school tries to be fair most of the time. I can think of examples when the teachers have taken endless trouble to listen to all sides of any argument, so that they can decide what's fair. And I know that most of you do the same and try to be fair to your friends.

But of course, not everyone manages to deal fairly with situations. In this story, someone lets their greed overcome any feeling of fairness they might have had. But things don't turn out quite as expected! Let's listen.

There was once a homeless man who was wandering the streets having just spent his very last coin. Now he had nothing. He had no idea what to do or where to go; and it was getting dark. Soon he would have to decide where to spend the night. Perhaps he would be able to find a doorway to sleep in, or a wall to shelter against. He hoped the night would not be too cold and that it would stay dry.

As the man walked along, he suddenly became aware of a wonderful smell. The smell of meat and hot bread. The smell of gravy and vegetables. The smell of deliciously piping hot food. The man couldn't remember the last time he'd eaten a really good, wholesome, solid, square meal. He followed his nose, turned a corner of the street, and came to a travelling food stall.

The stall was run by a large red-faced man wearing a huge striped apron. He had a pot of soup simmering on a small stove, and a pan of stew bubbling on a hot-plate. There were rolls of bread toasting in a small oven, and vegetables in dishes on the heated counter. Hot steam was rising from the food stall, and all around was the delicious smell of dinner.

There was a queue of people waiting to be served, and other people standing nearby, eating the food they'd just bought. It was obviously good food, judging by the way the people were enjoying it.

'I wish I could afford to buy some of that,' said the homeless man to himself. 'It's a long time since I've smelled anything as good, and even longer since I've tasted anything half as appetizing.' And he went to stand with some of the other people near to the stall so that he could continue to smell the wonderful food.

Suddenly, the stallholder looked up from his cooking and shouted, 'Hey! You! What do you think you're doing?'

The man, startled by the sharpness in the stallholder's voice, turned round to see who he was shouting at.

'Yes, you!' called the stallholder. 'Come over here and pay me your money!'

'I'm sorry,' said the man. 'I think there must be some mistake. I'm not in the queue. I haven't ordered any food. I'm not waiting to be served. I haven't any money so I can't buy anything.'

'Can't pay?' bellowed the stallholder. 'Then you're stealing. You're standing there smelling my food, breathing in the aromas of my cooking. Don't deny it, I've seen you! So, if you want to smell my food you have to pay for it. Come on, pay up, or I'll send for the police and tell them you're stealing!'

The man felt afraid. He hadn't meant to steal the smell of the food. He didn't know he had to pay just to smell it. And what if the stallholder should call the police, what would he do then? He'd never been in trouble before. He was suddenly aware that, as a homeless person, he didn't have many rights. What if they sent him to prison? The more the man thought about all this, the more worried he became.

Just then, a stranger stepped up to the stall. He spoke to the man behind the counter.

'Do you think it's fair that this man should pay for the smell of your food?' he asked.

'I do!' replied the stallholder. 'He can't have something for nothing. He has to pay, just like the rest of the customers.'

'Very well,' said the stranger. 'Then *I* will pay,' and he pulled a purse full of coins from his pocket.

The stallholder's eyes grew round with greed at the sight of the purse and the coins. But, the payment wasn't quite what he expected.

The stranger held out the purse and shook it hard. The coins rattled and jangled inside. He opened the purse and took out a huge gold coin. The stallholder's eyes opened wide. He was going to be paid well for the smell of his food.

The stranger held the gold coin between his thumb and first finger and tapped it hard on the metal counter. The sound rang out, clear and sharp.

The stallholder held out his hand, ready for the coin to be dropped in it, but the stranger rapped it again, hard, on the counter, and then . . . put it back in his purse.

'Hey! That's my payment,' said the stallholder, disappointment sounding in his voice at the thought of *not* getting the coin.

'But you've had your payment,' said the stranger, seriously.

'No I haven't! You've put the coin back in your purse!' the stallholder said, angrily.

'The sound of the money was your payment,' said the stranger. 'That seems fair to me! The man over there had a smell of your food, and now I've paid for it with the sound of my money. Perfectly fair! What do the rest of you think?' and he turned to the crowd that had watched this altercation with interest.

'It's fair,' they all said.

And the stallholder knew that his greed had not been fair, and that his customers knew it too.

'Come on,' said the stranger to the homeless man. 'I know a good place to eat. Come with me and I'll treat you to a good hot dinner.'

What do you think about that story? Do you think the stallholder was being fair to expect payment just for the smell of his food? He, of course, had had to prepare the food and cook it, so maybe you think he had a point? I think he was just plain greedy!

One of the most important things in life, I believe, is to try to treat people fairly. Unfairness is one of the things that upsets us most of all. If everyone in our world, from the smallest child to the most important politician, could try to treat everyone fairly, the world would be a better place.

~

Let's think about being fair. We can all play our part by being fair to our friends and the people in our families. We can make sure we're fair to people we meet by not making snap judgements about them; by being honest; by not being greedy or selfish. If we are fair to the people who are our neighbours, and they are fair to theirs, and in turn them to their neighbours, then everyone in the world could be treated fairly and equally. Let's do what we can to ensure that all the world's people are treated fairly.

Theme 9

Sport

Sports day

I know that nearly everyone in our school enjoys sport of one kind or another. Sport is good fun, and it's good exercise. Sport is exciting to watch and even more fun to take part in. Sport is often competitive and it is good to win, but taking part is just as important.

Do you know what 'sportsmanship' means? Yes, it's being fair and generous in sport; it's being able to say 'well done' to the winner even when you've lost; it's being brave enough to be a good loser.

I know that everyone in our school tries to be fair and good-tempered when they're involved in sport, and I know that people in our school don't cheat when they're playing games.

Someone wasn't quite so fair in today's story.

Everyone in the whole school was looking forward to Sports Day. The children in Mr Howard's class had been practising events for weeks, and he'd spent a lot of time explaining about the different races they were going to take part in, and how the actual day was to be organised. But two children didn't listen. They were too busy watching each other to take much notice of what Mr Howard was saying.

Leroy and Channah were great rivals. They were always trying to out-smart each other, to beat each other. It didn't matter what they were doing, it could be maths or swimming, reading or PE; each always wanted to do better than the other. Each wanted to be the first to finish, or to have the highest marks, or to do the best work, or to be the winner.

The day before Sports Day, Mr Howard took the children who were taking part out onto the playing field to time them in the 100-metre sprint.

He used a stopwatch and wrote down on his clipboard how long each person took. Everyone did their best. Leroy and Channah were the fastest and both took exactly the same time to run the 100 metres.

Channah felt extremely annoyed with herself. She had expected that her time would be better than Leroy's. She wondered how she could improve her time so that she would beat him and win the race tomorrow. She was determined to beat him and win, but she knew she'd already run as fast as she could. She decided that if she couldn't beat Leroy by running faster, she'd have to beat him by cheating. But how? How could she cheat in a running race?

Suddenly she knew. She remembered the toy racing car she'd brought to school a few days earlier: the toy car that Leroy had very much wanted. She would bring it to school tomorrow and use it to help her win the race and to make Leroy lose.

Sports Day arrived at last. The weather was as good as everyone had hoped it would be. The field was marked out for all the different events. The starting flag was ready, the finishing ribbon was stretched across the lanes, and the parents and governors and friends of the school were all gathered to watch. The whole school came out onto the field and the competitors took up their positions for the first race. The 100-metre sprint.

The children stood at the starting line. Channah made sure she was next to Leroy. She felt in the pocket of her shorts for the toy racing car. It was safely there. She held it tightly then pushed it to the bottom of the pocket.

The headteacher held up the starting flag. 'Ready . . . Steady . . . GO!' he shouted, bringing the flag down hard in the air.

They were off, all speeding as fast as they could down the track, Leroy and Channah quickly forging ahead of the rest, level with each other, both surging forward together. Channah knew she had little time to lose. The race would be quickly over.

'Now!' she thought, and she pulled the toy car out of her pocket, threw it onto the grass just in front of Leroy's feet, and kept on running. She mustn't look to see what he would do. She mustn't show that she knew anything at all about the car. She mustn't look guilty.

Leroy saw the car, just as Channah hoped he would. He thought it had accidentally fallen from her pocket. He thought she didn't know she'd dropped it. Now was his chance to have it. To claim it for himself. She wouldn't even know he'd got it. He slowed down, grabbed the toy car from the grass then picked up speed again and carried on with the race. But now, of course, Channah was well in front and was crossing the finishing line.

'Yes!' she shouted, punching the air. 'I did it! I won!' And she turned round to give Leroy a gloating grin of victory.

Channah stood proudly at the finishing line, waiting for Mr Howard to award her the first prize; to present her with the red rosette with a golden '1st' written on it. But to her astonished amazement, Mr Howard walked straight past Channah and presented the rosette to a boy called Calum instead.

'Why's he got it?' said Channah, angrily. 'It's mine! I won! I came first! I want the first prize, it's only fair. I beat everyone else.' And she glared crossly at Mr Howard.

'And we'll have less of that tone of voice, young lady!' said Mr Howard. 'In any case, you clearly weren't listening when we timed everyone for the heats in class. I said, quite distinctly, that the winner was to be the one who beat their own personal best; the one who beat their own record! Why do you think we did all that practising? Why do you think I spent so long timing you all individually? Callum didn't win the race, but he did beat his personal best. He's run faster than he's ever run before. The prize is his.'

'But *I* ran fast!' argued Channah, indignantly. '*And* I came first.'

'But you didn't actually run as fast as you did yesterday, Channah,' said Mr Howard. 'So you haven't beaten your own record.'

'I'm sorry,' said Channah. 'I didn't know.'

'No!' said Mr Howard. 'You didn't know because you didn't listen! Perhaps you could listen more carefully next time. Oh, and by the way, just one more thing,' and he turned toward Leroy, who was smirking because Channah had got into trouble, 'I think you have something that belongs to Channah?' he said, holding out his hand.

Leroy stopped grinning and gave Mr Howard the toy racing car.

'Thank you, Leroy,' he said. 'And maybe running a race with a toy car in your shorts pocket isn't the most sensible thing to do, Channah,' he added. And he looked at her in such a way that she knew he understood *exactly* what she'd done with the toy car, and why she'd done it.

'I'm sorry, Mr Howard. I'm sorry, Leroy,' she said.

'Sorry Channah,' said Leroy.

'Sportsmanship is about doing your best. Sportsmanship is not about cheating!' said Mr Howard, severely. Then he grinned at the children. 'Fair play and play fair! That's what we need. Now, on to the next race!' And Sports Day continued.

I wonder what you think of Channah's behaviour? I wonder what you'd have said if you'd been Mr Howard? I like the way Mr Howard said, 'Fair play and play fair!' at the end of the story. It's what we all need to aim for, and not just in sport.

~

Dear God, help us always to do our best. Help us to try to improve on our personal best, so that we achieve as much as we can. Help us to remember that hard work and honesty bring greater rewards than cheating. Help us never to spoil other people's efforts, but to value them. Amen

Alex cycles to Selby

I know that many of you here belong to sports clubs or gymnastic teams of one sort or another, and some of you belong to Cubs and Brownies and you're involved in sport there. I wonder if you can remember what it was like when you first joined? Being new, or the youngest, or the smallest is not always easy. But joining in, and getting involved, and doing your best is what is important.

Today's story is about someone who was new to a club, and who wasn't very confident.

Alex came home from football club practice with a glum face and news that the club needed a new strip and everyone was to raise some money for it.

'Well, what's wrong with that?' asked his mum. 'It's a great idea. If you all join in and help, you'll have the money in no time, and just think of the lovely new strip!'

'Yes, but everyone else'll do more than me. They'll all get more money than me. It's just not fair!'

'Oh, don't be such a softy,' laughed his mum. 'It doesn't matter how much each person raises. The important thing is that everyone joins in. Everyone's contribution is just as good as everyone else's, even if some people raise more than others, and some people raise less. It's just important that you all raise *something*. So, what is it you all have to do?'

'That's just it!' said Alex. 'The club leader said we could do what we wanted, 'cept that the parents have got to say we can,' and he pulled a letter out of his bag and waved it at his mum. She read it.

'Well that's all right,' she said. 'They suggest you get people to sponsor you to do something you enjoy doing. What's it going to be?'

'Dunno!' mumbled Alex, who at only eight, and one of the youngest, smallest, newest members of the local football club, still didn't think that anything *he* could contribute would be anywhere near as good as everyone else's efforts.

'Why don't you do a sponsored bike ride?' said his mum, enthusiastically. 'You like your bike; that would be a really good thing to do!'

Alex thought about it. He'd got a new bike for his birthday just a few weeks earlier and it was his best ever present. He rode it up and down the back lane with Tim from next door, and sometimes their mums let them both go to the park where there was a dirt track with dips and mounds. But best of all was when his mum and dad, who also had bikes, took him on the cycle path that ran near his house in York and went all the way to Selby. He'd only been a few miles on it, but it was good fun.

'But what would I do?' asked Alex.

'You could ride your bike to Selby and back,' said his mum.

'Selby!' declared Alex. 'And back!' he added.

'Why not?' said his mum. 'Your dad and I could do it with you, and we could get all the people we both work with to sponsor you, and you could ask our friends and neighbours to sponsor you as well, and maybe Miss Taylor from school. It'd be really good.'

'But, Mum, Selby's miles away! How far is it?'

'You're full of "buts", aren't you Alex?' laughed his mum. 'It's about 15 miles from here, so it's about 30 miles there and back.'

'Thirty miles!' said Alex. 'I've never done as far as that!'

'And you never will, if you don't try,' said his mum. 'So, how about it? Shall we tell your dad you're doing a 30-miles sponsored bike ride?'

'OK,' said Alex, and went off to get in some training with Tim.

When his dad came home, the three of them set a date of the Sunday after next for the bike ride, and his mum printed out some sponsor forms on the computer. Alex took them round to all their friends and neighbours and was surprised to find by the end of the week that he had £35 promised in sponsor money.

His dad took the forms to work at the start of the following week and the promised money grew to an amazing £65. And when his mum took them to where she worked, Alex was astonished to find he had £95 promised in sponsor money.

'But I wish I could make it to £100,' he said, looking in his money box and discovering that he had only 74p left.

'Well I don't think we can think of anyone else to ask,' said his dad. 'We've asked everyone we know and they've all been hugely supportive.'

'And £95 is a lot of money, Alex,' added his dad. 'All you have to do now, is the bike ride!'

Sunday arrived and the weather was good; perfect in fact for a bike ride, warm but not too hot, dry and not too windy. Alex's dad packed up a picnic which they put in panniers on his bike. They each had drinks on their own bikes. At ten o'clock they set off, with much waving and shouts of good luck from the neighbours and from Tim.

Now 30 miles on a bike is a long way when you're eight and not very tall, and Alex spent a lot of time glancing at the cycle-computer on his handlebars. The miles seemed to be ticking by extremely slowly. But, there was plenty to see and his mum and dad kept pointing things out that were new to him.

'You'll have lots to tell Miss Taylor at school tomorrow,' they said.

At last, after several stops for a drink and a rest, they arrived in Selby and sat by the abbey for their picnic lunch. And all too soon it was time to set off on the return journey. But this was harder going. The journey back from Selby didn't seem quite as interesting as the journey there. And Alex was getting tired. The miles on the cycle-computer turned even more slowly still.

'Come on Alex, keep going,' said his dad.

'You're doing really well. Just think of all that sponsor money when you've completed the ride,' said his mum.

But Alex could only think of how much his legs were aching, and of how disappointed he was that he'd not managed to make the £95 into £100.

Another few miles further on and his dad suggested they have a rest and another drink. There was a bench to sit on at the side of the track, and two elderly ladies sitting there, their own bikes propped up against the seat. Alex was quite surprised that such old ladies *could* ride bikes!

'Hello,' they said as Alex sat down. 'Have you ridden far?' And Alex began to explain all about the football strip and the sponsored ride and how they were now on their way back from Selby, to where they lived in York.

'Well, I think that's wonderful,' said one of the ladies. 'My friend and I have been cycling for years; we were about your age when we got our first bikes. I'm glad to see a boy like you is keen on sport; it's such fun,' and she fished her purse out of her saddle bag and handed him a £10 note. 'That's to add to your sponsor fund,' she said. 'Good luck!' and the two ladies rode off.

Alex beamed at his mum and dad. 'I've done it!' he said. 'I've got the £100. In fact, I've got more than one hundred.'

'Not yet, you haven't!' said his dad. 'Come on! You've still got a ride to finish!'

And suddenly, Alex found some extra energy he didn't know he had, and he discovered that his legs were no longer aching.

The following week at football club practice, he received a round of applause and a special certificate for being the newest member to put in the biggest effort towards the fund-raising.

'I knew you could do it,' said his mum.

'I knew I could, too,' said Alex.

'But . . .' began his mum.

'You're full of "buts", aren't you, Mum,' laughed Alex.

And his mum laughed too.

Alex made quite a few discoveries in those few weeks. I wonder if you can think of some of them. Yes, he found that:

- *he could do something when he tried, even though he thought at first he couldn't,*
- *people of all ages can take part in sport,*
- *joining in and doing your best is important,*
- *it doesn't matter if someone else is better at something than you,*
- *all contributions are helpful whether large or small,*
- *sport can give you confidence,*
- *taking part in sport with friends and family is fun.*

Well done for thinking of all those discoveries.

$$\sim$$

Let's think about sport. Think of a sport that you enjoy taking part in. Think of why you enjoy it and why it's good for you. And maybe you can think of a sport you've not yet had the chance to try, but that you'd like to. Maybe you can think of a team sport, and how playing in a team can help you as a person. Perhaps you can think of a sport where you've had to try hard, and then you've had success, like Alex in the story. Let's think about doing our best in sports and always being fair to other people who are involved.

Tanni Grey-Thompson

I'd like you to think of your favourite sports personality. I wonder who it is. No, don't tell me, just think of them; see them in your mind's eye; imagine them doing something successful in their chosen sport. Perhaps you're thinking of your favourite footballer scoring a winning goal, or maybe you're thinking of a tennis star, or a swimmer, or an athlete. Perhaps your hero is playing rugby or cricket, or maybe you're thinking of a gymnast or skier, a cyclist or golfer. Just imagine them taking part in their chosen sport. I'm sure they're all doing something very active.

Now let me tell you about the person I'm thinking of.

She has broken more than 30 world records. She's won sixteen medals in the Paralympics – that's eleven gold medals, four silver medals and a bronze. She's won dozens of European titles, and six London marathons. And as well as all that, she has a university degree, and is a Dame Commander of the Order of the British Empire – an honour awarded to her by the Queen. So she must also be very active to have done all that.

But . . . she's in a wheelchair.

Her name is Tanni Grey-Thompson* and she is a wheelchair athlete.

Here's her story.

Tanni was born in 1969 in Cardiff, Wales. She was born with spina bifida,** which means she has something wrong with her spine. A healthy spine is like a protective tube of bone, with nerves – the spinal cord – running down the middle. In spina bifida the bones don't close properly round the spinal cord and the nerves can become damaged. Damaged nerves can't send messages properly to and from the brain, so someone with spina bifida may not be able to move their muscles or feel things in some parts of their body.

Tanni learned to walk like most children, but as she grew bigger, walking became more and more difficult, and by the time she was seven, she was using her wheelchair most of the time. But, even using a wheelchair didn't stop Tanni doing the things she wanted to do, and just like you, she enjoyed swimming, and going to school, and playing outside, and having her friends over.

When it was time for her and her parents to think about which high school she would go to, everyone said that it would be better for Tanni if she went to a special school for children with disabilities. But Tanni disagreed.

'I want to go to school with all my friends,' she said. 'And I want to do things, to get on. I know I have a disability, but it's not going to stop me!' she added. Her parents knew that she was already very competitive and ambitious, so it was agreed that she should go to the local high school.

---

*Further information can be found at http://news.bbc.co.uk/sport1/hi/other_sports/disability_sport/4354422.stm.

** Further information about spina bifida can be found at www.kidshealth.org/kid/health_problems/birth_defect/spina_bifida.html.

And once there, Tanni joined in *everything*, even though there were some problems. For example, some people believed she ought not to be at the ordinary high school with able-bodied children, they thought she should be in a special school just because she had disabilities. And there were problems in getting her wheelchair into some areas. Many buildings are simply not designed for wheelchairs. But, Tanni was determined and enthusiastic about having a go at everything she possibly could. She swam, she played tennis, she tried archery. You name it, she tried it!

She became interested in many sports, and gradually developed her love for athletics. And it was an interesting time for wheelchair athletics. The sport was being taken more seriously. She saw on television that wheelchair athletes had begun to take part in the London Marathon.

Tanni decided that she was going to be a wheelchair athlete. Her grandfather encouraged her and said: 'Aim high, even if you only hit a cabbage!' He meant that if you have a dream and a goal, you should do everything you can to achieve it, even though sometimes you feel like you're not getting very far.

Tanni worked hard and trained hard. She was dedicated to becoming an athlete and she was motivated. She was *determined* to succeed!

When she was just fifteen, she entered her first race. It was the 100-metre event at the Junior National Championships in Wales. She had arrived at the beginning of her career. Four years later she took part in the Paralympics – the world Olympic games for athletes with disabilities. That year they were held in Seoul, Korea, and Tanni won a bronze medal in the 400 metres.

But, for Tanni, a bronze medal was not enough. She continued to train hard. She also started at university and worked hard for her degree. She used every minute of every day to work towards her goals.

Four years after winning bronze in Seoul, she travelled to Barcelona in Spain with the British team for the 1992 Paralympics. The hard work paid off and Tanni won four gold medals and a silver.

Four years on again, and she went to the 1996 Paralympics in Atlanta, America. This time she won one gold medal and three silvers.

And another four years on, in 2000, she travelled with the British team to Sydney, Australia, and won four more gold medals.

The next Paralympic games, in 2004, was in Athens, Greece, and Tanni won two more gold medals.

And in between all those Paralympic events, Tanni won lots of European titles, she beat her own personal best many times. She won the London Marathon *six* times; she was awarded the MBE and the OBE by the Queen; she was voted BBC Wales Sports Personality of the Year in 2004; the Queen made her a Dame in 2005 for her services to disabled sport; and as well as all that she got married, and had a baby girl called Cerys.

What a list of achievements.

Tanni has now decided not to take part in any more Paralympics, but she still keeps her interest in sport, especially in helping young people achieve their potential.

When asked about her brilliant achievements, she says, 'For me it's not about pretending I don't have a disability. I'm just a very competitive person.'

I think Tanni Grey-Thompson is the most inspirational and outstanding sports personality. And I think she has something to teach every one of us, whether we are disabled in any way, or able-bodied. She has shown us that we can achieve whatever we want to achieve if we are determined and motivated, and hard-working and committed.

Now think again of that sports personality you were thinking about at the beginning of our assembly today, and I think you'll agree that they, too, show that you need to be determined, motivated, hard-working and committed. If you are to succeed.

I think we can learn a lot from our sports heroes.

~

Let's think about those sports people that we admire. Let's think what it is about them that makes them so successful. Of course they all have skill in their particular sport, but they are also dedicated and committed to doing well. They are hard-working and determined. They are motivated and they want to succeed. We can do well in our aims and ambitions if we try to be dedicated, motivated and hard-working. We can do well if we are determined to do well.

Theme 10

Anti-social behaviour

Snooks

One of the main problems with anti-social behaviour is that the people who behave in an anti-social way usually don't care about the people they hurt or inconvenience, nor do they usually really understand the damage that they do.

Perhaps if we all thought a bit more about the consequences of what we do, about what happens as a result of our actions, the world would be a better place.

In today's true story, someone really upset the people of Aldeburgh, on the south-east coast of England, by what they did. Here's what happened.

If you go to the town of Aldeburgh, on the Suffolk coast, and stand beside the sea in front of the model yacht pond, you will see a beautiful bronze statue of a small dog.* His name is Snooks and his statue has been there for almost 50 years.

Snooks belonged to two of Aldeburgh's doctors; Dr Robin Acheson and his wife, Dr Nora. Snooks followed Dr Robin everywhere, even going to patients' houses with him, but he also went on walks by himself, all around the town. Soon, everyone knew Snooks, and everyone liked him. He was quite a character; friendly, but a bit bossy!

One day, Snooks became very ill and had to go to the vet for an operation. He'd been eating pebbles and had to have several of them removed from his stomach. Everyone in the town was worried about him and kept asking the doctors how he was. Fortunately Snooks made a full recovery and returned to his walks round the town.

---

*A photograph of Snooks can be found at http://woodbridgesuffolk.info/Suffolk/Aldeburgh.htm.

Eventually, of course, Snooks died of old age, and sadly, only two years later, Dr Robin died. The people of Aldeburgh wanted to put up some kind of memorial to the doctor, and whilst they were discussing what this should be, someone said, 'Why don't we have a statue of Snooks made? Everyone loved Snooks, and since he was Dr Robin's dog, it would be an ideal memorial.'

And so it was decided. A bronze statue of Snooks, standing just 60 cm high, was made and it was mounted on a small plinth and placed on the sea front beside the model yacht pond, where everyone could see and admire it. A plaque was put on the plinth to explain that this was Snooks and the statue was in memory of Dr Robin Acheson.

The statue of Snooks became a much-loved and well respected landmark of Aldeburgh. Snooks featured on postcards and on advertising posters, leaflets and press articles about the town. Everyone who visited Aldeburgh saw Snooks and learned his story. Hundreds of children came to see Snooks, and over the years, so many of them were held up to stroke his nose, that Snooks' bronze nose began to wear away!

Snooks by now was famous. He brought a smile to the face of everyone who saw his statue.

Then, one snowy night in February, just a couple of years ago, someone stole him.

No one saw who did it. No one heard anything. Snooks was on his plinth at five o'clock on the Wednesday afternoon, but gone by Thursday morning. Word soon spread through the town and the people were in uproar.

'How could anyone do this?' they asked.

'It's so upsetting.'

'I feel so angry!'

'I can't believe anyone could steal a statue that means so much to us all,' they said.

More people added their voices and their opinions. 'Snooks was so important to our town.'

'The children will miss him!'

'We'll *all* miss him, he means so much to us.'

'I feel so sad.'

'It's a pity that someone should waste their time on such vandalism.'

'It's tragic that Snooks' statue could be stolen, when it's such a personal memorial that we have all looked after and honoured for so long.'

And so the comments continued. One after another, people expressed their feelings of sadness and anger, that someone could do this.

No one knew why Snooks had been stolen, or where the statue had been taken. Was it a cruel joke? Was someone going to sell the bronze statue? Were they going to melt down the valuable bronze metal for money? No one knew.

The one thing everyone *did* know, however, was that the town was not going to be without its Snooks. The town mayor and the town clerk were inundated with phone calls, letters and visits.

'What are you, the town council, going to do about our statue?' the people demanded.

'We can't live without our statue of Snooks.'

'If no one finds him, we must commission another statue.'

'We're not going to be beaten by the thieves.'

So the Aldeburgh Town Council called a meeting at which the matter of the stolen Snooks statue was fully discussed.

'We have had such a huge response from the people of Aldeburgh, and even further afield,' said the town mayor. 'This has affected everyone because Snooks was, and is, such a feature of our town. People want a new Snooks and are willing to pay towards a new bronze statue. We must arrange to have one made as quickly as possible.'

The story ends there, so to find out whether a new bronze Snooks was made, or whether the original one was found, you'll have to go to Aldeburgh and stroke Snooks' nose! If it's almost worn away, it must be the original Snooks; but if his nose is new and unworn, then it must be a new, replacement Snooks! But, whichever it is, Snooks is still a much-loved and well-respected landmark of Aldeburgh.

Whoever stole Snooks can have had no idea of the hurt and upset, the anguish and sadness that he or she caused by that single act of greed or vandalism or whatever the reason was for taking the beautiful bronze statue. And that's the trouble with anti-social behaviour; the people who carry it out, don't stop to think about the damage and hurt they cause.

~

Dear God, help us to remember that every thing we do has a consequence. There is a result to every action we make. Help us to think ahead and to do nothing that will hurt anyone or anything in any way. Help us to be considerate of other people's feelings, and to respect other people's property. Amen

Copycat monkeys

Everyone likes to be the same as their friends. We all like to fit in to the group of people we belong to, and that sense of belonging is fine and good, as long is it doesn't make us feel as though we have to do something we know is wrong.

I'm always telling you to think for yourselves, and everyone here knows I don't accept the excuse 'but so-and-so told me to do it,' when I ask why you've done a particular thing.

It takes courage to stand apart and think for yourself if the group wants you to do something that you know is wrong. But it's important to think for yourself. It's important to make your own decisions and not let yourself be pressured or persuaded into doing something you don't want to do. If you don't think for yourself, you end up following someone else just like sheep following the leader, or just like the monkeys in today's story.

It was market day in the village in South China and the troupe of monkeys who lived near the village gathered in the trees. There were almost 50 of them, old, young, male, female, but the undisputed leader of them all was an older male monkey with thick grey-brown fur.

The monkeys gathered here every market day, because there were rich pickings when the shoppers had all gone home and the market traders were packing up their stalls. Then the monkeys came down from the trees and searched the pathways and the ground under the tables for fallen nuts, fruit, bread and vegetables.

But, today they were especially hungry.

The market traders ignored the monkeys as they set up their stalls. They put out their fruits and vegetables, their pots and pans, they set out their clothes and lengths of cloth. The hatseller put up his stall at the edge of the market, under the shade of a tree, and as usual he used the tree branches to display some of his straw hats. The hats danced and bobbed in the breeze like so many heads nodding and talking with each other. He spread the rest of his hats on his table.

At last the market was ready and the customers started to arrive. But, no sooner had the first shoppers begun to fill their baskets that the old grey-brown monkey in the trees suddenly signalled to the rest of the troupe, and all 50 of them surged forward, shrieking and chattering; swinging, running, jumping, leaping onto the piled-up market stalls, grabbing anything and everything they could touch; stuffing food into their mouths and destroying the market stalls as they went.

The customers ran to escape the onslaught. The stallholders shouted at the monkeys and tried to chase them away, but the monkeys were too quick for them as they leapt from stall to stall, upturning tables and scattering goods. They dodged out of the way of the angry traders and escaped to the safety of the trees, clutching the things they had stolen. One or two of the braver traders tried to climb the trees to catch the monkeys but it was no use; the animals were too quick, too agile, too nimble. They sat in the treetops and laughed and shrieked.

The market was ruined. Most of the goods were destroyed and the food inedible. The stallholders began to clear up the mess.

The hatseller started to gather up his remaining hats, and as he did so he noticed the old male monkey had one of the hats in its paws. The hatseller watched the monkey and the monkey watched the hatseller.

Suddenly the hatseller jammed the hat he was holding on to his own head, and there, in the tree above him, the monkey did the same.

The hatseller had an idea.

He began to pick up the hats that had fallen to the ground and he threw them up to the monkeys.

'Hey, what are you doing?' called the other traders. 'Have you gone mad?'

'No!' said the hatseller. 'It's too late to save the food, but I think I can get the other things back. Give me one of your pots and pans and jackets and boots and anything else from your stalls. Then throw some more of the same things up to the monkeys.'

The traders did as they were asked and the delighted monkeys caught the things as they were thrown. The old grey-brown monkey grabbed one of everything and watched, curiously, to see what would happen next.

The hatseller pulled on a boot. The monkeys did the same. He put his arm in a jacket sleeve. The monkeys copied him. He put a pan on his head. The monkeys followed suit. He tied some trouser legs round his waist. The monkeys tied on theirs. He threw his hat up in the air and caught it. Fifty monkeys did the same.

'Now, put some big boxes in the space under the tress,' said the hatseller to the other traders. Again, they did as they were asked, whilst the hatseller threw his hat in the air again and again for the monkeys to copy him. They were now thoroughly enjoying this game with the hatseller, and so when he threw his hat into the boxes under the trees, they unsuspectingly did the same.

Quickly, the hatseller untied the trousers and threw them into the boxes, followed immediately by the jacket and boot and pan. The monkeys did exactly the same, and before they knew what they were doing, they had thrown all the things they had stolen from the traders, back into the traders' boxes.

'Well done!' said the traders. 'But how did you know what to do? How did you know they would copy you?'

'Gangs of hooligans are all the same,' said the hatseller. 'They just follow the leader, without thinking, like sheep, or in this case, like monkeys,' he laughed. 'You see, they just want to be the same as the rest of the gang, but doing something without thinking for yourself never works, does it monkeys?' he called, and the monkeys slunk away in the trees, knowing they had been outwitted.

The hatseller was right! Sometimes people can behave in an anti-social way, just like those monkeys; and just like them, they play copycat and follow the leader, without thinking. It's not a good idea to do the same as someone else without thinking for yourself.

Perhaps we can all think of a time when we've followed someone else and done something we knew was silly or dangerous. Let's remember how important it is to think for ourselves and not just do what someone else says without deciding for ourselves. Let's all be brave enough to make our own decisions. Let's remember that it's courageous to stand up for what we know is the right thing to do.

The litter picker

Everyone in our school is very careful not to drop litter and to make sure they tidy up after lessons like art and technology. But you might have noticed that people outside our school are not always so tidy! The other day when I was driving along a road near town, I was horrified to see a huge amount of litter at the sides of the road and festooning the trees. The wind was partly to blame for blowing it along, but the litter wouldn't have been there in the first place if people hadn't carelessly dropped it. And the trouble with litter is that the more there is, the more people think they can add to it.

Some people just don't care where they throw their rubbish; they behave in an anti-social way when they throw it where it will inconvenience and annoy other people. But I know a man who made a group of anti-social children behave in a different way!

The man is called Geoff and he lives in a small town not far from here. Geoff gets very annoyed when people drop litter and rubbish in his neighbourhood, and I'm afraid that although the town council have rules about dropping litter and fines for people who don't obey the rules, people still drop rubbish on the streets. Geoff became so angry about the litter in his neighbourhood that he decided to do something about it himself, so every day he goes out with a black bin bag and a pick-up stick and gathers up any litter he finds.

Now, there's a group of children who live near Geoff who think this is highly amusing. They laugh at him whenever they see him, they call him names and they torment him by dropping sweep papers and crisp packets on the pavement outside his house. They do this deliberately to annoy him, and they know that as soon as he sees them he'll come out of his house, looking cross, then he'll pick up all the litter they've dropped and put it in his own wheely bin. When Geoff does this, they laugh unkindly and throw down even more rubbish.

Geoff once tried talking to the children, reasoning with them and trying to explain why it's important to keep where we live clean and tidy. But they didn't want to listen. They just sniggered and ran away.

One day when Geoff was collecting litter from the bus stop area at the end of his street, he happened to pick up a £5 note. Someone must have accidentally dropped it as they were getting off the bus, but of course he had no idea who so he couldn't return it to the owner. But that £5 note gave him an idea.

The following day, just before home-time when the children usually came past his house, Geoff went out into the street and half hid the £5 note under a stone by the wall of his front garden. He made sure that part of the £5 was still showing, then he went back into his house and waited. Sure enough, a few minutes later the group of children came round the corner of the street, as they usually did, laughing and joking and dropping litter as they walked.

As soon as he saw them, Geoff hurried out of his house and started picking up litter as though he'd been doing it all afternoon. The children began to taunt him.

'Litter-picker-rubbish-man!' they chanted.

'Rubbish-man-trash-man!' they sang.

'Picking up litter 'cos you live in a dump!' they giggled.

'Found any good junk today?' they shouted.

Normally, Geoff would simply ignore the chants and jibes of the children, but today he surprised them by replying.

'Well yes, actually, I have found some good junk today!'

'Well yes, actually, I have found some good junk today!' mimicked one of the children.

'Go on then, what have you found?' said another child. 'Have you found some buried treasure?' and they all laughed again.

'Sort of,' said Geoff.

The children, intrigued by now, were unsure whether Geoff was telling the truth or teasing them. They said nothing, but watched as Geoff poked around under the stone by the wall with his pick-up stick, and pulled out the £5.

'This is what I found,' he said.

'You found a £5 note!' said the children, astonished.

'I did!' said Geoff.

'Are you going to keep it?' one of them asked.

'Well, I don't know who it belongs to, so I suppose I'll have to,' said Geoff. 'You see, it's amazing what I find when I'm picking up litter. You should try it some time!'

'You mean *we* could find money if we pick up litter?' asked one of the children.

'It's possible!' said Geoff.

'And could we keep it if we found some?' they asked.

'I suppose so, though you'd have to check with your parents and see what they thought.'

'I'm going to start searching!' said one of them. 'Come on, you lot. Get looking.' And they all started peering at the ground as they went on their way down the street, picking up the odd sweep wrapper here and crisp packet there.

The next day, just before the children came out of school, Geoff put a 50p piece on the ground by his gate, with a few bits of paper and a chocolate wrapper on top of it. Sure enough, a few minutes later they came along the street, but instead of dropping litter, like they usually did, they were picking it up and examining it carefully. When they got to Geoff's gate they picked up the bits of paper and found the 50p.

'Hey! Look at this! Can we keep it?' they shouted.

'Well, you found it, so I suppose it's yours,' said Geoff, smiling to himself. His plan seemed to be working.

The next day, when the children were at school, Geoff went to see two of their parents. 'Do you mind if they help me when I'm tidying up the litter?' he asked.

'We don't mind at all. In fact we'd be delighted if our children were more helpful in the community, but we don't think they'll want to help with litter collecting!'

'I think they might,' said Geoff.

For the next few days Geoff made sure that the children found some money on the ground on their way home from school. One day it was only a 1p piece, another day it was 5p. But those small amounts were enough to keep them interested in keeping their eyes on the ground and picking up any stray bits of litter they found. They were also so busy picking *up* litter, that they stopped dropping it. And they were so busy telling Geoff about any money they found, that they stopped calling him names and laughing at him.

Everything went well for a week or two, then Geoff stopped putting the coins down for the children to find. He wondered whether they would lose interest in picking up litter and keeping their eyes open for what they might find, so he decided to offer an incentive.

'If you help me keep these streets free of litter for the rest of the month,' he said, 'I'll give you that £5 note I found. You can share it.'

'Do you mean it?' they asked.

'Of course I mean it. I wouldn't have said it otherwise,' said Geoff.

So for the rest of that month the children and Geoff kept their local streets absolutely litter free. The children found a few more coins, quite by chance, that other people had dropped, and Geoff kept his word and added the £5 to their cash.

'Well? What now?' asked Geoff. 'You've helped me for a month and you've been paid. What about next month, and the month after that? I can't afford to pay you out of my own money, so are you going to give up your litter-picking job?'

'No way!' said the children. 'We're looking out for the next £5 note; only next time it might be a £10!'

'It might!' laughed Geoff. 'You never know!'

I wonder if the children did find a £10 note. I'm glad they stopped teasing Geoff and being unkind to him. And I'm also pleased that they stopped dropping litter and started taking pride in keeping their neighbourhood litter free.

I know that no one here would behave in an unkind way, like the children did at the start of the story, and I hope that no one here would think of dropping sweet papers or crisp packets in the street or park. I think we all have a duty to keep our streets and neighbourhoods free of litter so that they are clean and pleasant places to live in.

~

Theme 11

Working together

Three wise birds

I'm sure you've found when you've been working together on, say, a project in your class, that when several people put their heads together and put forward their ideas, there are far more ideas than you could have thought up by yourself. Or maybe you've discovered that if you take part in a quiz, for example, you're much more likely to get all the answers right if it's a team effort and several people are joining in.

There are many advantages in working together and it's something we in school are always encouraging you to do. Working together co-operatively leads to success, and it usually makes a community stronger. Just think what a wonderful world we would have if everyone in it could work together in harmony. If we all play our part in working together, we can bring this a step nearer.

But working together is nothing new! Today's story is from the Jataka Tales of Buddhism and is thousands of years old. Let's hear what it says.

There was once a king who had no children. One day in the palace garden he found a nest with three abandoned eggs inside. Normally he would have left the nest alone, knowing that the parent birds might return, but he realised that this was no ordinary nest. This contained the eggs of three different species. There was an owl's egg, a mynah bird's and a parrot's egg. The king decided that the nest and its eggs must be a message for him, so he gave the eggs to the royal nurse to care for and said, 'When these birds hatch they will be my children.'

A week later the owl egg hatched. It was a male bird and the king named him Avtara.

Let's think about the area we live in. Let's imagine we are walking down our street, or to the shops, or to the park. Let's imagine what we can see on that journey. Can you see tidy streets, or streets full of litter? If you can see tidy streets, let's make sure we keep them clean and tidy. If you can see litter and rubbish in the streets, maybe we could ask the council to provide litter bins? Let's do all we can to keep our neighbourhood litter free.

'The king has had a son,' he announced to everyone.

The mynah bird's egg hatched two days later. It was a female bird and the king named her Kandini.

'The king has had a daughter,' he announced to the world.

The next day the parrot egg hatched, and the king named him Jambuka.

'The king has had a second son,' he announced.

The king treated the birds as though they really were his children. He gave them gold and jewels and everyone in the kingdom had to address them as Prince or Princess.

But the people laughed at the king behind his back for thinking that an owl, a mynah and a parrot could possibly be royal princes and a princess. The king knew his people were laughing at him but he thought, 'They don't know how wise my children are. I must show them.'

So he arranged for a huge meeting to take place, of all his ministers and his government, and many of his people. As soon as everyone was seated he brought in his eldest son, the owl named Avtara, and asked him a question.

'You are a royal prince,' said the king. 'And as such you must be able to give advice. What advice can you give me as to how I should live my life?'

The people waited to hear what Avtara would say, expecting nothing more than a too-whit-too-whoo.

'You should be honest and truthful,' said Avtara. 'You should be prepared to admit when you are wrong. You should stand up for what is right.'

The people were astonished to hear how wise Avtara was, and they said he should be one of the king's advisers.

Next, the king brought his daughter, the mynah bird called Kandini, in front of the assembled people.

'You are a royal princess,' he said. 'And as such you must be able to give advice. What advice can you give me as to how I should live my life?'

The people waited to hear what Kandini would say, expecting nothing more than a screech.

'Do not cause anyone sorrow or pain,' said Kandini. 'Don't blame anyone for something they haven't done. Don't leave all the work for others to do, but reward those who work hard.'

The people were amazed to hear how wise Kandini was, and they said she should be one of the king's advisers.

Then the king brought his second son, the parrot named Jambuka, before the assembled people.

'You are a royal prince,' said the king. 'And as such you must be able to give advice. What advice can you give me as to how I should live my life?'

'The most important thing is to be wise,' said Jambuka. 'No matter how important a person you are, you are of no use if you are a fool.'

The king bristled at these words. Was Jambuka calling him a fool? Was he going to make a fool of him in front of the assembly?

But Jambuka continued. 'If you are to rule wisely, you must consult other wise people, for many heads are better than just one. If you think and act alone, you can only have a certain number of thoughts; you can only do a certain amount of work. But if you work together with others, the amount of work you can do multiplies, and the number of thoughts and ideas you can have is countless. Working together wisely is the most important advice, for that way ideas can be shared and progress made.'

The people were flabbergasted to hear what Jambuka said, and applauded him saying he should be the king's chief adviser.

Years went by and the kingdom prospered. The royal princess and princes worked hard and loyally in their positions as the king's advisers. The king acted on their advice, but especially that of Jambuka. He consulted people before making any changes in his kingdom; he involved people at every level when he made decisions; and he constantly worked with his people, asking their opinions, considering their ideas and listening to their suggestions.

Eventually, the king grew old and died. The people said, 'Jambuka should be our next king,' and the ministers asked him to accept the kingship.

But Jambuka said, 'I have no need of a kingdom, and you have no need of a king. This country runs successfully, and you know how and why it does. It is successful because everyone works together. Everyone is consulted. Every opinion counts. Carry on in this way and the country will continue to be successful.'

And Jambuka flew away to the forest where he had always wanted to live, and the country continued to run efficiently because every voice was heard and everyone worked together.

So, thousands of years ago, this story was being told to teach people the benefits of working well together. And, as we've discovered before, stories from a long time ago can still teach us things today.

~

Let's spend a few moments thinking about working together. Think about the last time you worked together successfully with someone else. Think about why and how that project worked well. Think about a time in your class, or in your

family at home, when something went really well because you worked together.
And think about something you're going to do today, or this week, which will
involve working together with someone else. Let's all make sure that we try to
work well and co-operatively together in everything we do.

Partage Field

Have you ever been in a situation where you've been working in the same place
as someone else but you've both been working independently? It happens quite
a lot. I'm thinking perhaps of when several of you are working at the same table
in the classroom but doing different activities, or maybe when you and your
brother or sister are both trying play different games in a small garden at the
same time. Does it sometimes cause problems? There needs to be some give-
and-take, some co-operation, and some working together in situations like that.

Today's story concerns several people who found a way of solving a problem
by . . . well, let's listen and hear what they did.

There was once a piece of land called Partage Field which joined on to the
back gardens of several houses in the village. No one who lived in the houses
knew who the field really belonged to, neither did they know why it was
called Partage Field. They simply believed that it had always been there and
that everyone whose garden backed on to it had a right to use the field as
they wanted.

Sometimes this caused disagreements; like when Mrs Prendergast wanted
to hang out her washing in the field, at the same time as the Riley's children
wanted to play football, at the same time as Mr Appleby wanted to exercise
his dog. Then the arguments would begin.

'But I need to hang my washing here, I haven't enough room to hang it in
the garden, and I don't want dirty footballs being kicked against it!' Mrs
Prendergast would insist.

'But we've nowhere else to play,' the Riley Children would moan.

'And I need somewhere safe to let Bessie run and exercise.' Mr Appleby
would say.

'But she chases our ball,' the children would grumble. And so the argument would continue.

One day a man from the council came and knocked at the doors of all the
houses whose gardens were next to Partage Field.

'Who owns that land?' he asked, pointing to the field.

And each householder assured the man from the council that *they* owned it really, but that they let the other neighbours use it. The man took the information back to the council offices.

'It's quite clear that a little piece of Partage Field belongs to each house,' said the council boss. 'We must divide up the field and draw up a new map.'

But when the man from the council went back to the householders with the new plans, they were aghast.

'This little bit of land that you say belongs to me, isn't big enough for our children to play in!' said the Rileys.

'And I can't hang a whole line of washing on this tidgy bit of land!' said Mrs Prendergast.

'My Bessie won't be able to exercise!' said Mr Appleby.

'Well,' said the man from the council, 'that's what the council has decided. You each own a little bit of the field and the council is going to draw up a new map to show that you do!' and he went back to his council offices.

'What are we going to do?' asked the neighbours. 'This new arrangement is worse than the one we had before! Surely we can do something.'

'We need to find out who Partage Field belonged to in the first place,' said Mr Appleby. 'We need to find someone with a long, long memory, who might know its history.'

'Mrs DeLaney is the oldest person I've ever heard of,' said Matthew Riley. 'She's 101.'

'Good thinking!' said Mr Appleby. 'She's lived here all her life. Let's go and ask what she knows.'

Mrs DeLaney lived in the nursing home and she was happy to have visitors asking about the old days in the village.

'I know Partage Field,' she said. 'I used to play there as a girl. It belongs to everyone.'

'But it must have belonged to someone in the first place,' said Mr Appleby.

'It belongs to everyone!' repeated Mrs DeLaney.

'But is must be someone's responsibility,' insisted Mr Appleby.

'It's everyone's responsibility!' said Mrs DeLaney.

'But . . .' began Mr Appleby.

'Look!' said Mrs DeLaney, sounding exasperated, and holding up her hand with her fingers spread out. 'Look at your hand!'

Mr Appleby held up his hand and spread out his fingers just like Mrs DeLaney's.

'What can you see?' she asked.

'I can see my hand,' said Mr Appleby.

'You can see a collection of fingers!' said Mrs DeLaney. 'Five fingers that cannot do very much on their own. Can you build a house with just your thumb? Can you bake a cake with just your little finger? Can you mend a bike with just your first finger? No! You can do all those things if you use all your fingers together, but you can't do very much using only one on its own. But, when they all work together there's no end to the things they can do. People are like fingers. You can't do a great deal alone, but if you work together, and use your common sense, you can achieve almost anything. Now, I'm tired and I would like to have a little sleep!'

'What did she mean?' said Matthew Riley as he and Mr Appleby walked back home.

'She's given us the answer to our problem,' smiled Mr Appleby. 'We can *all* own *all* of Partage Field. Come on!' And they went home and had a meeting with all the other neighbours who were involved.

A few months later the man from the council called round again to look at the field. The council was ready to finalise the new maps of the area and wanted to know exactly what kind of boundaries had been put up. The man from the council expected to see the field divided into the individual sections by fences and hedges, and so was astonished to see what the neighbours had done to Partage Field.

For a start, he didn't see a field! He saw a beautiful park laid out with lawns and flower beds. He saw trees and flowers. He saw a children's play area with swings and roundabouts and a huge grassed area for ball games. He saw an area with posts and clothes lines for drying washing. And he saw well-placed seats and benches where some of the neighbours were sitting talking.

'How are things going with the field?' he asked, cautiously, not quite knowing what the people would say. 'I thought you would have all marked your boundaries to show which is your own land. The council needs to know so that it can publish new maps!'

'There are no fences in Partage Field,' said Mr Appleby, 'because we haven't divided it up as you suggested.'

'But you must!' spluttered the man from the council. 'The council said you have to!'

'But the council doesn't own the land,' explained Mr Appleby. 'We do! We *all* own Partage Field; not bits of it, but *all* of it, and we have all worked together to make sure it suits us all. You see,' he went on, 'we have discovered that if we work together we can achieve almost anything, whereas on our own we can't do much.'

'But what about the new map?' said the man from the council.

'You don't need a new map. Partage Field is what it is on the old maps, and Partage Field it will remain on the new ones. Goodbye!'

And the man from the council went back to the council offices, leaving the neighbours to enjoy sharing Partage Field.

It's often quite surprising what can be achieved when people work together. I think old Mrs DeLaney in the story was absolutely right when she said, 'People are like fingers. They can't do a great deal alone, but if they work together, they can achieve almost anything.'

I know we have a school full of people who are good at working together. Let's make sure we keep it that way.

~

Let's think about the way our fingers work together to do the things we want them to do. Each one on its own has very little strength, but together they can do all sorts. Each one of us, as an individual, cannot make huge changes in our world, but working together, we can achieve almost anything, and together we can make the world a better place for everyone.

Mother Teresa

There are many people in the world who have achieved great things. But almost all those people have worked together with others to achieve their goal. Maybe you can think of your hero, or someone you've read or heard about, who has achieved something special, and you can probably think of the sort of people that he or she worked with in order to succeed. For instance, most of the great explorers had teams of people working with them. Most of our famous sportsmen and women work in teams, and even those who take part in single-handed events, like sailing or walking round the world, have teams of people supporting them. Jesus, of course, had the disciples to help him carry out his work. The famous astronauts of our time have huge support networks behind them, like the space centre at Houston that masterminds the American space exploration missions.

One of the most famous, and most admired, women of all time is Mother Teresa,* but although it's her name that is well known throughout the whole world, she, too, had many people helping her in her outstanding work. Here's her story.

---

*Further information can be found at www.ewtn.com/motherteresa.

Mother Teresa was born in 1910, in Skopje, Yugoslavia. She was the youngest of three children and her parents christened her Agnes. Agnes was a happy child, she quickly learned to read and write, and she was good at geography. She particularly liked reading about missionaries; people who were sent to other countries to teach about God, and she could find all the places where they worked on a map of the world, and tell about the work they did.

By the time she was twelve Agnes knew that she wanted to be a missionary when she was old enough, and when she was eighteen she set off for Ireland to train to become a nun and a missionary and teacher. It was a huge decision. It meant leaving her home and her country, learning a new and different language, and probably never seeing her family again. Someone who was in Ireland with her at this time said Agnes was, 'Very small, quiet and shy; quite ordinary in fact.' Agnes may have been ordinary but she was determined to serve God, for she felt that he had asked her to do his work.

After about a year in the convent in Ireland, Agnes was sent to India. Here she took her first vows and chose her new name. From now on she was known as Sister Teresa. And, as Sister Teresa, she started her first job; she was to be a teacher at the Catholic Girls' High School in the city of Calcutta. The girls who attended the school were the daughters of wealthy people living near to Calcutta, and Sister Teresa taught them history and geography. She lived at the convent attached to the school and very rarely went out. Life continued happily for the next fifteen years. Then, something happened which would change Sister Teresa's life forever.

She was sent for a few days to visit another convent to the north of Calcutta, and the poverty she saw on the way shocked and horrified her. Here, just outside the convent and school where she lived and worked in comfort, were children who were starving; people who were ill and had nowhere to go; people who were dying in the streets. Sister Teresa knew she had to do something. She knew that this would be her new work. But how? How would she get permission to leave her teaching job at the convent? And where would she live? How would she find the money to help the people who so needed it?

Sister Teresa started asking questions. This small, shy woman who had always quietly done as she was told, confronted the convent and church authorities by saying she wanted to start a new community: a community whose job it would be to help the poor people of Calcutta. She said, 'I heard the call of God to give up all and go into the slums to serve him among the poorest of the poor.'

Sister Teresa then began to set her ideas moving. She went on a nursing course for six months so that she would know how to help the people who were ill. She worked out how she could live in the slums of Calcutta without the safety and security of the convent. She worked out how she would clothe herself. For everything she had was owned by the convent and was not hers to keep.

After many months she received the permission she had been waiting for; she was allowed to leave the convent and live independently as a nun. Sister Teresa went into the streets of Calcutta and rented a tiny hovel to live in. She wore the ordinary dress of an Indian woman – a plain white sari and sandals.

She decided that the best way to start was with what she knew – teaching. She had no school room and no books, pencils or equipment, so she wrote in the dirt with a stick, and the few children in her class did the same. Her aim was to teach them to read and write and some basic rules of hygiene. Word soon got around that Sister Teresa had set up a school, albeit a school with no walls and no equipment, but the number of children turning up each day grew. And as the children got to know her, Sister Teresa began to visit their families and their homes, helping the sick and the dying to have care and dignity. The more help she gave the more help she realised was needed. How could she, on her own, give all the help to all the people who needed it?

But Sister Teresa did what she had always done; she trusted in God.

And she was not alone for long. Others had heard of her work and wanted to help. Within one year Sister Teresa had more help than she could possibly have imagined. Young women, nurses and teachers, came to work with her. Other people offered food and clothing, books and pencils, medical supplies and money; anything that might be of use. People even gave buildings for Mother Teresa, as she now was, to use as schools, hospitals and clinics.

So many young nuns had joined Mother Teresa that she formed a new order called the Missionaries of Charity. As the help and support increased so did the services they could give. Mother Teresa opened a special home for those who were dying, and she gave them care, comfort and dignity. She opened a home for babies who had been abandoned, and another for people who had the disease called leprosy and who were often turned out by their families because they were afraid of catching the disease too.

Within a few more years the Missionaries of Charity had spread to other countries and now there are communities throughout the world, helping people wherever there is need. When she was 87 years old, and just a few months before she died in 1997, Mother Teresa gave up her position as head of the Missionaries of Charity and handed it on to someone else, knowing that the work she had begun would carry on because there were so many people working together to make it continue.

Mother Teresa is an example to us all of how to help other people who need help. But, without all those people who worked with her, she would not have been able to help so many, and her work would not have continued after her death.

Mother Teresa has shown us that we can each do a little to help someone else, but if we all work together, we can achieve a huge amount.

~

Dear God, help us to learn by the example of Mother Teresa, that each one of us can help someone else, but that by working together there is no limit to the amount we can achieve. Please help us to put our talents and skills together to ensure that everyone in our world has food and shelter, education, care and dignity. Please help us to make our world fair for everyone. Amen

Theme 12

Unlikely heroes

The sand rope

I wonder if you've discovered for yourselves that sometimes the most unlikely people can be the ones to sort out problems? For example, if something needs doing in school, you Year 5 and 6 children might think that the job has to be done by you because younger children wouldn't be able to do it. Or maybe in your family a bigger brother or sister may think that you wouldn't be able to do a particular task because you're too young.

We are all guilty at times of thinking that only certain people are able to do certain things. But sometimes, the very person we think won't be able to do something, is the one who actually succeeds.

Let's listen to today's story. It's one of the Jataka Tales, which is a very old collection of between 500 and 600 stories, and every one has a message. See if you can spot the message in this story. You might even spot more than one!

There was once a king who ruled his kingdom with an iron fist. He was cruel and hard and unforgiving. He had no time for people he considered weak or frail. He showed no understanding or respect towards his people, and, as a result, everyone was afraid of him.

The king's counsellors and advisers were so afraid of him that they dare not say anything but that which they knew he wanted to hear. And so the king was never given sensible or wise advice; in fact he was never given any advice at all, because no one was brave enough to give him any.

Sometimes, as a diversion from his royal duties, the king would set people almost impossible tasks, just so that he could watch them become nervous and agitated, upset and distressed. Then he would laugh, and feel powerful and strong when he saw how uncomfortable they were.

One day the king was out in the palace garden when he decided to have a go on his swing. He liked to play on his swing, especially when he made it go so high that he could see over the garden wall and into the village beyond the palace grounds. Often when he was swinging high like this, he thought up some of his more unpleasant and nasty tasks for his subjects to do.

But on this occasion the swing was not in use. There was a notice fastened on it that said 'Danger! Out of Order'. The king was furious.

'Out of order! How can my swing be out of order! And why did no one tell me! And why has no one mended it!' he roared.

The king looked closely at the swing and realised why it was out of order. The rope was broken.

As he held the broken rope in his hand, he heard the shouts of some children playing on the other side of the wall. They sounded happy and that made him even more furious.

'They'll pay for this,' he muttered to himself, and he stomped off to see his counsellors. 'Those villagers,' he said to the chief counsellor. 'I want you to set them a task. Tell them I want them to make me a new rope for my swing. But, I don't want any old rope. No, I want my rope to be unique. I want my rope to be made of sand! If they can't do it by sunset tomorrow, they have to pay me one thousand silver pieces. Each!' he yelled.

The counsellor looked shocked. He knew the task was impossible and unfair, but what could he say? What could he do? He could hardly start arguing with the king! Well, not and keep his job! And his head! So he mumbled, 'Yes, Your Majesty,' and went to organise the proclamation.

The Royal Herald went to the village, the proclamation in his hand.

'Oyez, oyez,' he called. 'His Royal Highness, king of this country, hereby announces the task for this village, as follows: Villagers will make a new royal rope for the king's swing by sunset tomorrow. Failure to do this will result in each person paying, immediately, a fine of one thousand silver pieces to His Majesty. Post script: the said royal rope is to be made of sand. Here ends the proclamation,' and the Herald marched back to the palace.

The villagers were horrified. 'How on earth can we do that?' they asked each other. 'And, if we don't, how on earth do we pay? We haven't a thousand silver pieces between us, never mind a thousand silver pieces each,' they said.

'We must put our brains together,' said the oldest inhabitant of the village. 'We must think!' So the wisest, oldest and cleverest people of the village met and started to think.

'I know what we could do,' said a small girl.

'No you don't,' said the elders. 'This is a problem for the grown-ups!' And they put their heads together again and started to think some more.

'But I know what we could do,' persisted the small girl.

'Go away child!' said the elders.

'But I have an idea,' she insisted.

'Go *away*!' they said, beginning to become irritated.

'But . . .'

'AWAY!' they said, and the girl did as she was told.

The village elders and betters thought and thought. They put their brains together all through the night and well into the next morning, but not one of them could come up with a plan for making a sand rope for the king's swing.

The small girl tried again. 'I think . . .' she began, but they wouldn't listen and shooed her away again.

The village wise ones pondered and hypothesised, they experimented and fabricated all through the morning, but no matter what schemes and plans they came up with, what ideas they tried, nothing succeeded in making a rope out of sand.

'But if you . . .' began the small girl again. 'If you just . . .'

'GO AWAY!' yelled the elders. 'You're making a nuisance of yourself and preventing us from THINKING!'

The wise ones thought and thought again, all through the afternoon and into the evening. The daylight began to fade and still they had not been able to make a rope out of sand.

'We have failed,' they said, dismally, as the sun began to set. 'We will all be fined a thousand silver pieces that we do not have,' they wailed, as the king together with his counsellors and the Royal Herald swept into the village.

'Well!' demanded the king. 'Where is the sand rope for my swing?'

'We have worked all day, Your Majesty . . .' began the village elders. 'But . . .'

'. . . But we need some advice,' interrupted the small girl. 'You see, Your Majesty, we want to make the rope exactly right for you. We want it to be perfect. But, at the moment we don't know what kind of rope you want. Do you want it to be thick or thin? Do you want it to be plaited or twisted? What colour do you want the finished rope to be?'

'Well . . . I . . . I haven't really thought about that,' answered the king.

'Then if Your Majesty could give us a small sample of sand rope to look at, we will make some just like it,' smiled the small girl, knowing full well that the king couldn't possibly give them a sample to see, as there was no such thing as a rope made of sand. And if the king couldn't do it, he couldn't possibly expect the villagers to do it.

The king knew he had been outwitted by one small child.

The village wise ones also knew that the small girl had been far cleverer than any of them, and that they hadn't given her a chance to speak. They looked embarrassed and ashamed.

The king's counsellors waited to see what the king would do and say. They imagined he would be incredibly angry and that he would probably double the fine. But no! The king saw the funny side of what had happened and was secretly pleased that someone had stood up to him at last. He burst out laughing and told the villagers he would pay them a thousand silver pieces for having such an intelligent girl in their midst.

Well, did you find the hidden message? Yes, it was that it's not just the important leaders who can have good ideas. Everyone has a part to play in life, and sometimes the most unlikely people can come up with the best ideas.

Did you find any more hidden messages? Yes, there was a message about bullying; one about listening to people; one about being fair; even one about standing up for yourself and doing what you know is the right thing, even if you're told to do something else.

~

Dear God, please help us to know that everyone's opinion matters. Help us to remember that everyone has a right to be heard. Help us to remember that everyone can have good ideas, everyone is important, and everyone has a part to play in life. Everyone can make a difference. Amen

Gareth and the carol concert

Sometimes, the most unlikely people can save the day! When something goes wrong, it can be the people we least expect to be able to help, who do or say the thing which sorts out the problem.

This is exactly what happened in today's story. The events in the story really happened, only a couple of Christmases ago, and the people in the story are real people.

Let's hear what happened.

Gareth and Adam were excited about the Christmas carol concert their school was putting on for all the parents. The plans and rehearsals were well under way; both boys were part of the choir, and both had been working hard learning the words and the music. These two boys perhaps had to work a bit harder than everyone else, because they both had special needs. Adam, in Year 2, had some behavioural problems and found it hard to concentrate and to sit still. Gareth, in Year 4, was a boy with Down's syndrome which is a kind of disability that makes the people who have it find learning quite difficult.

The whole school was taking part in the carol concert. Every single child was involved, all 210 of them, aged between 5 and 11. Everyone had a part to play. Some of the children were singers like Adam and Gareth, some were dancers, some of them were actors or musicians, and others had speaking parts. Everyone had a job to do and everyone was important.

The children, with the help and guidance of the teachers, had been practising their different parts in their own classrooms until everyone knew what to do. Then came the exciting day when the whole concert was fitted together, like a giant jigsaw puzzle, for the first time.

The whole school gathered in the hall. A raised stage had been set up at one end, and the children sat at each side of it. The rehearsal began. This was the first time that each class was able to see what the others had been practising. The concert told the story of the first Christmas and the birth of the baby Jesus in the stable.

One by one, the actors, musicians, dancers and speakers went up onto the stage to do their parts. The choir, sitting at both sides of the stage, sang the carols. Everything was going perfectly. Then . . . disaster!

Adam had been waiting at the side of the stage to sing a solo part of a carol. But, although he was exceptionally good at singing – he was not very good at sitting still and waiting! He began to shuffle about, then he started to fiddle with the manger holding the baby Jesus, and finally he began to investigate the straw in the manger. He pulled at the straw and the entire manger came crashing down from the stage onto the hall floor. Mary began to cry, Joseph stepped back and bumped into one of the kings who also fell off the stage.

The teachers were furious.

'How could you be so silly?' they said to Adam. 'All you had to do was sit still and wait your turn. Now look what's happened!'

Adam began to cry and wouldn't sing his carol. He was sent back to the choir and told to sit next to Gareth.

Now Gareth may have found learning the carols difficult, and he wasn't very good at maths or writing, but he was exceptionally good at looking after people. Gareth was an incredibly caring and considerate boy.

'Don't worry. I'll look after you,' he said, gruffly.

The rehearsal continued, and apart from that one glitch in the middle, the rest of it went well.

When it had finished, the headteacher said to Adam, 'Are you going to be able to sit still, and sing your carol tomorrow, Adam, when we perform the concert for the parents?'

'Yes Miss,' promised Adam.

The day of the concert arrived.

The parents and visitors came in and became the audience. The whole school took up their places. The concert began. Everything went perfectly and exactly according to plan. Then, about half way through, Adam started to feel fidgety. He fiddled with his shoelaces and pulled at his jumper. He drew patterns on the floor with his finger. He stopped joining in the carols and forgot where he was in the story.

No one noticed, except Gareth, who had kept an eye on Adam, even though they weren't sitting together.

Adam started to shuffle towards the manger at the edge of the stage. His fingers reached out towards the straw. He began to pull at some wisps of straw that were sticking out. No one seemed to notice, except Gareth, who could imagine what was going to happen next. It would be just like the rehearsal all over again. The concert would be spoiled and Adam would get into trouble. Gareth looked horrified at the thought of it all.

He looked round for a teacher to tell, but no one was near. So, without hesitating, Gareth stood up from his place in the choir and walked calmly towards Adam. He took him by the hand and led him to the very front of the stage, immediately in front of Mary and Joseph and the baby in the manger. Then, Gareth put his hand in his pocket and took out an apple, which he gave to Adam, whispering something to him at the same time.

The audience watched, entranced. Everyone thought this was a well-rehearsed part of the concert.

Adam gently put the apple by the manger, alongside the gold, frankincense and myrrh, as though it was another small gift for the baby. Then Gareth led Adam away from the stage and back to his place in the choir, ready for him to sing his solo carol.

'Wasn't that a wonderful concert,' said everyone, afterwards.

'And wasn't that part lovely, where those two boys gave an apple as a gift,' they said.

Gareth smiled, and the headteacher said, 'Well done, Gareth. I think you saved the day. Well done!'

Without Gareth's quick thinking, the manger might have ended up on the floor again, just as it had in the rehearsal. And it was because of Gareth's kind and caring personality that he was able to help Adam and prevent a disaster in the concert.

I suppose that when rehearsals for the concert first started, no one would have thought that it would be Gareth who would prevent a disaster. But, sometimes it is the least likely people who turn out to be heroes. And of course, as we all know, everyone is good at something. It was lucky that Gareth was there, with his kind and caring attitude, to help Adam on the occasion of the Christmas carol concert.

~

Let's think for a few moments, of the people we know and of the things they are good at. Some of them may be good at making things, others may be good at solving problems, or thinking up original ideas, or writing interesting stories. Some may be good at art or games or dancing; or maybe singing, like Adam in the story. Some people may be good at looking after others, at being kind, at being thoughtful. Whatever they are good at, everyone has a part to play in our world, and everyone is a valuable and worthwhile person.

The tree with the difficult name

Sometimes we jump to conclusions about people. We think we know what they are capable of doing, or not capable of doing, without giving them chance to prove themselves. And sometimes we think that only big important people can change things in the world; we think that small unimportant people can't make a difference.

But, that's just not true. Today's story is a traditional fable from Africa, and it looks at this issue of who is capable of doing what. As you know, fables are stories which try to teach us something. Let's see what this story is trying to say.

Once upon a time a long time ago, there was a severe drought in Africa. The rains were desperately needed but didn't come. The animals were having great difficulty finding enough food for them all.

One day, a gazelle came back from searching for food to say that she had found a huge tree, beyond the old water hole, out towards the mountain.

'I've never seen a tree like it!' she said. 'It's enormous and covered on every branch with big ripe juicy fruits. There's enough fruit on that tree to feed us all for weeks.'

'Let's go and see it,' said the others, and so an enormous procession of animals paraded across the plain, beyond the old water hole, and out towards the mountain.

Sure enough, there was the tree, quite as big as the gazelle had said, and covered with fruits.

'But wait!' said the lion. 'We can't eat from this tree! You know the rules. We can't eat from a tree if we don't know its name. If we don't know its name, we could be poisoned by its fruits.'

The other animals reluctantly agreed with the lion. Then someone said, 'We must find out its name! That can't be too difficult. The old woman who lives at the other side of the mountain will know. She knows most things.'

'We must choose the fastest animal to go and find her,' said the lion. 'The sooner we know the name of the tree, the sooner we can eat its fruit and put an end to our hunger. Send the hare! He's a fast runner.'

So the hare was despatched to find the old woman who lived at the other side of the mountain and ask her the name of the tree. He found her straight-away, and she told him that the tree in question was an Oowungelema Tree, and that, yes, it would be quite safe to eat the fruit.

The hare ran back to the animals as fast as he could, saying to himself over and over again, 'Oowungelema Tree, Oowungelema Tree'. But, just as he was in sight of the animals, the hare tripped over a dead branch, and the name of the tree went clean out of his head.

'You silly animal,' said the lion. 'We'll send the gazelle this time. She can run just as fast as you.'

So the gazelle was sent to find the old woman who lived at the other side of the mountain.

'The tree is the Oowungelema Tree,' said the old woman. 'Keep remem-bering the name all the way home. Don't forget it!'

The gazelle said she wouldn't, and she set off to tell the animals the tree's name. But, on the way she saw a tiny new-born fawn, and she stopped to look at it and its mother. By the time she arrived back at the tree, she had completely forgotten its name.

'You silly animal,' said the lion. 'I can see there is no alternative but for me to go myself. I can be there and back in no time for I'm a fast runner, and *I* won't forget!'

The lion found the old woman and was told the name of the tree. He set off at a smart pace back to the animals, reciting to himself over and over again, 'Oowungelema Tree. Oowungelema Tree. Oowungelema-three. Two-one-three-in-a-tree. One-two-three-up-a-tree. Two-one-get-me-my-tea. One-hot-tea-in-a-tree,' until he had made utter nonsense of what he had been told, and had mixed up the name so much that he couldn't remember how it had been to begin with.

The animals were not pleased.

'You are supposed to be our king!' they said. 'You are not supposed to get things wrong!'

'I'm sorry,' said the lion. 'Let's send another animal instead.'

So they sent the bison, then the buffalo; they sent the hyena and the giraffe; they sent the elephant and the monkey and the rat and the tiger and the antelope and the rhinoceros and the mongoose and the zebra and even the mouse. In fact they sent every animal that could run, but not one single animal could manage to remember the name of the Oowungelema Tree, and bring the name back to the other animals.

'I could go,' said the tortoise.

'You?' said the other animals.

'Yes, me!' said the tortoise.

'You can't run,' said the lion.

'Well, *you* can't remember!' replied the tortoise.

The lion felt very put out by this, but he knew that it was true, so he agreed to let the tortoise try.

'It's a waste of time,' said the other animals. 'He's so stupid and slow and silly and small, *he* won't be able to bring back the name. If *we* couldn't do it, then *he* certainly won't be able to!'

The tortoise set off on his slow small legs, and eventually arrived at the home of the old woman at the other side of the mountain.

'Tell me the name of the tree, please,' he said. 'The others all tried but none of them could remember.'

'I expect they were all too fast,' said the old woman. 'You see, going slowly sometimes gets you there quicker in the end! Now, off you go! Go slowly, and as you go, remember the name of the Oowungelema Tree. Take care now!'

The tortoise set off again. He plodded. Step after step. It was a long way. He was very tired. He nearly gave up. But he kept on going. At last he saw the animals waiting for him under the tree. He struggled the last few metres.

'Well?' they asked.

'Oowungelema Tree,' whispered the tortoise.

At the sound of its name, the tree showered the animals with rich juicy delicious fat fruits to eat. And the animals gave the first fruits to the tortoise.

'Thank you,' they said to him.

So, what do you think the story is trying to say? Yes, it's saying that sometimes the most unlikely people can be heroes. It's saying that we don't have to be big important people to play our part or make a difference. Sometimes, the ones we think are the smallest or the slowest or the least capable, are the ones that succeed.

~

Let's try to remember that everyone has a part to play, that everyone is important, and that everyone deserves to be given a chance. Let's try to remember not to jump to conclusions about people, but to give them a chance to show what they can do. Let's not decide whether someone is capable of doing something, until we've given them a chance. Let us remember that everyone is good at something.

Ourselves and
the World

Theme 1

Neighbours

The greedy neighbour

Can you tell me what being greedy means? Yes, I knew you would be able to. To be greedy means wanting more than your fair share of something. We often use the word greed when we're talking about food, but greed can apply to other things as well. People can be greedy for possessions, or attention, or even for time. Greedy people always want more, and they rarely want to share what they have. It's difficult to like greedy people because they seem to want more than is fair, and none of us likes to think we are being treated unfairly.

Today's story is from Africa and is about someone who was unbelievably greedy. I'd like to know what you think about how this story ends!

There was once a rich man called Kdo who lived in West Africa. He had a large house, big gardens and huge fields of grain, mainly millet seed, which gave him an excellent harvest year after year. Kdo's nearest neighbours lived in the small village near his house and many of them worked for him. Some cooked for him or cleaned his house; others worked in his garden, and many more worked in his fields; ploughing the land, sowing the millet seed and gathering the harvest when it was ready. But, far from being grateful to his neighbours, Kdo paid them as little as possible and never gave them extra food.

The villagers worked so hard and Kdo's fields were so large that every year he gathered in more and more harvest. So much harvest, in fact, that he ran out of space to store it.

'You could share some of the grain with the villagers,' suggested someone, timidly.

'What?' roared Kdo angrily. 'You think I am going to *give* it away? My hard-earned harvest? You can think again!' and he refused even to consider the idea. But, he still had the problem of what to do with all that grain.

'I know!' he suddenly thought. 'I'll make bricks with it, and build a wall. A beautiful, big, high, secure, ENORMOUS wall that everyone will be able to see for miles around. I'll become famous for my wall and everyone will know how rich and important I am.' And Kdo gave instructions for the bricks to be made and the wall to be built.

The villagers were angry and upset that the grain was to be used in this way when many of them were hungry and hadn't enough grain to feed their families. But Kdo was a powerful man and there was little they could do, so they did as they were told and mixed the grain with clay and water, shaped the bricks and put them in the hot sun to bake hard.

Soon the bricks were ready and work on the wall began. It encircled all Kdo's land and stood taller than a giraffe.

'It's a stupid wall,' someone said. 'Now he can't see the countryside; he can only see the wall when he looks out of his house.'

But Kdo wasn't bothered about that. He felt safe and important behind his wall of millet bricks, and even more so when he needed to speak to the villagers about work he wanted them to do, because then he sat high up on top of his wall and shouted his commands down to them.

Life went well for Kdo for several months after his wall was built. And then the drought came.

Month followed dry month and no rain fell. Nothing grew. There was no grain and no harvest that year. The villagers begged Kdo to give them some of his stored millet, but Kdo wouldn't hear of it. He wouldn't share any of his grain. He wanted it all for himself and didn't seem to care that his neighbours were starving and in danger of dying. The villagers began to move away from the area to other parts of the country that were not so badly affected by the lack of water.

Kdo stayed on in his house and slowly used up all his store of food. The rain still didn't come. Kdo ate the grain that should have been used for planting. And still the drought continued. At last Kdo had nothing left to eat and began to eat the grain in the millet and clay bricks of the wall around his house. And still the rain stayed away.

Day by day, week by week, brick by brick, Kdo ate his great wall of grain. All the people in the village had left by now and only Kdo and his donkey remained. His servants had gone, his valuables had been sold, his food had been eaten. Kdo tried to sell his house but no one wanted to buy it. No one wanted to live in this place of drought and famine. Kdo knew that he, too, must leave.

He set out with his donkey to visit the king of a neighbouring country, whom he'd heard was kind and generous. The king agreed to see him.

'I think life has been very difficult for you in the area of the drought,' said the king. 'But I have plenty, so I will give you what you need.'

'Thank you,' said Kdo, suddenly remembering how he himself had not been so generous when his villagers had asked him for food.

'I heard tell,' went on the king, 'of a certain rich man who lived in your region. Such a strange tale I heard! They say he was so wealthy he built a wall of grain around his house. But I heard he built it so that he wouldn't have to share the grain with his neighbours! The tale is incredible! Have you heard this story? Is it true?'

'There *was* a man who built a wall of grain,' answered Kdo quietly.

'Is he still alive?' asked the king.

'He is still living, but he has lost all his wealth,' replied Kdo. 'Now he has nothing and he has had to go to the neighbouring king to beg for food.'

The king looked at Kdo, keenly. 'Do you think the experience has taught the man to be less greedy and selfish? Do you think he has learned to be a better neighbour?' asked the king.

'Oh yes sir, I do,' said Kdo. 'I'm sure that having seen what a good neighbour *you* are, your majesty, he will learn from your example.'

'So it *is* you,' said the king. 'You are Kdo; am I right?'

'Yes, sir, I am,' answered kdo.

'Then I will give you more than enough for your needs,' said the king. 'I will give you grain so that you can rebuild your life, become a farmer again, on condition that you learn from me and become a good neighbour.'

'I will,' said Kdo.

So the king gave Kdo many sacks of grain and Kdo set off for his new life. But, on the way, his hunger overcame him and he sat by the roadside and ate some of the grain. A handful of grain became a fistful, and a fistful became a sackful. Kdo could not stop himself greedily cramming the food into his mouth, all his promises to the king forgotten. But his stomach had become so unused to eating such a large quantity of food that Kdo became ill. Then he died.

The people in the area still talk about Kdo. They remember how un-neighbourly he was, even when the king was a good neighbour to him. They vow that they will never become like Kdo, for, 'What's the use of a wall of grain without neighbours to share it with?' they say.

I think those people who talk about Kdo are right when they say what's the good of having something if there's no one to share it with. Sharing what we have is good. It makes us feel good and it's helpful. Our world would be such a good place for everyone if we could learn to share the earth's food and its resources as fairly as possible.

So, what did you think of the end of the story? Were you expecting Kdo to die? Or did you think the story would have a different ending? How would you have made the story end if you'd written it? Maybe you could write your ending to the story. I'd be interested to read them.

~

Help us, Lord, to share what we have with others. Help us to remember that everyone in the world is our neighbour and that we should look after and help our neighbours. Help us to remember that many of our neighbours in other parts of the world don't have enough to eat, and they don't have a fair share of our earth's resources. Help us to do what we can to share what we have. Amen

Taken for granted

I wonder if you have a neighbour who you think you know really well? Maybe it's someone sitting next to you now, or maybe it's someone who lives near you at home. When we know someone really well, we can sometimes take them for granted. If they've usually done something for us, for example, we expect that they'll always do that for us. But, we should never take people for granted. And we should never lie to them. Here's a story about two neighbours where things didn't turn out quite as they expected.

Once upon a time there were two neighbours who knew each other very well. In fact, they knew each other so well that they had begun to take each other for granted. Mrs Smith assumed she knew everything about Mrs Brody, and Mrs Brody believed she knew exactly what Mrs Smith was thinking. They thought they knew each other so well that they began to treat each other quite casually, and to take advantage of each other.

One day Mrs Brody decided to go and visit her daughter in Scotland. She presumed that Mrs Smith would look after her house and garden whilst she was away, after all, her neighbour always looked after things when she went on holiday. So Mrs Brody packed her bags and set off for the train. Almost as an after-thought, she called in on Mrs Smith on her way to the station and said, 'I'm just off for a couple of days to our Jane's. You don't mind seeing to things, do you. Byee!' and she was gone.

Mrs Smith, although she didn't get the chance to say anything, actually *did* mind 'seeing to things' because she had planned to go and visit her own daughter in Wales for a few days.

'Still, I suppose I can go later,' she said to Bruno, her dog, as she went into the kitchen to do some baking. And that gave her an idea.

'Mrs Brody has got a brand-new set of digital weighing scales,' she remembered. 'They're much better than my old ones. I'll just pop next door and borrow them. She won't mind. It's not as if she'll want to use them herself, not with her being away at Jane's just now.' So Mrs Smith let herself into Mrs Brody's house and borrowed the scales from her kitchen.

Whilst she was there, she noticed Mrs Brody's lovely new mixing bowl and thought she'd borrow that, too. 'She won't mind,' she said to herself. And then she spotted Mrs Brody's electric mixing machine, her glass rolling pin and her cheerful pinny with the red hens on it. 'She won't mind me using those as well,' she said, as she tucked everything under her arm and went home to her own kitchen.

The baking session did not go very well. Mrs Smith was not very good at baking and she was extremely untidy. Soon her entire kitchen was in chaos; the cakes had burned, the pastry had stuck to the worktop and the draining board was sky-high with washing up. Then, catastrophe! Mrs Smith dropped a whole trayful of things. Mrs Brody's brand-new digital weighing scales, her electric mixer and her glass rolling pin crashed to the kitchen floor and smashed to pieces. Then, to make matters even worse, the corner of the cheerful pinny with the red hens on it caught fire on top of the cooker.

'Oh NO! Whatever am I going to do, Bruno,?' she wailed, as she plunged the pinny into the washing-up water and quickly began to pick up all the broken bits from the floor so that Bruno wouldn't hurt his paws. Mrs Smith spent the rest of that day, and two sleepless nights, wondering how she was going to explain the damage to Mrs Brody when she got back from Scotland. 'She won't mind a little white lie,' thought Mrs Smith, as she decided what she was going to say. And no sooner had she done so, than Mrs Brody returned.

As soon as she went in her kitchen she noticed the scales were missing.

'Ah . . . Yes . . . There was a bit of a problem,' said Mrs Smith.

'A bit of a problem?' echoed Mrs Brody.

'Yes, you see while you were away the mice got into your kitchen and they ate your scales. I'm afraid they did a bit more damage as well, for they ate your rolling pin and the mixing bowl, and they even ate your pinny. I'm sorry but there was nothing I could do.'

'Mice?' said Mrs Brody. 'Mice in my kitchen? Mice eating digital weighing scales and mixing bowls and glass rolling pins? That's very strange!'

'Yes, isn't it!' agreed Mrs Smith.

Mrs Brody did not for one minute believe what Mrs Smith was telling her. She guessed that Mrs Smith had borrowed the things and that something had happened to them. So she thought up a plan of her own.

'Oh well,' she said. 'Never mind. These thing can't be helped.'

And Mrs Smith was so relieved that Mrs Brody was taking the news so calmly and that she apparently believed the story about the mice, that she invited Mrs Brody round to her house for tea. 'Just to welcome you back from your holiday,' she said.

'That's very kind of you,' said Mrs Brody. 'I'll come round in about half an hour. Is that all right?'

'That's perfect,' said Mrs Smith, and she hurried home to get the tea ready.

Meanwhile, Mrs Brody went into her garden. She called to Bruno, and led him back to her house. Bruno was quite used to going into Mrs Brody's house, so he wagged his tail and waited for her to give him something to eat. Soon there was a delicious bowl of dog food on the floor. Bruno tucked in and Mrs Brody went round to Mrs Smith's for her tea.

Mrs Brody was just about to sit down when she said, innocently, 'Oh, by the way. I was just on my way round here when a brown bird swooped down from the sky and flew off with Bruno.'

Mrs Smith stared at her.

'The bird just picked him up and flew off with him. It was quite extra-ordinary. Maybe you'll never see him again!'

Mrs Smith dropped the plate of sandwiches and the teapot.

'Bruno?' she said. 'A bird has flown off with Bruno?'

'Yes,' said Mrs Brody. 'Just now. I saw it with my own eyes.'

'Don't be silly,' said Mrs Smith, beginning to sound angry. 'Birds don't fly off with dogs the size of Bruno!'

'Exactly!' declared Mrs Brody. 'And mice don't eat digital scales and glass rolling pins! Now, shall we both start being honest with each other, stop taking each other for granted, and stop making fools of each other, Mrs Smith!'

'I'm sorry,' said Mrs Smith.

'And I'm sorry too,' said Mrs Brody, as she went off to let Bruno out of her kitchen, and Mrs Smith retrieved the cheerful pinny with the red hens on it from the bin so that she could better explain to Mrs Brody exactly what had happened on the day she borrowed the scales.

Those two neighbours learned some valuable lessons from all that. They learned not to take each other for granted, and they learned not to take advantage of each other. Mrs Smith learned that telling lies isn't the best way of getting out of trouble, and I think Mrs Brody probably learned that teasing someone about their pets is very upsetting for them and best avoided.

~

Dear God, help us to remember that to have good friends and neighbours, we need to be good friends and neighbours. Help us not to take our friends and neighbours for granted, but to appreciate what they do for us. Help us to be kind, considerate and helpful to our neighbours. Help us to remember that everyone, in fact, is our neighbour. Amen

Khalid and the kite

I looked up the word 'neighbour' in the dictionary today. It said: 'A neighbour is a person or thing near or next to another.' Then it went on to say: 'A person who lives next door, near, in the same street or district, or in the next country.' It sounds, then, as though a neighbour can be just about anyone! And that's the thing about neighbours – they can be anyone. We don't usually choose them; they just happen to be people nearby.

And because we haven't chosen our neighbours, we might not like them! But we do have a responsibility to get on with them. You've heard me say in school that you don't have to like everyone, but you do have to get along with everyone in our community. It's just the same in your neighbourhood. I have a story about neighbours for you today.

Khalid and Ahmad live in neighbouring villages in Afghanistan, quite near the capital city of Kabul. They both like going to school, they both like playing with their friends. But . . . they don't like each other! However, they do both like flying their kites. Kite flying is a national pastime in Afghanistan and it's both a sport and an art.

One day, when Khalid had saved up enough pocket money to buy a new kite, his dad took him into Kabul to choose a new one. There were lots of kite shops in Kabul, but Khalid knew exactly which one he wanted to go to. It was Noor Agha's shop. Noor Agha was the most skilful kite maker in town. He could build enormous kites, almost two metres across, out of tissue-thin paper and slim strips of wood. He could make as many as 30 kites in a single day, and every one of them would fly perfectly.

Khalid hadn't enough money to buy one of Noor Agha's special kites, but he was able to buy a small plastic one. It would do for now. One day, when he could afford it, he would have one of Noor Agha's magnificent hand-made kites.

Khalid and his dad set off home again to fly the new kite, but when they got to the village a kite-flying contest was just about to begin. The competitors were getting their kites ready.

'Shall we go somewhere else to fly yours?' asked his dad.

'No, let's watch the contest,' said Khalid. 'I can fly mine later.' They'd just joined the crowd when Khalid noticed Ahmad and his father were also there, ready to watch the match. The two boys glared at each other.

Soon, there were a dozen or so kites in the air, some of them huge and most of them brightly coloured. Khalid liked one in particular. It was a brilliant turquoise kite with a vivid black, red and white design on it. Khalid was sure it was one of Noor Agha's kites. As the kites danced and swooped, the contest began. Each kite flyer chose another kite to challenge. Each competitor tried to make his kite string rub against his opponent's string, like a saw, until he had cut right through it. Most of the kite strings had been coated with wax, or even glue and powdered glass, to make them as sharp as knives. The kite flyers made their kites dance and swoop, dive and swirl, as they tried to cut the strings of their opponents. Sure enough, first one and then another string was cut, and first one and then another kite fell to the ground. As the kites fell, the children ran after them. If they found a fallen kite it was theirs to keep.

'Go on, Khalid,' said his dad. 'Run after one and try to claim it!'

But Khalid had his eye on the brilliant turquoise kite with the vivid black, red and white design. It was still flying strongly and now had only one other kite in competition with it. It was a final challenge between the turquoise kite and a yellow one. Khalid wanted the turquoise kite to win the contest, but he also wanted it to lose; for if it lost he was in with a chance of running for it and claiming it for himself.

He noticed that Ahmad was also watching it carefully.

He waited.

The turquoise kite climbed into the sky again. It dived towards the yellow one, but too late, the yellow kite dipped below it and sliced through the turquoise string like a blade. The yellow kite soared, triumphant, into the sky, the winner, whilst the defeated turquoise kite floated towards the earth.

Khalid leapt to his feet. With his eyes always on the kite, he ran towards the place where he guessed it would land. But the wind took hold of it and whisked it further and further along the ground. Khalid continued to run after it. If only he could reach it, grab it, claim it, it would be his.

But someone else was also chasing the prize. Ahmad was just as determined to claim the kite for himself. The two boys closed in on the kite. They both grabbed it at exactly the same time.

'It's mine, I saw it first!'

'No you didn't. It's mine, I got it first.'

'Get off! I'm having it.'

'Oh no you're not, it's mine.'

Then the fight started. The kite fell to the ground, torn, broken and almost forgotten, as the two boys scuffled and fought and rolled on the ground.

Suddenly, a figure loomed over them and a large voice said, 'And what good is the kite to either of you if it is broken and useless?' And they looked up to see Noor Agha standing over them.

'You two are neighbours, are you not?' he said.

'S'pose so,' mumbled Ahmad.

'Sort of,' said Khalid.

'You live in neighbouring villages, don't you? And you go to the same school?'

'Yes,' they both agreed.

'Then you're neighbours. You don't have to like your neighbours, but you do have to get along with them if you're all to live together in peace. Now, get up, the pair of you!'

Khalid and Ahmad got to their feet and looked suitably ashamed.

'Now! This is what we'll do,' said Noor Agha. 'I will give you each one of my kites, if, IF, you challenge each other only with your kites and not with your fists. In other words, no more fighting! Agreed?'

'Agreed!' said Khalid and Ahmad.

They were taken, with their parents' permission, back to Noor Agha's shop, where he gave them each one of his smaller kites. He told them both they could come to him for advice about building their own kites if they wanted to. They did!

And that's how Khalid and Ahmad, in time, became not exactly the best of friends, but not the worst of enemies. They learned, through a shared interest, to get along with each other, because, as everyone knows, that's what neighbours do.

They were lucky, weren't they, that Noor Agha was prepared to help them. He knew the value of working together and getting along.

We don't usually choose our neighbours; they're the people who just happen to be near us. The person sitting next to you now is your neighbour. The people who live in your street, the families who live in our town, the people who live in France and in the rest of Europe; they are all our neighbours. In fact, everyone is our neighbour, since everyone is near someone who is near someone else!

We don't have to like everyone, but we do have to get along with everyone. That way, our world will be a better place.

~

Let's think about our neighbours and try to be thoughtful, kind and helpful to them. Perhaps you could think of someone who's sitting near to you now; someone who isn't a special friend, but someone you could try to help, or be kind to, today. Perhaps you could think of a way you could help someone, either at school or at home, to show you were trying to be a good neighbour.

Theme 2

Journeys

The rabbit-proof fence

Can you remember the most recent journey you went on – apart from your journey to school this morning? Maybe you were coming home from your holidays, or from visiting someone. I wonder if it was a long journey or a short one. I wonder if it had been planned a long time or if it was more of a last-minute sort of journey. There are, of course, many different kinds of journeys.

Today's story is about a girl in Australia and a journey she made over 70 years ago. It's a true story. The girl was called Molly Craig and she was just fourteen at the time of the story. Molly's father was a white man, and her mother was an Australian aborigine, but Molly was unfortunately born at a time when children like her were forced to leave their families to go and live in homes hundreds of miles away, where they were taught to be 'white'.

Molly lived in a town called Jigalong, in Western Australia, with her mother, her grandmother, her little sister Daisy who was eight years old, and her cousin Gracie who was just six. For the past few weeks Jigalong had been busy with activity because the men had come to build a fence.

You might think a fence is pretty unimportant, but this fence . . . *this* fence was to be thousands of miles long! This was to be a rabbit-proof fence.*

You see, Australia had a problem with rabbits. There were millions of them. The authorities decided that the only solution was to build an enormously long fence to keep the rabbits out of the farmlands and to stop them eating the crops. Molly, Daisy and Gracie went down to the fence every day and watched the Jigalong section being built.

---

* Further information can be found at http://en.wikipedia.org/wiki/Rabbit-proof_fence.

'It's good and strong,' Molly said. 'It'll keep the rabbits out.'

'It sure will,' said the workmen. 'Those rabbits will never get through this fence.' And they continued building, with wood and with wire, out of Jigalong and away to the south.

A few days after the fence men had gone, some more visitors came to Jigalong, but these people were not so welcome. In fact these people were the visitors the Jigalong mothers had been dreading seeing. These were the people who had come to take their children away.

'You know it's for their own good,' said the man with the list of names. 'Your children will go to new homes. They will have a much better life. They will go to school and learn to read and write. They will learn how to be servants and farm workers for the white people. You know it is for their own good. And you know it is the law!' And without giving the mothers the chance to say goodbye, the children were bundled into the cars and driven away.

Molly screamed and kicked and cried. She looked out of the back window of the car and could see her distraught mother and grandmother standing in the middle of the dusty road.

'You'll soon forget her,' said the woman in the car.

'I won't,' screamed Molly. '*And* I won't stay with you. *And* I'll come back home again. *This* is where I live.'

'You'll never come here again,' said the woman. 'You're going to a new life.'

Molly, Daisy, Gracie and the others were taken to a railway station and put on a train. After two days they arrived at the Moore River Settlement which was to be their home whilst they learned how to work for the white people.

Molly did as she was told and kept out of trouble, but all the time she thought of home, and how she could get back there. And all the time she did her best to look after Daisy and Gracie. She was determined that the three of them would stay together. She was determined to look after them.

One day, Molly was outside scrubbing the steps of the main building, when she heard some workmen talking.

'Last section's just about finished,' said one. 'Then it'll link up with the other branch and the main fence.'

'Let's hope it does the trick and keeps the rabbits out,' said the other. 'We can't afford to lose any more crops.'

Molly stopped to listen. Fence? Rabbits? she thought. Were they talking about the rabbit-proof fence?

'Hey, mister,' she shouted.

They stopped to look at her.

'Is it near here? The rabbit-proof fence?' she called.

'Sure is,' said one of the men. 'Just a mile over there. See that tree? Just a bit further on. Why do you ask?'

'Just wondered, that's all,' said Molly, but an idea was growing in her mind. 'I saw part of it being built,' she said. 'Near Jigalong.'

'Jigalong, you say? Well, I never been there, but I know it's about a thousand miles north of here.'

'A thousand miles!' thought Molly. 'A thousand miles is an awful long way,' but the idea in her mind grew a bit bigger.

That night it rained. And rained and rained.

'We can do it now,' Molly said to Daisy and Gracie. 'If we leave now they won't find our tracks for ages because of the rain. We can walk back home. It's a long journey, but we can walk it. I know we can. We *have* to!'

'I don't want to!' grumbled Daisy.

'It's too far,' cried Gracie.

'We don't know the way,' said Daisy.

'We'll follow the rabbit-proof fence,' said Molly. 'It'll lead us home to Jigalong.' And she got the two children up and dressed with no one noticing and they set off, into the rain and the night, to follow the rabbit-proof fence.

And so began their difficult and dangerous journey. They had no food, no water and no warm clothes. They scavenged food from farmers and aborigine hunters. They cooked what little meat they could find over an open fire. The two younger children tired easily and were tearful, but Molly looked after them, encouraged them, and even carried them when they became too exhausted to go any further. She knew she was responsible for them and that without her they would not be able to survive. She was responsible for them because they were her family, and because it was she, Molly, who had brought them on this journey.

Molly led them across the desert trying hard not to draw attention to themselves in case they were recaptured and sent back to the Moore River Settlement. All the time she thought of home, and all the time she followed the rabbit-proof fence, convinced that this would lead them safely back to Jigalong.

But what Molly did not know, was that the rabbit-proof fence had several branches to it. It was like a huge tree, with one main trunk and lots of offshoots. Several times, when she met farmers or aborigines, she was told they were walking in the wrong direction, and then they had to retrace their steps and pick up the main trunk again. And several times Molly had to hide the three of them, when she realised that the people from Moore River were trying to find them to take them back to the settlement.

But, Molly, Daisy and Gracie followed the rabbit-proof fence for one thousand one hundred miles, and nine and a half weeks. And, at last they reached Jigalong and home.

Molly was determined, from first being captured, that she was going to return to her home. She could have escaped on her own. She may well have had an easier journey if she hadn't had the two younger children to care for. But, she had a responsibility to them and she certainly wasn't going to fail that responsibility. She was determined that all three of them would make the journey home, together.

Molly and Daisy are still alive today. They are old women now but they still live near Jigalong. No doubt they still talk of the journey they made all those years ago, of all those miles and all that time. And of course of the rabbit-proof fence that helped them.

Let's spend a few moments thinking of the journey that Molly, Daisy and Gracie made, and of the way that Molly cared for the younger two children. Let's remember how determined she was to go back to her home, and how she felt responsible for the younger two children. Let's think of ways in which we can show responsibility to people younger than us.

Scamp gets lost

Journeys are usually interesting, often exciting, and sometimes unpredictable – in other words you don't always know just how they'll turn out. You can set off thinking you know exactly what's going to happen, and mostly it does, but just sometimes, things turn out quite differently from what you expected.

In today's story, based on a true one, someone went on a journey they didn't expect, and someone else went on a journey they thought would be very sad. Here's what happened.

Scamp looked at the open garden gate and wondered what to do. He was a small coffee-coloured cairn terrier, who was Mrs McDonald's pride and joy. He was six now and had lived with her since her was a puppy just twelve weeks old. Scamp often went out of the gate with Mrs McDonald, but he was always on his lead, except when they got to the moors, then he was allowed to run about on the springy grass and hide in the Scottish heather. But he always had to come back when she called him, and he was never allowed out on his own.

Scamp looked again at the open gate.

He nudged it a little more open with his nose, and stepped out on to the pavement. No one called him back. No one seemed to notice him. He walked a little way along the path, getting used to the feel of not being on his lead. Then he walked across the road, over the bridge and out towards the moors. He knew this route. He'd been here many times before, but never, ever on his own.

Scamp ran across the grass, sniffing the air, following the scent of rabbit and hare. This was exciting. He felt free and adventurous. He ran and ran, stopping here and there to look at something new. He discovered parts of the moor he'd never seen before. He felt like an explorer.

Then suddenly he heard a bang! It sounded like a gun he'd heard once when he was out with Mrs McDonald. She'd called him back and put him on his lead again, but she wasn't here now to keep him safe. He knew he must get away, and fast. He bolted across the moors and ran and ran until he was completely out of breath and could run no more. Scamp looked around. He had no idea where he was, but there in the distance he could see houses and rooftops. His house must be there, he thought, so he plodded towards them. But there was nothing here he recognised. The streets, the houses, the scents and smells, were all different from the ones he knew. He sat down outside a shop and realised he felt hungry.

Just at the side of the road, parked with its back door open, was a van, and inside Scamp could see an open packet of half-eaten sandwiches. A piece of meat was sticking out of the bread. Scamp jumped into the van, snatched the meat, and was just about to jump down again when two men came out of the shop.

'Right Bert!' said one. 'Ready for off?'

'Certainly am,' said the other. 'It's a long drive. Best get going.' And before Scamp knew what was happening the back door was slammed shut, the engine started and the van set off. Scamp trembled with fear, but found some old sacks to curl up on, and waited to see what would happen next.

After a long time, the engine stopped, the back door was opened again, and one of the men was startled to see a small dog leap out and dash off down the road. Scamp had no idea where he was, even less idea of where he was going, but knew he wanted to be as far away from the van as possible. He wandered the streets and eventually found himself in a yard at the back of a pub. He searched around in the bins for something to eat but two fierce dogs rushed out at him and he ran away. He wandered around for three or four days and nights, becoming more hungry and scared and tired. At last he wandered into a garden and lay down under a bush.

'Mum?' called a boy from the window. 'There's a dog in our garden. Can we keep him?'

'Don't be silly, Alex,' a woman answered.

'But, Mum? Look! Can we keep him?' Alex said.

'Of course not! He must belong to someone!' said his mum.

'He doesn't look as though he does,' saidAlex.

'He *does* look a bit thin and bedraggled,' said his mum.

'Can we give him something to eat?'

So Alex and his mum went out and gave Scamp his first meal in almost a week. They made him a dry bed in their shed to sleep on.

'So, *can* we keep him?' Alex asked again.

'No, Alex. He belongs to someone else. They'll be worried about him. Just think how you'd feel if he was yours and he'd got lost,' said his mum. 'We'll look after him until we find the owner. Now come and help me make some posters to put up in the shops to let people know he's here.'

But despite posters and telephone calls, enquiries to the police and to Petwatch, no one living locally had reported a missing dog.

'*Now* can we keep him?' said Alex.

'Only if we can't find the owner,' answered his mum.

'Yes! I'm going to call him Benjy,' shouted Alex and he went out to give Benjy a hug.

'If there's any question of keeping him, we must take him to the vet to have him checked over,' said Alex's mum later, so off they went with Benjy to see the vet.

'He looks as though he's been well cared for in the past,' said the vet. 'I think he's lost. We'll just scan him to see if he's micro-chipped*. If he is, then we'll know straightaway who the owner is.' The scanner was held over Benjy's back and immediately the vet knew he belonged to someone. He turned to the computer and typed in some numbers, and there was Scamp's and Mrs McDonald's name and address.

Alex burst into tears. 'I wanted to keep him,' he said.

'But his owner will want him back, Alex, and Scamp will want to go back to his own home,' said the vet. 'I'll ring Mrs McDonald and tell her Scamp's safe, then we'll make arrangements to get him back to her.'

---

* Further information about micro-chipping animals can be found at www.identichip. co.uk.

'We'll do that,' said Alex's mum, suddenly. 'We'll take Scamp back home.'

So the next day, Alex and his mum put Scamp in the car and drove all the way from Yorkshire to Scotland. Alex was very quiet in the car, and was feeling upset about having to give the dog back, but when they arrived at Mrs McDonald's he had no doubt at all that they had done the right thing in bringing Scamp back to where he belonged. Mrs McDonald and Scamp were overjoyed to see each other again.

'But I *did* want to keep him,' said Alex, near to tears again as he hugged Scamp goodbye.

'I think we will get a dog, Alex,' said his mum. 'I know how much you'd like to have one.'

'Now, that's a very funny thing,' said Mrs McDonald. 'Because I happen to know that the breeder where I got Scamp from has some puppies that are looking for homes. She lives just down the road. Would you like to see them?'

Alex beamed at his mum. 'Can we, Mum? *Can* we?'

And that's how Scamp went on a journey he didn't expect, and how Alex went on one too, and came back home with a puppy instead of feeling sad!

I imagine that Scamp enjoyed his journey back to Scotland much more than his journey to England. And I imagine that Alex enjoyed his journey back to England much more than his journey to Scotland. I'm sure I don't have to tell you why!

It was lucky for Scamp that Alex and his mum were kind and helpful people who were concerned for the stray dog and prepared to try to find out who he belonged to. And it was helpful that Mrs McDonald had had Scamp microchipped when he was a puppy, otherwise they'd never have found each other again. It's good that the journeys turned out so well for everyone in the end.

～

Let's think about our pets and the ways that we are responsible for them. Let's make sure we are responsible owners and that we look after the animals in our care properly. Let's make sure we never do anything to hurt or frighten animals, and that we respect all living creatures.

When we go on journeys, let's make sure our pets are well looked after if we have to go without them, and properly cared for if they come with us.

Julie's dad

Every single one of us here is on a journey right now! We're all on our journey through life. Some of us have been on that journey quite a while, but you are only just beginning yours and you have lots of exciting parts of your journey still to come.

Older people, of course, have been on their journey through life a long time, and sometimes we can look at an older person and forget that he or she has an interesting life story behind them. We sometimes don't stop to think about the exciting adventures they've had, or that they have fascinating and intriguing stories to tell.

I have a friend called Julie, and although I've met her father a few times, I actually knew very little about him . . . until the day he told me about an adventure he'd had; a journey he'd been on, when he was a young man.

Here's his story.

Julie's dad found himself crouching in a tiny wood in Normandy in northern France. It was gloomy and wet. He was injured. He had a broken nose, cuts to his face, a sprained thumb and a damaged shoulder. In a field nearby lay his crashed plane. It was 1944 and France was seeing some of the worst fighting of the Second World War. Julie's dad was a fighter pilot and his plane had just been hit. It seemed unbelievable that only an hour ago he'd been about to have his breakfast at his airfield in England, yet now he was here, alone, in danger, shocked and injured, hiding in a wood in a foreign country.

Julie's dad, Flight Lieutenant George Pyle, expected at any moment to be captured by Nazi soldiers. There were plenty in Normandy, and for the moment they were in charge. He knew he had to get away; away from the plane which would soon be discovered; away from the area. But he knew he was at least twenty miles from the beachhead and British soldiers and safety. Twenty miles was impossible to cross on foot when you were injured and surrounded by the enemy.

Mr Pyle crawled out from the wood, looked at his little pocket compass, and headed north, towards the sea. Suddenly, he heard voices. He pushed through a hedge to get away from whoever was coming, but was dismayed to find himself standing in front of two strangers in the middle of a farmyard. There was nothing for it but to hope for the best, trust they were friendly and try to explain who he was and why he was there.

Mr Pyle spoke hardly any French and the two French farmers spoke no

English, but they quickly realised that this was the pilot from the crashed aircraft. The two Frenchmen glanced around to see that no one was looking, then bundled Mr Pyle into the farmhouse. He had no idea where they were taking him, but soon found they were trying to help. The farmer's wife sat him at the table, provided food and coffee, gave him an old coat so that his uniform would be less conspicuous, then the two men led him across their land and pointed out the direction he needed to take. Mr Pyle wanted to pay them for the coat and food, but they refused to take any money and wished him good luck. Mr Pyle realised, as he left them, that although they had been so kind to him, he didn't even know their names.

Mr Pyle struggled across the Normandy countryside. He was in considerable pain from his broken nose and damaged shoulder, and it was difficult to climb over gates and through hedges, but he knew he must keep away from the roads if he were to stay hidden from the Nazi soldiers.

After less than a mile, he came face to face with another French farmer, digging potatoes in a field. Another French farmer who could have given him away to the Nazis. But once again, Mr Pyle was given help and friendship. This farmer, just like the others, offered him food and drink and showed him the way to go. Once again, the family would take no payment for their kindness.

A little further along his journey, Mr Pyle was stopped by a fiercely barking dog. Here was real danger, not so much from the dog itself, for it was chained up, but the barking might bring soldiers and others to see what the fuss was about. Sure enough, someone came to investigate: another Frenchman in work clothes. Mr Pyle again tried to explain who he was and what had happened. This man took one look at the pilot and knew he could walk no further. He was too tired and too badly injured to carry on. Once again Mr Pyle was taken to a farmhouse just like the others. Once again he was given a warm welcome and food.

Then the farmer left, and came back a short time later with another man. This was Monsieur Jacquier, the local school teacher and Monsieur Jacquier quickly took charge. He decided that Mr Pyle must stay at the farmhouse until he was well and strong enough to continue on his journey. They found a store room where they could put a bed for him and where he could hide if any German soldiers should come to the farm. They gave him ordinary clothes, just as a French farmer would wear, so that he would look as though he belonged to the village. They sent for the local doctor to treat his injuries.

Each day, different villagers came to give him food and to see how he was. But this led to a problem. Each day more and more people knew that a British airman was hiding in the village. The more people knew about him the more danger everyone was in. For if the Nazi soldiers found out about him, not only would Mr Pyle be imprisoned or even shot, but the lives of the villagers would be in danger, too. They could be executed for helping him. Mr Pyle would have to go.

So, Monsieur Jacquier arranged for a new hiding place. This time it was in a stable with some horses. But then came a new problem – Mr Pyle was allergic to horses! After only a few days he had to be moved again. He was taken to Madame Eudine's house and given a place in the barn to sleep. And it was here that he had a sudden reminder of the danger he was in, and a very narrow escape.

He'd been hiding in the barn for several days when Madame Eudine decided it would be safer for him in the house. She took him to a small room in the attic and removed everything from the barn that would show he'd been there. No sooner had she done this than a Nazi soldier came to the farm. He demanded food; he wanted an omelette, and whilst Madame was making this he searched all the farm buildings . . . except the house. Mr Pyle waited in the attic. Still. Silent. Hardly daring to breathe. He could hear the soldier talking downstairs to Madame Eudine. Would she give him away? But he need not have worried about that. Madame Eudine was as loyal and trustworthy as all the rest of the people who'd helped him so far.

But more danger awaited Mr Pyle. More Nazi soldiers were nearby and Monsieur Jacquier decided the only thing to do was to go back. Back to where the journey had begun. Back to the site of the crash. Flight Lieutenant Pyle had travelled on a dangerous journey of several weeks, only to end up exactly where he'd started!

And that might have been the end of the journey, but in fact it was only a new beginning. Monsieur Jacquier alerted the French Resistance to Mr Pyle's problem. The Resistance was an organisation of people who worked against the enemy, and helped the Allies. The Resistance helped Mr Pyle continue on his journey, constantly hiding him and moving him, and exactly nine weeks all but a day since he crashed his plane in the Normandy countryside, Mr Pyle was delivered safely to a British Royal Air Force Unit.

Later, Mr Pyle said, about all the French people who had helped him on his journey, 'I was a stranger arriving suddenly and unexpectedly amongst them, yet no one hesitated to hold out the hand of friendship, despite the dangers in doing so. They hid me, looked after my injuries, shared their food with me, and always gave me every consideration and courtesy. I owe them a debt I can never ever repay.'

When we look at older people, like Julie's dad, it's very easy to think they've always been old, and that they've never had any exciting adventures. But everyone has a story to tell about their journey through life. Maybe you know someone who is quite old, and you could ask them about their adventures when they were young.

Julie's dad's journey home would have probably been very different if all those people hadn't helped him along the way. He might not have even got home at all without their help.

~

Let's think for a moment about the journey through life that we're all making. Let's try to do whatever we can to help the people we meet along their journey. We can all try to be kind and helpful, to be considerate and polite. We can all try to respect others and be friendly towards them. If everyone tries to help everyone else on their journey through life, we will have a better world.

Theme 3

Problems

Alex Thompson's yacht

Every single person in the world has problems of one sort or another from time to time. Maybe you've already had a problem today; I know I have! This morning I had a huge problem because I couldn't find my car keys, then, when I'd found them and got to school I discovered that I'd left something behind at home that I needed. Another problem! Later, I discovered a problem with the office computer and just before I came in to assembly there was a problem with someone on the phone. What a morning!

Problems present themselves all the time. They're part of life. But the important thing about problems is how we solve them. We have to think our way through problems and decide what to do. Problem solving is interesting, though we might not always think so at the time.

Today's story is about someone who had a serious problem, and how he, and someone else, dealt with it.

The yachtsmen were ready, and after months of training and preparation, the race was set to begin.

This was the world's toughest, solo, round-the-world, yacht race: the Velux Five-Oceans Race. Each boat had just one man to sail it. (The women's race was separate.) The race would take weeks of sailing through some of the world's most difficult sea conditions. The distance each yacht had to travel was 30,000 miles. Right round the world.

The starter sounded and the yachts set off. At first all went well. The yachts ate up the sea miles, travelling further and further on their journey. The yachtsmen settled into a routine: checking the course, altering the sails to suit the wind; a few snatched hours of sleep; a meal prepared in a tiny galley; more work on the boat, maybe a few repairs; another hour of sleep; and so on, day after day, night after night. Sailing single-handed round the world is hard, tiring, relentless work.

After several thousand miles the yachts had spread out. Mike Golding was in second place and sailing well as he began to cross the southern ocean. He was already gaining on the lead yacht. At this rate he would catch up and even overtake the leader. He would be in first position. If he could keep the place he would win the race! What a wonderful, beautiful thought.

Eighty miles behind Mike's boat was Alex Thompson's yacht. Alex was pleased with his position and knew there were many thousands of miles still to go. Plenty of time for him to move ahead and take second or even first place. Alex finished the jobs he was doing, set the boat on automatic pilot, and went to his bunk to catch an hour or two's sleep. He noticed the worsening weather.

An hour later the storm struck. The waves towered over the tiny yacht, hurling themselves on to its deck. The wind howled and screamed, and snow and ice beat down with the rain. Suddenly there was an enormous crash as a huge wave smashed into the hull, throwing the boat on to its side. Alex was thrown from his bunk. He snapped on his safety line and climbed out of the cabin to see what had happened.

As he moved to the deck, the yacht turned right side up again, but it wouldn't balance; it bobbed and tilted. Alex realised that the keel – the huge part underneath the hull that helped the boat to balance and to stay upright, had torn off. Without the keel, Alex couldn't control the boat. Without help he could well drown. Alex struggled on the heaving boat to reach the radio equipment, and sent out a mayday signal to alert the nearest boat or ship to the fact that he was in serious difficulty; that he was in danger.

The nearest boat was eighty miles away.

The nearest boat was Mike's.

Mike picked up the mayday signal on his radio and looked out at the storm. It was already behind him; he was heading into calmer waters. If he turned back to help Alex, he, too, would be sailing in the storm. He, too, would risk damage to his boat. He could risk his own life.

Mike knew that if he turned back he would certainly lose his hard-won second-place position. If he turned back he would definitely lose all chance of winning the Five-Oceans Race. What a problem! What a decision to have to make!

But, if he sailed on, Mike knew he would be ignoring Alex's mayday signal. If he sailed on and Alex died, how could he live with his conscience? Mike knew, almost without thinking, what he must do. He knew that all sailors have an unwritten rule that says you must respond straightaway to help anyone who is in danger at sea. Mike knew that saving Alex was much more important than winning the race.

Mike turned his yacht round and sailed back towards the eye of the storm. The waves were more than five metres high now and the winds were gale force. The nearer to Alex he travelled, the worse the storm became. At one point an enormous wave smashed against his yacht and snapped the mast in two.

At last Mike reached Alex's yacht and he could see how damaged it was. Alex was already in his survival suit, but the sea was too rough, the wind too strong and the night too dark for Mike to attempt the dangerous boat-to-boat rescue. Alex and Mike would have to wait until first light in the morning to attempt to get Alex safely off the broken yacht. They both spent a cold and miserable night trying to stay in contact in the churning sea.

By dawn the next morning it was light but the sea conditions were just as bad as the night before. It was still too dangerous to attempt a boat-to-boat rescue. If Alex tried to jump aboard Mike's yacht and missed, he would be swept away and would drown.

They decided there was only one way to do the rescue. Alex launched his tiny life-raft whilst Mike sailed alongside it, trying to keep it as steady as possible in the heaving sea. After four near-attempts, Alex waited for exactly the right moment and dropped from his yacht into the raft. One false move and he knew he would drown. But his judgement was sound. He landed safely in the bobbing raft. Mike, still struggling to keep *his* yacht alongside the raft, tried to pull Alex to safety, but it took more than two hours before he was able to do so. Both men were now exhausted but they were at least on Mike's yacht, and they both watched as Alex's boat turned over again then sank to the depths of the southern ocean.

They then both battled to secure the broken mast so they could sail the 1000 miles to Cape Town to carry out proper repairs.

Mike was allowed to re-enter the race when the repairs were done but he'd lost ten days of sailing time and was given a two-day penalty for turning back. He didn't win the race, or even come second or third, but he did save Alex's life; and, several months later, Mike was awarded the OBE – the Order of the British Empire – by the Queen for his courage in rescuing Alex.

I'm sure none of us will ever have to solve such a dramatic problem as that one faced by Mike and Alex. It all turned out so successfully because they both kept their heads, they didn't panic. They stayed calm and thought it through. That's the thing about problems: you have to stay calm, think hard, and do the best you can with the information you have at the time.

~

Let's think of any problems we might have to solve. Maybe something's lost, or maybe someone is upset, or maybe we're finding something difficult to do. Let's consider for a moment what we might do to solve the problem.

Let's remember that almost all problems have a solution. And let's follow Mike's example in the story, and make sure we're always ready to help someone if they need us.

The jewel in the lake

Problems are funny things! They come in all different shapes and sizes. They can be very small or they can seem so big as to be almost insurmountable; so big that it seems they can never be solved. But for every problem there's a solution, an answer.

Sometimes the answer can be right under your nose, although you don't notice it straightaway. Sometimes there isn't, in fact, a problem at all, when you really stop to think about it.

Here's an old story from Asia, in which a king has a problem, or at least he thinks he does! I wonder if you can work out before the end of the story what the solution is!

The king opened his bedroom door late one moonlit night, and just as he entered the room he saw a magpie fly away from the open window. 'It must have been sitting on my windowsill,' thought the king. 'It might even have been in my room, poking around to see what it could steal. I know what magpies are like; they steal bright shiny things given half a chance!' and he started to look round his bedroom to see if anything was missing.

Sure enough, a beautiful opal jewel that he knew he'd left on the dressing table wasn't there. The jewel was one of his favourites; a huge, pearly-white, shimmering stone that glowed with hundreds of soft, muted colours when he held it to the light.

'That thieving magpie!' the king shouted. 'It's stolen my opal,' and he ran outside to see if he could see where the magpie had gone. The king knew that there was a magpie's nest in the huge tree overhanging the lake, and he went straight there to look for the bird. There was no sign of it, but there, in the middle of the lake, he could see his jewel. It was large and round and glowing pearly-white in the darkness.

'The magpie must have dropped it as it flew towards the tree,' said the king, as he hurried back to the palace to find some servants who could fish the jewel out of the lake.

They gathered together fishing nets and buckets and rowed out to the place where they could see the shimmering opal. The king stood on the bank and directed the operation.

'Left a bit,' he shouted, then, 'No! Go a bit further to the right! No! A bit more to the middle. Yes! It's there! Fish it out!' The servants followed his instructions as best they could, but try as they might they could not fish the jewel out of the lake. They rowed back to the shore.

'There's only one solution to the problem,' declared the king. 'You'll have to drain the lake!'

'Drain the lake?' said the servants, horrified. 'But that's an enormous job!'

'It's the only way to get me back my opal,' said the king. 'Just do it!'

So the servants began the mammoth task of draining all the water out of the lake so that the king's jewel could be found. But it wasn't there. The servants dug about in the mud at the bottom of the lake; they sifted through the leaves and debris; they even looked at all the filters that were fitted to the ends of the pipes that had channelled the water out of the lake and into the nearby river. But, no jewel.

'Well, it *must* be there!' said the king, beginning to feel angry that the jewel was still lost. 'Look!' he suddenly shouted, pointing to a bucket of water standing at the edge of the mud. 'It's in there!'

The servants rushed towards the bucket and there, glimmering in the murky water, was the jewel. They tipped out the water, expecting the jewel to pour out with it onto the grass. But . . . nothing.

Then one of the servants refilled the bucket with water. 'Look!' he said. 'It's back. But it's not the jewel that's in there, it's the jewel's reflection! The jewel must be up in the tree.'

'Just as I thought!' yelled the king. 'I was right all along. That thieving magpie *did* take my opal and he's put it in his nest up in the tree. Quick! Climb up there and get it for me, before it gets lost again.'

The servants all swarmed up the tree, grabbed the magpie's nest and brought it back to the king. He plunged his hands into it and felt around, but no jewel. He tipped the nest upside down and shook it, but no jewel. He threw the nest down in disgust. 'I just don't understand this,' he said. 'First it's there, then it isn't, then it's back again,' and he looked again in the bucket of water. There was the jewel, gleaming and shimmering in the moonlight.

The king emptied out the water again onto the grass and could no longer see the jewel. He refilled the bucket, and there was the jewel once more, shining and dancing in the moonlight.

'The moonlight!' said the king, quietly, and he looked up at the night sky. There, hanging huge and round in the sky was the moon. A bright shining circle of silver. He looked again into the bucket of water. There, hanging huge and round, was the moon. A bright shining circle of silver. The king realised that the jewel in the water was not his opal at all, but the reflection of the moon.

'But, if that's the moon I can see, where is my opal?' he asked. 'I saw the magpie fly off with it!'

'Did you actually *see* the magpie fly away with your jewel?' asked one of the servants, tentatively.

'Well, yes!' said the king. 'That is . . . I didn't actually *see* it, but I did see it, if you see what I mean.'

The servant looked confused.

'I did see the magpie,' went on the king, 'though I didn't see it actually steal the jewel. But it must have, mustn't it?'

'Shall we go and look in your bedroom, sir,' said the servant. So they did. And there, on the floor by the dressing table, was the missing opal.

'Oh dear!' said the king. 'I *am* sorry! I've made you do all that work for nothing, haven't I?'

'Never mind,' said the servant. 'At least the problem is solved.'

'But there wasn't a problem, was there?' said the king. 'I only thought there was because I jumped to conclusions and I didn't think. I'm sorry. Next time I have a problem, I'll think hard before I do anything at all.'

'Good idea, sir,' said the servant, and he went back to the garden to begin the task of refilling the lake so that everything would be back to normal in the morning.

Well, did you guess that the jewel they could see was really the moon? I thought you would! And did you guess that the jewel wasn't missing at all, but that the king had jumped to conclusions? Yes, I thought you'd have got that right as well.

We can all jump to conclusions at times, and we can all see problems where they don't exist. We need to think before we do anything. Clear thinking can get us a very long way!

~

Dear God, help us to think before we act or speak. Help us to think logically and with common sense. Help us to think our way through problems which might occur, and to work out the best solution. Help us not to jump to conclusions, but to work things out clearly and calmly. Amen

The granite quarry

There are two ways of tackling a problem. You can try to put right what you can see is wrong, or you can look back to the beginning and try to find out what caused the problem in the first place.

For example, suppose we had a leak in the roof. We could put a bucket under the leak to catch the drips, and that would solve the problem short-term because it would stop the water pouring all over the floor. But of course it wouldn't solve the long-term problem because the leak in the roof would still be there. To solve the problem once and for all we would have to have the roof repaired.

I wonder which you think is better: to solve the short-term problem, or the long-term one. Let's see what you think of this true story.

There is a quarry in India which is famous for its granite. Granite is an extremely hard stone, and is very popular at the moment in our country and Europe and America for making expensive worktops for kitchens. It's so popular just now, in fact, that the quarry can hardly keep up with the demand for granite. More and more granite is wanted by rich people in the West, so more and more workers are needed to extract the stone from the quarry.

But, there's a problem.

The workers are expected to work very long hours for very little pay, but, more importantly, the work is hard and dangerous.

First, they have to use dynamite to break up the stone in the ground and the hillsides. Dynamite is a powerful explosive, but there are few safety measures and there are many accidents. Often, the men working with the dynamite can have their arms or legs blown off when an explosion goes wrong. When that happens, they are taken to the local hospital but often there is little the doctors can do, and the injured workers die. If they do survive, they are usually expected to carry on working again even though they may have only one arm or one leg.

When the stone has been blasted out of the ground by the dynamite, the huge chunks of granite have to be carried to the cutting area. There is no machinery to do this, so the blocks are carried by men, wearing their ordinary clothes and usually flip flops on their feet. There are no protective steel-capped boots for them to wear. Often the blocks of stone are dropped and the men have crushed toes or feet or legs. When this happens they are taken to the local hospital for operations and treatment.

Once the stone gets to the cutting area, men and boys – even boys as young as six or seven have to work – start to cut and shape the granite. Sometimes women and girls do this work as well. There is some machinery for splitting the granite into slabs, ready to be sent to the factory for polishing, but most of the work is done by hand. There are no protective gloves for the people to wear. The tools are sharp and dangerous, and they often slip causing fingers and hands to be badly cut. When these accidents happen, the workers are taken to the local hospital.

As the stone is being cut, great clouds of stone dust blow about. The workers have no protective masks and so they end up breathing in the dust, and many of them become ill because of this. Some of them have to be taken to the hospital.

The extra demand for granite at the quarry meant more workers, and more workers meant more accidents. More accidents meant more hospital space was needed, so it was decided that the hospital should be extended. An extra operating theatre was built to deal with the huge number of accidents; extra doctors and nurses were taken on to deal with all the patients who needed care. But no matter how much busier the hospital became, it never seemed to be able to deal with the ever-increasing number of ill and injured workers.

Until, at last, someone realised that they were only solving the short-term problem. They were trying to treat the people who were injured and ill, but no one was looking at why the problem was there in the first place. The hospital was doing the best it could, but no one was looking at the quarry and the conditions the people there were expected to work in. And until *that* problem was solved, there would always be people who needed the hospital.

It's only now, in recent months, that the owners of the quarry have started to think about improving the working conditions of the people they employ. And there's still a long way to go.

(Of course, the story raises another issue as well. It raises the issue of people in wealthy countries wanting goods as cheaply as possible from people in poorer countries. We can talk about that another day, but you might like to think about it and maybe discuss it in your class.)

I wonder what you think of the story. Which do you think was the more important? The short-term solution to the problem or the long-term solution? I think the answer was that they needed both. They certainly needed the hospital, but if the workers had better working conditions, perhaps it wouldn't be needed as much.

There's an old proverb, a saying, that maybe you've heard, that goes: 'Prevention is better than cure'. I wonder if you can tell me what it means. Yes, it's better to stop something happening in the first place, than to have it go wrong and then have to try to put it right. It's a way of warning us to think ahead, to try to make sure we don't do something that could prove to be dangerous, or that could hurt us. I wonder if anyone can think of a good example of 'Prevention is better than cure'.

Yes, those are good answers:

- Wearing a cycling helmet is better than treating a banged head.
- Not playing football near windows is better than repairing the glass.
- Tying your shoelaces is better than going to hospital with a broken leg.
- Looking before crossing the road is better than having an ambulance come to pick you up.

~

Let's just think for a moment. Let's remember to think before we do anything. Let's try to anticipate any problems that might happen because of something we do. And if we do meet problems, let's think carefully about how to solve them. Let's also think about where everything comes from that we use. Let's make sure that we don't cause problems for other people, in other parts of the world, by the things we want to have.

Theme 4

Rules

Picasso breaks the rules

Assembly preparation: It will be helpful to have two or three books illustrating Picasso's work, especially those showing his early (more conventional) style of painting, and his later style. The following suggested paintings to look for are readily found in most books about Picasso.

Earlier works:
'Girl with bare feet' 1895
'The altar boy' 1896
'The disinherited ones' 1903
'Portrait of Olga in an armchair' 1917

Later works (painted after 'Les Demoiselles d'Avignon', The Girls of Avignon, 1907):
'Three musicians' 1921
'Maya with a doll' 1938
'First steps' 1943
'Child playing with a toy truck' 1953

I wonder if you have heard of a famous painter called Picasso. Maybe you've seen some of his paintings in books in our library, or even been lucky enough to see one of his actual paintings in an art gallery or museum. I have one or two books about Picasso here, so that I can show you the sort of art work he did.

Some people believe Picasso was the most important artist of the twentieth century. This is because he broke the traditional rules of art and brought new

Further information about Picasso's life and work can be found at www.picasso.fr/ anglais and the painting *Les demoiselles d'Avignon* can be seen at www.moma.org/ collection/conservation/demoiselles/index.html.

ideas and a new freedom to painting and sculpture. He paved the way for the modern art of today. Here's his story of breaking the conventional rules of art, and painting in a new and original way.

Pablo Picasso was born in Spain in 1881. And he was *born* an artist! It is said that he could draw before he could talk, and that the very first word he spoke was 'pencil'!

Pablo Picasso's father was called Don José and he was a teacher of drawing and painting at the local art school, so it was natural for him to teach his son to draw and paint, and from the age of seven, Picasso had art lessons from his father. When Picasso was only thirteen, he finished a picture that his father had begun earlier. When Don José saw how skilfully his son had finished the painting, he said there was nothing more he could teach Picasso, and he gave him his palette and brushes and said he would never paint again. Don José never did paint again but he concentrated on helping Picasso with his art education and with his career as an artist.

When Picasso was fourteen, he went to art school in Barcelona to learn the traditional rules of painting pictures. The rules said that paintings must be realistic; they must look exactly like the real person or view or animal that the artist could see. The rules said that the paintings must be accurate, they must have true colours, they must show perfect perspective (that means things in the distance must look as though they were in the distance, near things must look nearer and bigger than far-away objects). The rules said that paintings must be tidy and that the brush strokes shouldn't show. The rules said that artists should paint portraits and landscapes, animals and religious pictures. Picasso followed the rules. He proved himself to be a skilful and confident painter, completing all his assignments very quickly. When he was sixteen, Picasso won gold medal in a local art competition. Everyone said he was a very gifted artist and that he would go far. But no one knew then just how far Picasso and his art would go.

In 1900, the first year of the new century, Picasso went to live in Paris. Paris at that time was not only the capital of France, but was also the art capital of the art world. Dozens of artists from all over the world came to Paris to work and talk and experiment with exciting new and different ways of painting. Picasso joined them.

He lived with several other artists in a building called the Floating Laundry. The artists were so poor that they couldn't afford furniture so they painted cupboards and bookcases and shelves on the walls to make it look as though they had some! Sometimes they had no money to buy paints, so they bought pencils and did drawings instead.

Soon after arriving in Paris, Picasso held his first exhibition. He was still only nineteen years old. He was still following the rules of painting. The art critics loved his work. 'Picasso is a painter, absolutely and beautifully,' they said. But the critics were to change their minds by the time of his next exhibition, because Picasso began to paint without following the rules!

He began not only to paint what he could *see*, but also what he could *think*. He began to look for the shapes in what he could see, and to draw and paint them even if they didn't really look like the object or person in front of him. He began to move the shapes around on the paper and canvas, and to draw and paint them in the wrong order. He began to experiment with colour and to paint objects in colours they would never have in real life. He began to paint pictures as patterns instead of trying to paint reality.

Then, Picasso painted a huge picture called 'The Girls of Avignon'. It was more like a pattern than a realistic picture, and the art critics hated it.

The public didn't like it because they couldn't understand it.

Even Picasso's friends and fellow artists didn't like it.

No one wanted to buy this huge painting that everyone thought was ugly.

'You should stick to painting what people want to buy,' said one of Picasso's friends.

'You're a talented painter. Paint what people can understand,' said one of the critics.

'You're good at drawing, so draw,' said someone else.

But Picasso had faith in what he was doing. He had faith in himself. He knew he didn't want to paint like everyone else. He knew he wanted to break the rules. He also knew that these were rules he *could* break because he wasn't hurting anyone else. The only person who could suffer if he didn't keep to the rules was himself, because if people didn't like his paintings they wouldn't buy them and he wouldn't have any money.

So Picasso took his painting back to the Floating Laundry and turned it to face the wall then no one would have to look at it, but *he* would know it was there. Then he concentrated on painting *his* way. He painted more and more pictures using flat shapes fitted together like a jigsaw. He drew the back and the front and the side of something all in one picture as though you could see all those views at the same time. He started to stick bits of paper and card and fabric onto his pictures. He invented collage. He began to make sculptures out of all kinds of things like bicycle saddles, tin cans, handlebars, bits of metal, even shopping baskets. Nothing like this had ever been done before.

By now the art critics were changing their minds about Picasso's work. They began to admire it and to recognise his ability. Art dealers in Paris were beginning to see that Picasso's work was not 'rubbish' as some had said, but the work of a talented artist, a genius in fact, and they wanted to buy it. Art dealers began to compete with each other to buy his work and Picasso became rich and famous.

One day a dealer came to Picasso and asked to buy the picture he had painted all those years ago; the painting Picasso called 'The Girls of Avignon'. But Picasso refused. 'It's not for sale,' he said. 'You didn't want it then, so it's not for sale now!' Picasso had known all long that that painting would be important. He had known all along that it was right for him to break the rules of painting and to find a new way for art.

Today, the paintings we know as 'modern art' owe their beginnings to Picasso for daring to stand out and break the rules. Usually of course, we all have to keep to the rules: rules in school, rules on the road, the rules or law of the country. Those rules are there to help us all live safely and well in our communities and our world. But sometimes, when breaking the rules doesn't affect anyone else, and doesn't affect our safety, it's possible to break the rules, like Picasso did, in order to discover something new.

Picasso knew that breaking the rules wouldn't hurt anyone. He knew that breaking the rules of painting would allow him to experiment and discover something new, but I don't suppose he knew when he painted 'The Girls of Avignon' just what an effect that painting would have on the art of the future.

Let's think of all the rules that we need to keep. Rules like those we have in school so that we can all be safe and well; rules that we have in games so that we can play fairly; rules like the Highway Code that help us to use the roads safely; and rules like the laws of our country which help us all live together in our communities. Let's think also of our own rules, of that voice inside each one of us that tells us what is right and wrong. Let's remember that breaking the rules to discover something new has to be done carefully and with thought, so that we, and everyone else, stay safe.

The bee who wanted to be different

Most of you here have been involved in deciding what rules you need for your class, and many of you have been involved in making the rules we need for our school. And we all know why we need rules: when we belong to a family or a community we need to have rules to live by so that we can all get along together and live side by side in a peaceful and productive way. Can you imagine what it would be like if there were no rules at all? It would be chaos and no one would be happy.

Sometimes we might feel as though we don't want to keep to the rules, and sometimes it can even be right not to stick to the rules. Some of the most creative people in the world have made discoveries by not keeping to the rules! The secret is knowing when it's all right to break the rules, and when it's not! If breaking the rules means affecting other people, or doing something unsafe, then usually it's not a good idea.

Today's story is an Aesop's fable, told to warn people about breaking the rules in a community. Here's what happened.

The bees were having their first lesson in cell building. The young bees were taught how to make beeswax, then how to form the wax into honeycombs. Honeycomb, as you probably know, is made up of hundreds of tiny six-sided shapes which fit together perfectly. Some of the six-sided cells would be for the queen bee to lay eggs in, and some would be used as storage cells for the golden honey when it was made.

But, one bee wanted to be different.

'I don't see why I have to be the same as everyone else,' she grumbled. 'I don't want to make cells that shape. I don't see why they have to have six sides. Six is a stupid number!' and she began to make beeswax cells that were a different size and shape from everyone else's.

'You can't do that!' exclaimed the other bees when they saw what she was doing.

'Oh yes I can,' she replied. 'Just watch me!' and she made another cell with three short sides and two long ones.

'Take that cell out and make a proper hexagon!' said the teacher bee behind her.

'See! We knew you'd get into trouble,' giggled the others.

The bee who wanted to be different watched as the teacher moved away to look at another bee's work.

'I won't do it that way!' she said, defiantly. 'I'll do it my own way!' and she continued to make unevenly shaped cells with any number of sides except six.

At the end of the morning the teacher asked each bee to fit the cells she had made to the cells made by the other bees. They all began to do as they were told and soon the honeycomb began to grow; all the cells fitted together beautifully, except of course, the ones made by the bee who wanted to be different. Her cells had corners and angles that stuck out in all directions, and sides which were too long or too short to fit any of the other cells.

'I'm sorry,' said the teacher bee. 'But you can't share this honeycomb! If you want to be different and make a comb of your own you'll have to go and live somewhere else. If you want to live here with us you'll have to fit in. You'll have to work *with* the rest of the bees, not *against* them. If you can't do that then you'll have to leave.'

The bee who wanted to be different looked at the teacher. She thought she was joking and was all ready to laugh, but then, to her horror, she realised that the teacher really meant what she said.

'But where will I go?' she said plaintively. 'Where will I live? This beehive is my home, I don't know anywhere else.'

'I'm sorry,' said the teacher bee, 'but honey bees live together in a community. They work together. They support each other and fit in with the rest of the hive. If a bee doesn't want to do that, then she must go and live alone, perhaps in a hollow tree or a crack in a rock. If she wants to be different then she must live differently. Do you still want to be different?'

'Yes!' shouted the bee who wanted to be different, though the truth of the matter was that she didn't want to be different at all; she wanted to fit in with the rest, to belong, to have friends, but she was being defiant and difficult.

'Yes!' she shouted again. 'I want to be different. I don't want to do things like you say I should!'

'Then out you go,' said the teacher. 'There's no place for you here,' and she chased her out of the hive, over the field, across the moor, and beyond.

Poor little bee! Do you think that was a fair ending for her? How would you have ended that story, if you'd written it?

I can see what Aesop was getting at when he wrote the story. When people or animals live together in a community they have to fit in with the community, if it is to work well. There are times when it's all right to be different, but not when you need to be part of any kind of family.

Maybe you could have a go at making a tessellated pattern using six-sided shapes? Then try to fit in some oddly shaped, irregular sections, and see what happens. You'll understand why the other bees were so annoyed with the bee who wanted to be different. Or maybe you could have a go at rewriting the story? You could show me what you've written!

~

Dear God, help us to know that we need to work together, and not against each other, in our families at home and school, and in our neighbourhood. Help us to know that working together and playing together makes for strong communities. Amen

Bill gets a job

As you know, rules are there to help us live together in our communities and to keep us safe. Rules can be broken, but it's best to really think about them first, and then only to break the rules if doing so doesn't hurt anyone in any way. The other thing about rules is that they have to have common sense applied to them in the first place. It's no use thinking up rules if they're just plain silly.

See what you think of this true story. It was in the newspapers a short time ago.

Bill works for a big DIY store in Yorkshire, and has just been nominated for a nationwide competition called 'Worker of the Year'. Nothing unusual in that, you might think; after all, lots of people are excellent workers and many of them are nominated for awards like that. But Bill is rather different, because for more than 25 years, no one would give him a job at all.

Bill is 41 now, but when he was only a few months old, he had some bleeding in his brain and had to have an emergency operation. The operation saved his life but unfortunately it left him unable to see. Ever since then, Bill has been blind.

When he was five, Bill went to a school for blind children, and he did all the things that all children do at school. He learned to read and write, he did maths, he took part in games and PE, and he did all the other subjects that everyone does. He left school, like the rest of his class, when he was sixteen, and was looking forward to getting a job and starting work. He wasn't sure what he wanted to do, but he knew that whatever job he did, he would do it to the best of his ability.

Bill sent off hundreds of application forms, and went for dozens of interviews, but no one would give him a job.

'We're very sorry,' said the people at the first interview he went to. 'It's impossible for us to give you work. It's the rules. It's because you can't see. You would be a danger to yourself and to the rest of the workers. We can't give you a job here.'

At the next interview the boss said, 'I'm sorry, Bill. I just can't take the chance. It's Health and Safety rules. It just wouldn't be safe to have you working here. I'm sorry.'

At the next interview they said they had no job that Bill could do and that they couldn't possibly employ a blind man.

The next place said he was a risk to everyone and that the rules wouldn't allow him to work.

And so it went on. Place after place, job after job, everyone said the same thing; Bill couldn't see therefore he couldn't work. And most of the bosses blamed the rules.

Finally, someone told Bill that he should give up even trying to find work because the rules said a blind man couldn't ever be in a work situation. No one would ever give him a job.

Bill was saddened and disappointed that no one was prepared even to give him a chance. 'If someone would only let me try,' he said, 'I could *prove* that I was capable and that I wouldn't be a danger to anyone.' But no one was prepared to give him that chance.

Bill needed money to live, but with no job he had no wages. He had to apply to the social security for a disability benefit – money which is given to people who are unable to work, so that they can buy food and clothes and pay for somewhere to live. And with no hope of ever being able to get a job, Bill began to feel fed-up and despondent and depressed. Weeks turned into months, and months turned into years. Bill felt as though his life was being wasted. So many people had told him that he would never have a job, that he would never be of any use to anyone, that he began to believe it.

Then, after 25 years of being unemployed, Bill heard about a national charity called the Shaw Trust. Someone told him that the charity helps people with disabilities to find work and to become independent. 'Maybe they could help me?' thought Bill, and he went along to meet them.

'Of course we can help,' they said. 'We can give you support and guidance and help you to find the opportunities that are out there.'

Bill was astounded. No one had ever talked to him about help and guidance before, and no one had ever mentioned opportunities!

The Trust gave Bill the confidence to try a work experience placement. He loved it! He set off every morning and felt, at last, as though he was part of the working world. But the work experience was only for a month. After that Bill was back at home with no job. All his old feelings of self doubt came back, and once again Bill felt his life was wasting away; only this time the feelings were even worse because he had experienced what it was like to go to work.

The Shaw Trust, however, had not given up on him; they'd heard of a huge new DIY store that was about to open. The store needed a warm-hearted person to be their 'meeter and greeter' – someone who meets customers with a friendly word as they come inside to do their shopping. 'It's just the job for Bill,' they'd said, and they arranged for him to go for an interview.

'You're exactly the sort of person we're looking for,' said the bosses at the store. 'We need someone with a friendly smile and a kind word for every-one. Someone who is approachable and who will make the customers feel relaxed. How about it Bill? Would you like the job?'

'Would I like it?' laughed Bill. 'You bet I would!'

So Bill started work at the store. 'It's changed my life,' he said. 'Going out to work and meeting people every day has given me a purpose in my life. It's made me feel much more self-confident. I am earning my own living now, and not relying on benefits. It's brilliant!'

A spokesperson at the store said recently, 'Bill is the first person our customers meet when they come in. They always come away from him with a smile on their face. He's a valuable and popular member of our team. He works so hard and puts such a lot of effort into everything he does that he deserves to be nominated for our nationwide 'Worker of the Year'!'

I think it's quite likely that Bill won the award for 'Worker of the Year'. What do you think? Do you think he deserved to win? I don't suppose he would want to win, though, because of his blindness. I think he would want to win on merit – because of how he did his job, regardless of the fact that he is blind.

I wonder what you think of the workplaces that wouldn't give him a job for all those years? Do you think they were right to follow the rules that said blind people can't work? I think everyone must be given a chance to prove what they can do, because of course, as we all know, everyone is good at something and everyone is valuable.

~

Dear God, help us to remember that everyone must be given the chance to prove what they can do. Help us to remember that rules which stop people being given that chance are unfair and unjust. Help us to be fair to everyone we meet; and to appreciate what people can *do, and not presuppose there are things they can* not *do. Amen*

Theme 5

Caring for animals

The cormorant

I have seen, on television, people swimming with dolphins. Have you? I've also seen television documentaries and nature films showing people swimming with whales and even sharks, though with certain types of shark it's necessary to swim inside a protective cage.

I've never swum with any of those creatures, but I did once swim with a cormorant. It was a magical experience that I will never forget, though it didn't have a very happy ending. Here's what happened.

The first time I saw the cormorant I could hardly believe my eyes. I was on holiday in Majorca and I was swimming in the sea in the early morning. There was a tiny bay almost surrounded by rocks and it was a beautiful and safe place to swim. There was no one else in the sea with me, just a few people walking by the shore. The cormorant was standing on a rock, only a very short distance away from me. I stayed as still as I possibly could and floated just a little nearer to the rock. The cormorant stood still and watched me, and I watched the cormorant.

It was absolutely beautiful. I think it was only a young bird. It had sleek dark brownish-black feathers and a long body with a pale-coloured front. It had black shiny beady eyes and big webbed feet. It had a long beak with a little hook on the end. I had never been so close to a cormorant before and I felt very lucky to be so close without it flying away.

Suddenly, it plopped into the water and started to swim; not away, but backwards and forwards in the same patch of water I was in. And how it could swim! It could dive without making even the smallest splash; it could dart incredibly quickly under the water; it could twist and turn so fast I could hardly watch it; and it could catch fish. There were lots of small silvery-coloured fish in the water, and every so often the cormorant would dive straight towards one. It never missed.

After about five minutes of swimming near me, the cormorant climbed out of the sea onto a rock and stood with its wings outstretched, as if it were hanging them out to dry.

The next morning I went again down to the sea to swim, not really expecting to be lucky enough to see the cormorant again, or at least not expecting it to be in the water with me. But it was there. Just as beautiful as the day before. It darted about in the water catching small fish for its breakfast. It didn't seem concerned about my being there; it didn't seem to be afraid of me. I was able to swim near it and it sped past me and around me, its feathers shining like silver in the diffused sunlight and leaving a trail of sparkling silver-white bubbles behind it.

Every morning when I went to swim, the cormorant was there. Sometimes there might be someone else swimming at the same time, but there were never more than one or two people. Later in the day, when lots of people came to swim, the cormorant would stand on the rocks, a little way off, watching, listening, and hanging its wings out to dry. Lots of the holiday-makers had never seen a cormorant before, and many of them took photos or clips on their video cameras. Everyone was careful not to frighten or startle the bird. People moved quietly and gently when they were near it. No one wanted to do anything to harm the cormorant.

The cormorant gave a great many people a great deal of pleasure just by being there. I liked watching the new tourists arrive and seeing the look of surprise on their faces when they saw the cormorant for the first time.

On the last day of my holiday, when I had packed my case and was almost ready to leave for the airport, I decided to take one last walk down to the sea, and say goodbye to the cormorant, if it was there.

When I arrived at the rocks where the cormorant usually sat, I saw a small crowd of people. They were all talking quietly and one woman was crying. It seemed that the cormorant was hurt. It had a large wound on the side of its head. There was a lot of blood. The cormorant was clearly in pain and it couldn't walk or swim properly.

'What happened?' I asked a man who was standing there.

'A boy has been throwing stones at it,' he said. 'I tried to stop him but I was too late. The damage was already done. I don't think the cormorant will live.'

That boy had thoughtlessly injured, probably killed, a beautiful creature. He had spoiled the pleasure of many people on holiday, who had enjoyed just watching such a lively bird. Everyone else had respected the cormorant and had done their best not to frighten it or harm it in any way. In return, the cormorant had trusted the people. And then a boy, a human being who should have known better than to harm a living creature, had destroyed that trust.

I don't know whether the cormorant survived. I hope it did, but I doubt it. I do know how angry I felt about that child's cruelty, and I know I shall never forget the joy I had when I swam with the cormorant.

~

Let's think about our responsibility towards other creatures who share our world, our pets and all the other wild creatures. Every living creature on our planet has a right to be here. The greatest enemy of most living things is us: people. Let's think about our duty to look after all living things, and about ways in which we can care for the animals, birds and insects we come into contact with.

Let's do what we can to support those groups of people who are trying to conserve our planet and to make sure no living creatures become extinct. Let's make sure that each one of us does nothing to hurt any living creature.

Angeline and the cats

There have been lots of stories written about animals and the people who care for them: I'm sure you can think of at least one. Today's story is one I came upon quite by accident when I was on holiday in south-west France.

We were following the map on our way to the coast when suddenly there was a deviation sign. The road ahead was closed because of some work they were doing, and all the traffic was directed a different way. The deviation took us through a small village called La Romieu.

We decided to stop in the village square to have a look around and were soon intrigued by the life-size statues of cats! They were everywhere. Beautiful stone sculptures of cats sitting on window sills, hiding in nooks and crannies, prowling by the side of doorsteps. The sculptures are not old. They were made by an artist who heard a grandmother telling the story of the village to her grandchildren and he felt it was important that the story shouldn't be forgotten. So he made stone cats and put them all round the village square in order that everyone who saw them would know the legend of Angeline, a young girl who saved the village almost 700 years ago. This is her story.

In 1338 there lived in the village of La Romieu a woodcutter, Vincent, and his wife Mariette. They enjoyed life in the village, for although it was remote – far from any other village or town – it had good fertile soil for growing all the food they needed. Vincent and Mariette gathered wild strawberries and blackberries from the forest, they grew fruit and vegetables in their garden, and they kept hens and pigs and a cow. Their neighbours grew corn in a field nearby and Mariette swapped some of her vegetables for some of their corn and was able to grind it into flour to make bread for Vincent and herself. No-one in the village was ever short of food. Life was good and the young couple were happy.

When they had been married for three years, Mariette had a baby girl. They called her Angeline and thought life couldn't get any better . . . but then . . . something dreadful happened.

Vincent was killed by a falling tree when he was working in the forest.

Mariette was heartbroken and became ill and depressed. One day, only two months after the death of Vincent, a neighbour came to the house and found Mariette dead, with the baby Angeline in her arms.

The neighbour took Angeline to her own home and adopted her as one of her own family. Angeline was a very quiet child, who seemed to prefer animals to people. She was particularly fond of cats, and her adoptive mother gave her two kittens to keep as pets. There was a male and a female.

When Angeline was about four, there was a dreadfully harsh winter. The village and the surrounding area was held in the grip of ice and snow for months on end. When the spring finally arrived it was late and short, and the summer that followed was cold and wet. Nothing grew in the gardens and fields. The harvest that year brought in almost nothing. There was little food for the animals and even less for the villagers. All they could do was wait and hope for better things the next year.

But, the following year was just as bad if not worse. The whole area suffered from the famine. The villagers had eaten all their stored food and had to eat the remaining animals to stay alive. They had to eat the hens, pigs, cows, sheep, and even the cats and dogs.

Angeline's family knew how upset she would be at the thought of having to kill and eat her own pet cats, so they defied the village rule and let her keep the two cats. But no one could know they were there, so the cats were hidden in the attic and only allowed out at night to hunt for mice and voles when no one would see them.

The famine became worse. The old people and very young babies in the village and the surrounding area began to die of starvation. Angeline's family managed to stay live by eating roots and sometimes mushrooms.

Then, after two disastrous years, the weather improved. The crops grew again and the villagers were able to harvest enough fruit and grain to last them through the coming winter.

But another disaster awaited them.

Because all the cats had gone, the vermin had multiplied until there was a plague of them. There were hundreds of rats and mice over-running the village. They were everywhere. In the store houses, in the kitchens, behind the sheds, in the attics. In the cupboards, under the stairs, behind the walls, in the wardrobes. And they were eating everything they could find. The grain stores and larders were being emptied by the rats and mice.

The villagers, who were already weakened by two years of famine, knew they could not face yet more starvation. Yet starve they would if the problem of the rats and mice could not be overcome.

Angeline, now nearly seven, confessed to everyone in the village that she had *not* done as she was told. She had *not* allowed her two pet cats to be killed and used for food like the rest of the cats. But where were they? everyone wanted to know.

'They are in the attic,' said Angeline. 'But they are not in the attic on their own!' And she told all the people how the two cats, the male and the female had, during the last two years, had several litters of kittens. There were now over twenty cats in the attic!

'You could all have one of my cats to look after,' she said. 'They are *very* good at catching mice!'

And so Angeline gave every family in the village one of her cats. Soon the mice and rat population was under control and enough food was saved to keep the villagers alive for another year, until the next harvest.

Angeline and her cats had saved the village.

And that might have been the end of the story, but, the legend goes on to say that as Angeline grew up and grew into a woman, her face began to change and she began to look more and more like . . . a cat!

Perhaps the ending is just a made-up part, although the rest of the story is said to be true. However, I did notice that one of the statues in the square of La Romieu, the only bronze sculpture, is of a half girl, half cat-like creature, and*

---

* Further information, together with photos of some of the sculptures, can be found at www.la-romieu.com/anglais.

underneath is a small plaque inscribed 'Angeline'. Whether the story is true or not, I don't know, but it's an interesting one, and I like stories about people who care for animals.

~

Dear God, help us to look after the animals in our lives. Help us to take care of our pets; to remember that they can't take care of themselves and that they need us to look after them. Help us to understand their needs so that we care for them properly. Help us never to harm them, or injure them or neglect them. Amen

Goats for peace

I wonder how many of you have seen a real live goat. Most of you, I expect. I wonder what you know about goats. Yes, you know a lot of facts:

- *The males are called billy goats and the females are called nanny goats.*
- *The young are called kids. (I bet you didn't know that when the females are pregnant we say, 'they are kidding'!)*
- *The kids are often born as twins.*
- *Goats give milk that people can drink.*
- *They are very lively, sociable, adventurous animals and they can jump.*

I wonder if you know that they are called 'domesticated animals' – that means animals that have been bred to live with and be of use to human beings. They were one of the first animals ever to be tamed by humans, and have now been living alongside us for about 10,000 years! They are extremely useful to us.

You might think that rather strange, especially since not many of us keep a goat! So why are they so useful? Well, listen to this story.

Kwame and his family live in Africa in a country called Rwanda. They used to live in a village where Kwame, like most of his neighbours, had a small plot of land on which he grew fruit and vegetables and where he kept a few animals. The villagers were able to provide enough food for their needs.

But then there was a terrible war within the country. Soldiers came and simply took away everything the people in the village owned. They destroyed their homes and took the animals. The villagers had to run for their lives.

When the war was over and Kwame and his neighbours started returning to their homes, they had nothing. The houses were gone, there was no food, no animals, nothing left to sell. They tried to stay alive grubbing for roots and eating leaves and berries. There was a small amount of food sent in every so often by other countries, but it only lasted for one or two days then it was gone. Kwame knew that if they were to survive they would have to start again; they would have to rebuild, replant and restock with animals. But without any money, it was impossible.

People in Britain and other wealthy countries knew that the Rwandans needed help, and needed help fast, but they also knew that simply sending in food wasn't the best long-term answer. The best solution to the problem was to help the Rwandans to help themselves! The best solution to the problem was to help the Rwandans to start their lives again. The best solution was . . . goats!

So the Charities Advisory Trust* in Britain set about finding money, and finding goats, to help the villagers of Rwanda. They also wanted to help similar villagers in other countries affected by war, where needy people, through no fault of their own, were too poor to buy animals for themselves.

But a goat, you may think! What use is a goat!

A goat is a good way of taking the first step out of poverty. A goat gave Kwame and his family that first step.

The goat needed very little land. It was tethered and allowed to eat the hedgerow bushes. Every day one of Kwame's children would take it out for a walk so that it could eat some of the roadside plants and bushes. The goat gave manure which was used to fertilise the newly planted vegetable patch. Fertiliser meant better, bigger and more vegetables. The goat, as well as the family, could now eat better. The goat had the outer leaves of cabbages and cauliflowers added to its food.

The goat gave milk. Milk for the family to drink and also milk to sell. Milk to sell meant money for Kwame's family to spend on better food and more seeds to plant. Eventually Kwame's goat had twin kids. A kid to keep and a kid to give back to the goat bank.

A goat bank, you might ask? What is a goat bank?

The bank, dealing in goats instead of money, was set up by the Charities Advisory Trust. The bank gives a goat to a needy family, just like Kwame's, and when the goat has kids, and it usually has twins, the first female is given back to the goat bank to be passed on to the next needy family.

---

* Further information can be found at:
www.charitiesadvisorytrust.org.uk
www.goodgifts.org
www.vetaid.org
www.oxfamunwrapped.com

Kwame's kid, the one he kept for himself, was allowed to grow up until it too had kids. He was able to keep the new babies. These kids could be sold if Kwame needed money for school fees for the children, or for medical bills. Kwame's family was moving out of poverty.

The Charities Advisory Trust has now given over 50,000 goats to the goat bank, and much of the success is due to ordinary people, like you and me, who have given money to 'buy a goat'.

Of course, goats need looking after. And whilst they are helpful to the human beings they live with, the human beings must also be helpful and show responsibility to the goats. It is always the job of human beings to look after animals, even if those animals are providing a service to the human beings. The animals must be treated properly. They must be fed and cared for; they must be given medical care if they need it. And that's where VETAID comes in.

VETAID works together with the Charities Advisory Trust and its job is to help small farmers, like Kwame, to understand about animal health and so have healthier animals and crops and a successful farm.

You might like to find out more about VETAID, or the Charities Advisory Trust, or 'Goats for Peace'. In fact, maybe our school could think about buying a goat for the goat bank! What do you think?

~

Let's think for a moment about all the food that we eat in a single day. We have three main meals and often extra treats in between as well. We have shops to go to where we can buy the things we need. Let's think about Kwame's family, and how little they had at the beginning of their story. Let's remember the difference a goat made to their lives. Let's remember that many people in our world don't have enough food. Let's remember that animals can make a difference to their lives, but that the animals, too, must be cared for and looked after.

Theme 6

Caring for the environment

Mulunga escapes from the humans

When the first astronauts went into space and saw our planet Earth from a long way away as it had never been seen before, they all said how beautiful it is. Almost all of them also said that our planet Earth looks very fragile. One astronaut described the Earth as looking like 'a beautiful, shimmering, fragile Christmas tree ornament'. Another said that the Earth looked so small from where he was in the spaceship, that he could hold up his thumb and make it disappear behind it. 'I could obliterate it with my thumb; that's how fragile it is,' he said.

And there's that word again: 'fragile'. Do you know what it means? Yes, it means delicate; easily broken or damaged. When we look at our world and see its rocks and mountains, it's difficult to think of it as fragile, but it is. It can be easily damaged and altered beyond repair. We human beings have a duty to look after our world, sometimes we're not as good at caring for it as we should be.

And this is nothing new! Today I have a story from the Yao people of West Africa which is thousands of years old. Let's hear what the people in this story did.

Chameleon was hungry, so one day he decided to make a trap out of grasses and set it in the river to catch fish. He watched and waited. After a while he pulled up the trap and was delighted to see it full of fish. Chameleon chose a fine fat fish to eat and gently put the others back in the river.

The next day he set the trap in the river again, but this time he caught nothing. He ate a grasshopper instead. On the third day he put his trap in the river once more and watched and waited. There were no ripples on the surface, no air bubbles rising, so he expected to find nothing in the trap. But, when he lifted it out of the water, there in the bottom were two of the strangest creatures he had ever seen. They were tiny and pale. They had thin bodies, skinny arms and legs, and little heads with tufts of hair on top.

'Whatever can they be?' said chameleon to himself, as he took them, still in the trap, to Mulunga, the Creator, to ask what he should do with them.

'Ah!' said Mulunga, 'I was wondering when they would appear. They are called humans, and you have a man and a woman in your trap. Set them free, let them walk on the earth, and watch!' said Mulunga.

Chameleon opened the trap at the edge of the water and watched the two small pale humans climb out and up the banking to the dry grassy ground at the top. As soon as they reached the top of the banking, the humans began to grow. And grow. And grow. Until they were bigger than baboons but not as tall as giraffes.

Chameleon continued to watch.

The humans collected some dry twigs and sorted through them. They each chose two sticks and began to rub them together.

'What are they doing?' asked Chameleon. But before Mulunga had the chance to reply, the sticks had made sparks, and the sparks had caught fire. The humans pushed some of the fire together and piled on more twigs and dry grass. But the rest of the fire they ignored. It raced along the ground, consuming grass and branches and trees on its way. It reached a small wood and burned that. It travelled as far as the forest and ran, out of control, to the other side. The animals, birds and insects in its way fled, terrified, to safety.

Chameleon watched, horrified.

But the man and the woman didn't care. They were interested only in their small fire, which they tended carefully. The woman stayed near it, constantly feeding it more twigs and branches, but the man walked away from the fire, into the wide open space where the buffalos ran. He sharpened a long thin stick on a stone, then hid by a rock. When a young buffalo passed by he threw the spear in its side and killed it. The man dragged the dead buffalo back to the fire and the woman cooked the meat. They ate what they wanted and threw away the rest.

Chameleon watched. 'Why do they take more than they need?' he asked. But no one was there to answer, because Mulunga had walked away in sadness.

The next day, and the next and the next, the humans made fire and killed animals. Then they began to argue and quarrel.

'Why should I stay by the fire all day,' shouted the woman. 'Why can't I go hunting?'

'And why do I have to go hunting all the time,' argued the man. 'Why can't I stay and tend the fire?'

But neither of them treated the fire with caution. Neither of them treated their world with respect, and their fires spread throughout the land, spoiling and destroying the countryside. The animals were so afraid that they all ran away and took refuge all over the world; anywhere to get away from the man and the woman who were ruining the Earth. Chameleon climbed to the top of the tallest tree to escape from them, and spider climbed so high up his silken thread that he disappeared into the sky.

Soon, only Mulunga remained and he was unhappy and upset and disappointed to see the humans destroying the beautiful and peaceful world he had so carefully created.

One day, Mulunga noticed spider high up in the sky.

'How did you get there?' he asked.

'I climbed up my silken thread to get away from the humans,' answered spider. 'It's safer up here, away from them! Do you want to come?'

Mulunga looked sadly at the lovely world he no longer wanted to live in, and he climbed up spider's thread to escape.

They say that Mulunga never went back to Earth. They say that he's still hiding in the sky and that's why no one can see him. They say that he was so puzzled by the behaviour of the humans that the only thing he could do was run away and hide, as far away as possible, just like spider, chameleon and the others.

The Yao people of West Africa tell that story to make themselves remember that human beings have a great power over our environment. We can look after our planet Earth and respect it. We can look after the other creatures who share our world. We can look after the people who share our world.

Or, we can destroy our beautiful planet. We can be greedy and selfish and cruel. We can allow other creatures to become extinct and we can gobble up all the Earth's resources. We can ignore the other people who share our world and we can take what they have and leave them to starve.

The choice is ours.

～

Let's stop and think about the planet we live on: planet Earth. It's fragile and could easily be destroyed. We human beings are intelligent creatures and have a duty to look after our world. We need to take care of it for the future. We need to take care of it so that it survives.

Polar bear

What do you know about polar bears? Yes, you know quite a lot:

- *The polar bear is the largest species of bear and the largest land carnivore.*
- *They live in the north polar region which is in the Arctic Circle.*
- *They live in extremely cold and icy conditions.*
- *They are a creamy white colour.*
- *They are good swimmers.*
- *The cubs are born in a den under the snow.*
- *The female gives birth to one to three cubs in winter.*
- *Cubs are blind and helpless when they are first born.*
- *They are white so they are camouflaged against the snow.*
- *Polar bears can attack human beings.*

Well done, that's quite an impressive amount of information. Polar bears are beautiful animals but there is a real danger they could become extinct. The Worldwide Fund for Nature* says that all our polar bears could be extinct within the next twenty years, if we don't urgently do something to slow down global warming. Just think, by the time you are grown up with children of your own, there may be no polar bears left in our world.

A few days ago I watched a television programme about polar bears and the frozen Arctic Region where they live. Here's what happened.

The television camera crew had spent weeks finding, then tracking, the polar bears. They were not easy to find. The area where the polar bears can be found is enormous. They live all along the Arctic coast and on the sea ice and ice floes where they often float for hundreds of kilometres. The polar bears roam this inhospitable environment, searching for food: mainly seals and walrus, but also fish, seabirds and even reindeer.

The crew wanted to film in January, in one of the coldest places on Earth. The sea ice of the Arctic Ocean in winter is almost 7 metres thick, and it expands to cover a huge area, only melting back in the spring and summer.

---

* Further information on the Worldwide Fund for Nature and climate change can be found at www.panda.org.

But this January, the television crew were surprised to notice that the temperature was *not* below freezing, and the sea ice at the edge of the land was already breaking up. This usually didn't happen until later in the summer. They were puzzled.

The camera crew flew by helicopter over the frozen sea, constantly looking, searching, for the polar bears. They knew they were likely only to find male bears; the females would be in their dens under the snow, waiting for the birth of their cubs. But the males would be out searching for food.

At last they spotted a bear. He was alone. He was a big male, stocky and strong; his hind legs longer than his front legs. The crew could see his large furry feet that acted like snowshoes as he plodded through the drifts.

They filmed the bear as he strode out onto the sea ice towards a hole in the ice where they could see the black water shining below. This was a breathing hole. A space in the ice-covering where seals come up for air. The polar bear knew it was a breathing hole. He waited. Still. Silent. Unmoving.

Suddenly a seal surfaced for air. The bear, without a second's hesitation plunged through the ice and snow surrounding the breathing hole. Snow and splinters of ice flew everywhere, like a white explosion. Underwater, the seal darted away, but the powerful polar bear, its webbed feet moving like flippers, dived after it, swimming strongly. The seal was no match for the polar bear. In one swift movement it seized the seal in its jaws and swam back to the edge of the now-broken ice hole. Still with the seal in its jaws, it heaved itself out of the water back onto the ice, shook itself dry with a massive scattering of silver drops, and devoured its meal.

The crew returned to base with their film, but agreed to follow and film the polar bear again, for several more days, to build up a picture of its life on the ice. So the next day they set out again. They followed him, watched him and filmed him. He found no food that day, but the crew were not concerned. They knew that polar bears have to spend over half of each day hunting, and that many attempts to catch seals are unsuccessful. They knew that even in good hunting areas, a bear may catch only one seal every four or five days.

But, when the camera crew had been following the polar bear for more than a week and not seen him catch anything to eat, they began to worry. They were also becoming increasingly worried about the state of the sea ice. With each day that passed, the ice was melting more and more. It would soon be too soft and unstable to support the weight of a polar bear. This in itself wasn't a problem, as the bears are good swimmers, but they need solid ice to be able to pull themselves out of the water. Soft, melting ice is not firm enough to support them.

On the ninth day of tracking the polar bear, they saw him hunting a young seal. The seal was quick and agile, and the bear was now tired with hunger. He swam after the seal, further and further away from the solid land of the coast; further and further into the melting and unstable ice of the sea.

The young seal darted this way and that, always managing to evade the bear. The bear, visibly tiring now, could only thrash about in the icy, slushy water in a hopeless attempt to catch it. The seal made one last dive, down, down, and away from the bear. It escaped, leaving the polar bear exhausted in the water.

The bear knew it must reach land. It tried again and again to climb onto the ice. But the ice was too soft, too broken; the bear too tired. It became weaker and weaker. The camera crew, in their helicopter, could do nothing to help, they could only watch.

Again the polar bear made a desperate attempt to climb onto the melting ice. But it was by now too weak with exertion, too weak with hunger. It fell back into the dark water. And disappeared beneath it.

The camera crew knew it had died.

What a sad ending for that polar bear. But, it might be a sad ending for all polar bears. The ice caps at the north and south poles of our world are being seriously affected by global warming. The ice caps are melting. Some scientists believe that the Arctic Ocean's ice will be gone completely within 30 years. That sounds like a long time – but not when you think that it's been there for two million years!

If the ice melts, then food which the polar bears eat will no longer be available, and the bears won't survive. Scientists believe that if the Arctic ice melts it will affect many other parts of our world.

Part of global warming is natural. The Earth has warmed up and cooled down by itself over millions of years. And the Earth has always been able to take care of itself. Until now. Now, the changes are happening too quickly. And the speed of the changes is due to how we, human beings, are treating our world. We are using up fossil fuels like oil, petrol and diesel. We are causing air pollution and we are allowing too many 'greenhouse gases' to affect the world's atmosphere.

Maybe you could find out more about global warming, and find ways that we can help to look after our world.**

~

** International Polar Year runs from March 2007 to March 2009 and is the largest international collaborative Polar project ever undertaken. www.ipy.org.

Dear God, help us to know what a beautiful but fragile world we live in. Help us to care for our world by looking after our environment. Help us to be aware that everything we do has an effect on our planet. Help us to think carefully about the things we buy, and how they are packaged, and how we get rid of our rubbish. Help us to be aware of the needs of the animals in our world, and to do nothing to destroy their environment. Amen

Food miles

Assembly preparation: you will need:

- A lunchbox containing an egg sandwich, a pot of yogurt, an apple and a banana.
- A bag containing an apple, a carrot, an onion, a few green beans and a drawing/picture of a fish.
- Cards (listed below) for selected children to read out.
- Eleven children to help.

I wonder what we're having for school lunch today. And I wonder what those of you who have brought a packed lunch, have got in your lunchbox? I've brought *my* packed lunch into assembly today, and I'd like some volunteers to help me to show you what I've got. (**Two children take out items one by one, say what they are and show them to the assembly.**)

Where do you think I bought these items? Yes, of course, the supermarket. And how far do you think these items have travelled, to get here to our assembly table? Yes, those are interesting answers. Our nearest supermarket is only a couple of miles up the road, so it's fair to think that all the food for my lunch has travelled just a couple of miles.

But suppose I told you it had travelled thousands and thousands of miles! Supposing I told you it had travelled nearly twice round the world! These four children are going to tell you where my lunch is from.

Child 1 (reading from prepared card): *The wheat for the bread in this sandwich has come from Canada. That's 4,600 miles away. The butter is from Denmark. That's 650 miles away. The eggs are from near here.*
Child 2: *The strawberries in this pot of yogurt were grown in Israel. The milk came from France. The plastic pot was made in China. All the different parts of the yogurt have travelled 7,800 miles to get here.*
Child 3: *This apple is a Braeburn apple from New Zealand. It has travelled 11,500 miles to get here.*

Child 4: *This banana is from the Fiji islands. It has travelled 9,800 miles to get here.*

Wow! That's quite a lot of travelling my lunch has done. And I thought it just came from the supermarket! Those of you who are really good at maths will be able to add up all those miles: 4,600 + 650 + 7,800 + 11,500 + 9,800. I had to write it all down to do the adding up, and it comes to an unbelievable 34,350 miles! That's the equivalent of going right round the world and half way round again!

There's a lot of concern at the moment about the huge distances our food is travelling. One in every three vehicles on our roads is carrying food, or something to do with food. This travelling is called 'food miles' and food miles measure the distance any food has to travel to get from where it's grown, to our plates. Food miles matter because all this food travel means more pollution from lorries and transporters, more carbon dioxide being emitted, and more global warming.

And the silly thing is, much of the food doesn't *have* to travel so far.

Take a look in my shopping bag! **(Two children take out items one by one and show them to the assembly.)**

Apples, carrots, onions and green beans all grow quite happily here in Britain. But, *these* apples, carrots, onions and beans didn't grow here. These four children are going to tell you about them.

Child 5 (reading from prepared card): *These fruits and vegetables were all bought in big supermarkets not far from here. This apple grew in America. It travelled 11,500 miles to get here.*
Child 6: *This onion grew in Australia. It travelled 10,000 miles to get here.*
Child 7: *This carrot grew in South Africa, and travelled 6,000 miles to get here.*
Child 8: *These green beans grew in Kenya and they travelled just over 4,000 miles to get here.*

That's another incredible 31,500 food miles. And I really don't think those food miles are necessary, because all those foods grow here, right under our noses, here in Britain. Some foods, of course, don't grow here, and if we want to import them we know they have to travel the food miles to get here. For example we can't grow our own bananas or pineapples or kiwi fruits here in Britain because the climate is too cold, so we have to import them from where they grow. But maybe we don't have to import as much as we do. At the moment we bring in 95 per cent of all the fruit we eat.

You've heard me say before that I think having common sense is one of the most important skills anyone can have. I'm not sure that we are using common sense when we choose to buy foods that have travelled all those miles, when it's not necessary.

For example, do you know that some of the fish that is caught in the seas around Britain is sent to China to be processed? Then it's sent back again to Britain. That's 10,000 food miles for each lorry-load of fish to end up right back where it started. I'm not sure that's common sense. It's like this fish here going all the way round the edge of our hall, just to end up where it started. (Child with fish picture walks it round the hall.)

And do you know that we in Britain used to grow thousands and thousands of apples? Well, we have dug up nearly all the apple orchards, and now we buy foreign apples and make them travel thousands of food miles to get here.

And do you know that we grow delicious raspberries and strawberries in Britain? The trouble is, they only grow for a very short time in June and July. If we want to eat raspberries and strawberries in winter, they have to travel thousands of food miles across the world. Maybe we should just enjoy them when they come into season in Britain, and look forward to them the rest of the year, like people used to do.

The problem with food miles is that there are more of them every single year, as supermarkets get bigger and smaller local shops disappear. Air transport and road transport uses up diesel and sends out carbon dioxide which adds to global warming.

We can't help using up *some* food miles, but maybe we should all think a bit more carefully about where the food comes from that we eat. Maybe we should try to cut down the number of food miles our food has to travel to get to our tables. There's plenty of food for thought here!

I am certainly going to try to look more carefully at where my food comes from. It was a shock to me to realise that my lunch has travelled one and a half times round the world to get to me. I will try to buy local food when I can, so that I can play my part in trying to cut down food miles, and the environmental impact that goes with those miles.

Maybe you could find out more about food miles,* and where the food you like comes from.

---

* Further information can be found at:
www.bbc.co.uk search 'food miles'
www.fwi.co.uk/foodmiles
www.coolkidsforacoolclimate.com/Causes&Effects

~

Let's think for a moment about our food. We are lucky that we have an enormous amount of choice in the food we can have. But maybe we have too much choice. Maybe all that choice is having a bad impact on our planet. Let's stop to think, when we eat our meals, about where the food is from; whether it's travelled a long way, whether it's travelled by air or by road or by sea. Let's ask ourselves if the food miles it's travelled could be lessened in any way. Let's all do our best to look after our world, and do nothing to pollute it or damage it.

Theme 7

Global awareness

Tsunami: after the wave

I wonder if you know what a tsunami is. Yes, I thought many of you would know. It's a tidal wave that's caused when there's an earthquake under the sea. Some of you may well remember the terrible tsunami just after Christmas in 2004. Others of you will have heard of it, I'm sure.

The news of the tsunami, and the televised pictures of some of the damage it caused, had a huge impact on people all around the world. People were shocked by what had happened, and all over the world people acted quickly to raise as much money as they could to help the survivors of the disaster.

Let's hear of what happened to one girl called Sylvia.

Sylvia was eleven years old, and she lived with her mother and father, her older sister and her nine-year-old brother on the island of Sri Lanka. Sri Lanka is just off the south-eastern tip of India. Sylvia and her family lived by the sea, in a small house almost on the beach.

But everything in Sylvia's life changed one day near the end of 2004.

It was 26 December, the day after Christmas Day, and it began just like any other morning. The sun climbed in the sky and shone on a bright sparkling sea. The tourists were already out on the beach, or sitting on their terraces having breakfast, or swimming, or planning what to do with their day. Sylvia and her brother were at home. But, unbeknown to anyone, far out to sea and hundreds of miles away, there was a powerful earthquake deep under the ocean.

The earthquake caused a massive tidal wave, a tsunami, which grew and grew as it neared the land. It took everyone by surprise as it smashed onto the land at just after nine o'clock in the morning.

Sylvia's house, like all the other houses on the shoreline, was washed away, together with everyone and everything in them. The first Sylvia knew of what was happening was when the sea suddenly burst into her house and carried her away, further and further into the open ocean. She had no idea of what had happened, or where she was. She only knew that she was very, very frightened. Sylvia was swept so far out to sea that she could no longer see the land. There was no one else near her. No one else to help her.

Sylvia saw that there was lots of debris in the sea with her. Lots of bits of broken building, pieces of wood, even plastic beach furniture. She managed to grab hold of a large log that floated past her, and she clung on to it to stop herself from drowning. She managed to cling on to the log for more than 24 hours until an army helicopter flying overhead spotted her and sent down a life-line to rescue her. She was airlifted to hospital. Sadly, her little brother and her best friend from school were not so lucky and they both died.

The tsunami was devastating. It killed more than 250,000 people, destroyed houses, and left millions of people homeless. And although building work has started, to clear away all the debris and build new homes, life is still not back to normal for many people, including Sylvia.

Sylvia now lives in a special temporary camp with her mum, dad and older sister, together with many other people who lost their homes and members of their families.

'Life is a bit better now,' says Sylvia. 'But whenever I hear the sound of the waves I start to remember what happened on that day. Or if I hear the sound of pouring rain I remember and it makes me very frightened again.

'And it's difficult to live here in the camp,' she says. 'People sometimes start rumours that another tsunami is coming. I would feel safer far away.'

People everywhere wanted to help the victims of the tsunami. People everywhere realised that we all have a responsibility to other people who live in our world, even if they live thousands of miles away, because we all belong to one global family, our human family.

People everywhere raised money as quickly as they could to help the victims of the tsunami who had lost everything; their homes, their clothes, their belongings. It's hard for us to imagine what it is like to lose everything you have. The money that was raised was sent to charities like Christian Aid, who tried to ensure that it was sent where it was needed. Some of the money went towards practical things like setting up temporary camps, or building new houses, but some of the money was put towards helping people like Sylvia deal with what had happened.

One of the groups supported by Christian Aid helps Sylvia to do 'normal' things again; things she and her friends used to do before the tsunami.

'They play with us and teach us new games,' she says. 'They teach us songs and dance. Most of the time we play.' Sylvia is being helped to be an ordinary child again, and to put the tsunami behind her. It's working because she now has hopes for the future.

'My dream is to be a teacher, one day,' she says. 'I go to school again now, and I want to work hard so that one day I can be a teacher.'

Sylvia's dream may well come true, because people from all over the world wanted to help the victims of the tsunami. We all need to help each other no matter where in the world we live. We are all neighbours in our world.

～

Dear God, thank you for our homes and our families and our favourite things. Help us not to take these things for granted, but to remember how lucky we are to have them. We think of Sylvia and all the other millions of people who were affected by the tsunami, and by other natural disasters. Help us to remember that everyone in our world is our neighbour and part of our human family.

Story © Christian Aid, London, UK (2005). Adapted by the author.

Send my friend to school

Assembly preparation: you will need a purse with six £1 coins and a selection of items which cost about £6 each. Several children can help with counting the cash and displaying and describing the items.

I'm standing here, looking at you all, and I can see nearly 300 different people. Different! Can you tell me something that makes you different from, say, your friend? Yes, height, hair colour, clothes, names. We are all different.

But I can also see nearly 300 people who are all the same. All the same! Can you tell me something that makes you all the same? Yes, you're all children, you all come to school, you (nearly!) all work hard, you all learn similar things, you all belong to our school family. You are all different, yet the same.

And it's just like that all over the world. There are children everywhere who are all different yet all the same. Children come from different countries but they all like to play. Children speak different languages but they all like to learn.

But, do you know that 100 million children can't go to school? Some of them have to go out to work; some of them have families who can't afford to send them to school; some of the girls get married when they're very young, and their families don't think it's worth educating them.

Before I tell you today's story, I want you to look at this. What is it? Yes, it's a purse with some money. I'll choose someone to count it for me. £6. And over here I have some things which all cost about £6 each. I'll choose someone else to show you what they all are. Now, I'd like you to remember all these things that are worth £6, whilst I tell you the story.

Venkatamma is eleven. She lives in Andhra Pradesh in southern India. She goes to school. Nothing very unusual about that, you might think! But, Venkatamma has only just started to go to school. Until just recently she had to work every day, and going to school was just a dream.

Venkatamma's job was to spend every day looking after ten buffaloes. It was hard work. Buffaloes are very large animals and she had to make sure they didn't wander off, or get lost. She had to make sure they were taken to places where there was enough grass for them to eat, and where there was water for them to drink.

The buffaloes that Venkatamma had to care for were not her own animals, or even the animals belonging to her parents. They belonged to a man who owned them; and who also owned Venkatamma. He had bought her several years earlier from her parents.

They hadn't wanted to sell her, but they were poor and they had no choice. They couldn't afford to feed her or keep her. So Venkatamma was sold. The man paid her family £6 for her. That wasn't £6 a day, or £6 a week, or even £6 a year. It was just £6. He bought a girl for £6.

One day, one of the buffaloes that Venkatamma was looking after escaped and got into a neighbour's garden. It trampled the fruit and vegetables and made a dreadful mess. When the owner of the buffaloes heard what had happened he was furious with Venkatamma and beat her. She was hurt and frightened, but she managed to run away to her sister's house.

Venkatamma kept crying and she stopped eating. All she would say to her sister was, 'I want to go to school.'

After three days, her sister took Venkatamma to the Bridge School, which is run by an Indian organisation called Gramya, which is supported by Christian Aid. The Bridge School is for children, like Venkatamma, who have never been to school before.

She has been going to school for almost a year now, and is doing very well. She is a bright girl and she so much wants to learn. 'I would like to go to university,' she says. 'I want to become something important like a teacher and feel that I am helping the community.'

Selling a child for £6 is something that we can't imagine, here in our country, where children have rights, and where it is the responsibility of adults to look after and care for children. It's also hard for us to imagine children not being able to go to school.

Why do you think it's important for children to go to school? Yes, so that they can read and write; so that they can get a better job; so that they can go on to college or university; so that they can learn how to be healthy; so that they can live a better life.

Education is a really important way to help people stop being poor, and that's why charities like Gramya and Christian Aid are working so hard to help children all around the world to get an education.

In 2005, children from all over the UK and Ireland took part in something called 'Make Poverty History: Send My Friend to School'. They asked the leaders of the world's richest countries to help send more children in poor countries to school. But, we're not there yet. There are still millions of children in the world who don't have the chance to go to school that you have. Maybe we could do something to help. Maybe we could play a part in making poverty history. Maybe we could help send a friend, somewhere in the world, to school.

~

Let's spend a few moments thinking about all the opportunities we have, here in our school, to learn new skills, to find things out, to get an education. Let's make the best of the opportunity we have, and not waste our time or our talents. Let's remember the millions of other children in the world, who don't have the chances we have. Let's remember that although we are all different, we are also all the same. We need the same chances in life. Let's play our part in making the world a fairer place for everyone.

Story © Christian Aid, London, UK (2005). Adapted by the author.

Chakrabadra and the Gurkhas

We all know that there are many people in other countries of our world who don't have the same advantages that we do, here in Britain. For example, many people don't have clean water, or enough food. Many people don't have proper houses to live in or access to medicines and doctors. Often people find themselves in desperate conditions because of natural disasters like earthquakes or floods, or even because of wars.

Many people in Britain think it's our duty to help people in poor countries, because we have so much and they have so little; but some people think that other countries are too far away and that we should only help those in need here, in our own country. I wonder what you think.

Today I'm going to tell you about a group of people who live in another very poor country a long way away, but who also have strong connections with Britain.

The people are called the Gurkhas and they live in Nepal, a country which lies along the Himalayan Mountains between China and India. Nepal is a beautiful country with spectacular mountain scenery, but it's also one of the poorest countries in the world. Most of its people live in hill villages, but there are few roads linking them because the mountains make road building difficult and expensive. Nepal often has earthquakes and landslides and monsoon floods, so life in the mountain villages is full of danger and uncertainty. Many houses get swept away by these natural disasters and if they do, there is little the owners can do about it. There is no money for them to rebuild their homes and start again. They have to rely on friends or family to take them in.

Life in Nepal is harsh and difficult, but despite this, or maybe because of it, the Nepalese people are strong and brave, proud and loyal. And because they have these qualities, they have been welcomed into the British Army for the past 200 years. The British Army has special Gurkha Regiments where the Gurkha people can learn to become soldiers and serve *our* country.

Chakrabadra is one of thousands of Gurkha men who fought for the British Army during the Second World War. Chakrabadra proved himself to be a brave and loyal soldier. Just before the end of the war he found himself in Burma on the wrong side of a river when the bridge across it was blown up. He couldn't get back to the rest of his regiment and was captured by the Japanese and sent to a prisoner of war camp. The conditions there were dreadful and he saw many of the other prisoners die of starvation or ill-treatment. Somehow, Chakrabadra stayed alive, and when the war ended he was given a medal for his bravery, then was released and sent home to Nepal. The British Army no longer needed him because the war was over.

Chakrabadra went back to his house in the small village where he'd lived before joining the army and picked up the threads of his old life again. In summer he grew food for himself and his wife in the tiny garden they had made on the hillside. In winter when there was snow on the ground and the air was freezing cold, he tried to keep their house warm by cutting down trees for firewood and burning the logs. Life was difficult but not impossible.

Chakrabadra saw more and more of his countrymen come home from the war, some with terrible injuries and some unable to walk. There is no welfare service in Nepal, no National Health Service or free doctors and medicines, so Chakrabadra and his friends simply tried to help each other as best they could.

Things carried on in this way for several years, but as the Gurkha men grew older, they became less and less able to look after their homes, their families and themselves. Many soldiers in Britain who were growing older had war pensions paid to them, so that they had enough money to live. But there was no war pension for the Gurkhas, because they had only served in the British Army for the six years of the war. A soldier had to have served for fifteen years if he was to have money from a war pension.

It soon became clear to people in Britain that the Gurkhas, who had worked so hard for the British Army, needed help. A group of people got together and formed the Gurkha Welfare Trust.* Their aim was to raise money to help the old Gurkha soldiers and the wives of soldiers who had died in the war. In their first year the Gurkha Welfare Trust raised enough money to help almost 1500 ex-soldiers.

Chakrabadra is one of the men the Trust helped. Every month he is given 3333 Nepalese rupees, which sounds a lot, but is the same as about £20. £20 isn't much for a man and his wife to live on for a whole month, but it buys basic food for them both. The only problem is that Chakrabadra has to go and collect his pension from the nearest Trust Welfare Centre, which is a full day's walk there and another day's walk home again.

One of Chakrabadra's friends who also served in the British Army is no longer able to walk, and the only way he can get to the Welfare Centre for his pension is by paying a young man to give him a piggy back. The journey is difficult for both the porter and the passenger; it takes several days to do the

---

* Further information can be found at www.gwt.org.uk.

trip down and back up the mountain, and it costs almost half of the old soldier's pay. The Trust knows that the money spent on porters means less money is spent on good food, so they now give extra money to the people who need carrying, so that they can pay their porter.

Chakrabadra and the other ex-soldiers are given medicines and treatment if they need them, and they are given money for fuel in the winter, together with warm blankets.

The Gurkha Welfare Trust is trying to give help to the Gurkha soldiers who have so bravely given their help to Britain during the last 200 years.

If you thought that we should only help people in our own country, I wonder whether this story has made you change your mind. The Gurkhas live thousands of miles away from us, here in Britain, yet they have helped us enormously in the past. I think that perhaps we have a duty to help them now, when they need help. I wonder what you think.

∽

Dear God, please help us to be aware that there are so many people in so many countries in our world, who do not have the advantages that we have. Help us each to do what we can to make our world as fair as possible for everyone. Help us to know that everyone in every country belongs to the same world family, and that everyone, no matter how far away they live, is our neighbour. Amen

Theme 8

Myths

How darkness came to the world

(The three stories in the theme of Myths are intended to be read in consecutive assemblies. However, each can be treated independently if preferred.)

Everyone here knows that there are lots of different kinds of stories. There are true stories, fairy stories, fables, myths and legends. There are stories that are funny, or far-fetched, or serious, or even tall! Everyone in our school can write stories of their own, and everyone has an imagination to help them.

You all know that story telling itself is very old. It's the oldest form of entertainment. People were telling each other stories even before they thought of music or drama. Some of the oldest stories of all are called myths, and they were told thousands of years ago to try to explain the things that couldn't be explained!

For example, people then didn't understand why it was dark at night, or why the sun seems to move across the sky during the day, or why the stars shine, or why there are mountains. So they made up stories to try to explain the world in which they lived; to try to explain the world's mysteries.

Here's a story from Sierra Leone in West Africa which tells why the night is dark.

Once, at the beginning of time when God first made the world, it was always light. The sun shone golden during the day and the moon shone silver at night. Both day and night were as light and bright as each other, and although the golden day and the silver night were different, they each gave the same amount of light and everyone could see clearly.

One day, God wanted a basket of something taking to the moon, so he called to the bat to help him.

'You can fly high, and you can fly well, bat,' said God. 'I want you to take this basket and deliver it to the moon.'

'What's in it?' asked the bat. 'What is it for?'

Now God had been going to tell the bat that the basket was full of darkness, but he was annoyed that the bat had asked, so he said, 'It's none of your business! Just do as I ask!'

'But what will I say to the moon when I give it to her?' asked the bat, not unreasonably.

'Just tell her to look after it, and I'll come and explain later what she is to do with it. Oh, and one more thing. Tell her on no account to open it until I say she can.' And God tied a piece of string round the basket to keep the lid very firmly in place. He tied a knot in the string and tied the ends in a bow. 'There!' he said. 'Now don't forget to tell her not to open it until I say.'

'Very well,' said the bat, and he flew off with the basket held firmly in his teeth.

The bat had intended to fly straight to the moon with the basket and have his dinner later, but he suddenly felt rather tired and hungry, so he put it down on the grass and went to find something to eat. Whilst he was gone, a meercat came by and noticed the basket on the ground.

'Whatever can that be?' he said to himself, walking all round it and peering this way and that. 'I've never seen anything like it.'

As he walked round the basket a second time, two mice came scurrying by.

'What's that?' they squeaked, as they scampered up to it.

'I don't know,' said the meercat. 'I don't know where it's come from.'

Whilst they were all staring at the basket, a rat walked by.

'What are you looking at?' he asked.

'This round thing made of woven twigs,' said the mice. 'We don't know what it's for.'

'It looks like a nest to me,' said the rat. 'Ask the eagle, he'll know what it is.'

So the animals went to fetch the eagle and ask him to come and look at the nest.

'Doesn't look like a nest to me,' he said. 'It hasn't got a way in . . . or a way out,' he added. 'The beetle might know what it is.'

Just then a beetle came by, but didn't know what the basket was either, so they asked the ant and the lizard, the hare and even the spider, but no one knew what the object could be or where it could have come from.

Then a hyena strolled by.

'What are you doing?' she said.

'Looking at this thing,' they all replied. 'We don't know what it is.'

'Well, that's easy,' said the hyena, poking the basket with her paw. 'It's obviously a present for me, that someone has put here. It will, quite definitely, have something to eat inside it. Anyone who knows me knows that I like food,' and she prodded the basket again.

'Look!' she went on. 'It's tied up with string. So, if it's tied up, it's clearly intended to be *untied*. That's all we have to do. Untie it.'

'Oh, I don't know,' said the meercat.

'Better not!' said the rat.

'Might be dangerous,' said the lizard.

'There could be a *snake* in there!' said the mice.

'It might not actually be for you,' suggested the spider, timidly.

'Not be for me!' shrieked the hyena. 'Of course it's for me! Open it. Now.'

So the mice climbed on top of the basket and undid the bow and chewed through the knot in the string. The lid slipped a little and a tiny bit of darkness escaped.

'What's that?' asked the rat, alarmed.

'Whatever it is, it's mine and it's escaping,' said the hyena, jumping onto the basket and banging down the lid.

And exactly at that moment, the bat came back from his dinner.

'What are you doing with my basket?' he shouted.

The animals all stood still.

'Your basket?' said the hyena. 'But it's mine. It was left here for me!'

'It's not your basket, it's mine,' said the bat. And then he went on, 'Well, actually it's not mine, either. It's God's. I'm to deliver it to the moon, but on no account is she to open it until God says she can.'

The animals were silent.

'You haven't opened it, have you?' said the bat.

'Well, only a little,' said the hyena. 'Look!' and she opened the lid a bit more just to show what she meant.

Suddenly, more darkness escaped and the bat flew this way and that, trying desperately to recapture the darkness and push it back in the basket.

'I've got to put it back,' he said over and over again. 'I've got to deliver the basket to the moon.

'He'll never do it,' said the hyena, as she and the other animals went back to their homes.

And the hyena was right. The bat never did succeed in catching the darkness and putting it back in the basket; but ever since that day, when the twilight comes, he begins to fly about everywhere, trying to recapture the darkness so that he can deliver the basket to the moon, just as God asked him to do.

The stories and myths of how the world and everything in it began are interesting, but you might wonder what they have to do with us today. Well, they show that people, no matter where they are from, have always believed that a great power, that some people call God, is responsible for our world and its creation.

And whether we believe the old stories or not, we can all marvel and wonder at the beautiful and extraordinary world we all live in today.

~

Let's think for a moment about how special the daytime and the night-time are. The daytime gives us sun and light, warmth and the chance to be outdoors. The night-time gives us velvety darkness and the moon and stars. Daytime and night-time give us different animals, different insects and birds. Our world looks and sounds and smells and feels different in the daytime from the night-time, yet both day and night are remarkable and special in their own way.

The moon who wanted more

Yesterday's story, a myth from West Africa, explained why the night is darker than the day, and how that came about. Today's story is a Jewish myth which explains almost the same thing, but in this story, the way it came about is very different. Here's what happened.

Way back, at the beginning of time, when God had just made the world and everything in it was new, the sun and the moon were equal. The sun was big and gold. The moon was large and silver. They were both as bright as each other and they were both extremely beautiful.

The sun and the moon took turns to shine. They each shone for the same length of time, and with the same power, and for a while all was well.

But then the moon began to want more.

'Why should I have to share the skies with *him*?' said the moon to herself. 'Why should I have to hide half the time? I want to shine *all* the time. After all, I am much more beautiful than the sun, anyone can see that, so I should be given more light, more time and more sky.'

The moon decided to go and tell God that she thought she ought to have more power, more brightness and more sky-time than the sun.

'And why do you think that?' asked God.

'Because I deserve more,' said the moon. 'I am better than the sun and I am certainly more beautiful.'

'And who says that you are?' asked God.

No one needs to tell me!' replied the moon. 'It's perfectly obvious. And anyway, I just *know* I'm better than the sun.'

'So what do you want me to do?' asked God.

'I want you to make me bigger than the sun,' she said. 'I want you to make me brighter than him, and I want you to give me more time in the sky. In fact, I think I ought to have *all* the time in the sky. The sun could go and live somewhere else, like under the earth for example.'

'You are very conceited!' said God. 'You are very big-headed and full of your own importance. But I will certainly make some changes for you!'

As soon as God had spoken, the moon began to feel herself changing. She smiled to herself as she waited to grow larger and brighter. She wondered how it would feel to be the most powerful light in the sky and she wondered what the sun would think when he saw what had happened. But the smile on her face soon turned to tears as she realised that she was not growing bigger; on the contrary, she was shrinking and fading and fast disappearing.

'What's happening to me?' cried the moon. 'What are you doing to me?'

'You are greedy,' said God, angrily. 'So I am going to take away your light. You will be as nothing in the sky and no one will be able to see you.'

'I'm sorry,' cried the moon. 'I'm really sorry. I shouldn't have wanted more than my fair share. I shouldn't have been so big-headed. Please forgive me. Please put everything back as it was.'

God saw how truly sorry the moon was for her behaviour, and he didn't want to punish her further. 'I'm sorry, Moon, but it's too late to go back. Things have gone too far and changes must be made,' he said, gently, as he hung her, pale and silvery, in the sky.

'I won't make you shrink to nothing,' said God. 'But I can no longer allow you to be as bright as the sun. However, I will give you a different light; a softer, paler light, and I will give you some time in the night to shine your light. But I will also give you a reminder of your greed.'

'A reminder?' said the moon, timidly.

'You will always remember your greed,' said God. 'Because every month I shall let you grow large and round and bright, but every time you do so I will make you disappear again until you are nothing in the sky.'

'But what if you forget to make me grow again?' asked the moon, tear-fully.

'I shall not forget,' said God. 'And so that you'll know I have not forgotten you, I shall give you the stars to keep you company, then you'll not be lonely.' And God sprinkled a scattering of a thousand stars in the sky around her.

'But what will I *do* in the sky?' asked the moon, who imagined year after year of boredom if she were not allowed to spend her time shining.

'I shall give you a job to do,' said God. 'You can help mark the time. From this day on, each day will start not with the sunrise, but with the appearance of the first three evening stars.'

And from that time on, the Jewish people have counted the start of each day from the sight of the first three stars in the evening. They have counted the days and weeks, months and years, by the moon instead of the sun. And they have said special prayers of God, in the light of the moon, each time it is new in the sky.

This myth explained to the Jewish people not only how the sun and moon turned out to be different, but how and why the passage of time is marked as it is in the Jewish faith. Many religions count their months and years quite differently from the standard months and years that we use in Britain today. Maybe you could find out about the Jewish calendar, or the Muslim one, or the Chinese calendar, for example.

This myth also explains to everyone who hears it, that it's wrong to be greedy and try to get more than your fair share.

Dear God, help us to be willing to share what we have with others. Help us not to be greedy or selfish. Help us to think about the needs of other people, and not just about what we want. Help us to be considerate towards other people, and especially towards our friends and family. Amen

Raven lets out the daylight

We have heard a story from West Africa, and a story from the Jewish religion about the sun and the moon. Today I have a very different story from the Indian peoples of North America that's also to do with the sun and the moon and the stars. But this story is in two parts. See if you can tell where the first part ends and the second part begins. You might recognise something about the second part of the story.

At the beginning of time everything was dark. Raven beat his wings against the darkness to make earth, and people came to live along the shoreline, then Raven stole fresh water to make rivers; but still everything was dark. Raven felt sorry for the pale, sickly people with only fish to eat and with only darkness around them.

Raven knew that the Old-One-who-lived-at-the-source-of-the-river had the sun and moon and stars hidden in his house, so he decided to steal them so that he could give light to the poor pale people. Raven turned himself into a human baby and had himself born to the daughter of the Old-One-who-lived-at-the-source-of-the-river.

Almost as soon as he'd been born, the baby began to crawl. He crawled all over the house, his sharp raven eyes darting everywhere. In no time he had seen what he was looking for. There, hanging from the rafters of the house, were three large, black, drawstring bags. Just the right size, thought Raven, to contain the sun, the moon and the stars.

The baby held out his fat little arms towards the bags and began to cry. His mother cuddled him and gave him some milk but nothing would stop him crying. At last she said to her father, the Old-One, 'Let your grandson play with the smallest bag. It's clearly what he wants.' But the Old-One said no, and refused to discuss it further.

The baby cried louder and longer until at last his grandfather, the Old-One, could stand it no more and gave him the bag to play with. For a while the baby rolled the bag on the floor, then suddenly, he pulled the draw-string, and *whoosh* the stars flew up the chimney and disappeared into the sky. The grandfather was furious and told his daughter in no uncertain terms to keep the baby under control and quiet.

The baby's mother did her best, but soon the baby grew fractious again and cried and cried, holding up his fat little arms to the remaining two bags hanging from the rafters.

'NO!' roared the grandfather. 'He CANNOT have another of my bags to play with!' But the crying persisted and when the Old-One could stand it no longer, he gave the second bag to the baby to keep him quiet.

For a while the baby rolled the bag on the floor, then suddenly, he pulled the drawstring, and *whoosh* the moon flew up the chimney and disappeared into the sky. The grandfather was furious and told his daughter she really must keep the baby under control and must DEFINITELY keep him quiet. All went well for a while, and the Old-One nodded in his chair, then the baby began to bawl again.

'NO! Absolutely NOT!' yelled the grandfather. 'He is not going to have the last of my treasures to play with!' But the baby cried and cried and waved his fat little arms towards the last bag hanging from the rafters. His mother became distraught because the baby was so upset, and so, to keep everyone quiet, the Old-One lifted down the bag and gave it to the baby . . . but not before he'd tied the drawstring in a triple turn and then a double knot.

'There!' he said, throwing the bag to the floor for the baby.

Raven knew he would be unable to undo the bag, so there was nothing else for it; he turned himself back into a raven, picked up the bag in his beak and flew up the chimney with it. He flew high into the sky, over the moon and the scattered stars, on and on until he came to the river in the darkness where the poor pale people were fishing.

By now he was extremely hungry.

'Give me some of your fish to eat, please,' he called to the people, but they were selfish and rude and told him to go away.

Raven flew a little further down the river and asked the next group of people he came to for something to eat. 'I'll give you some daylight if you give me something to eat,' he said.

But the people were selfish and rude and told him they didn't believe he had any daylight, so they weren't going to give him anything to eat. Raven flew further and met another group of people, then another and another, and at every group it was the same. Raven asked them for food, and they refused.

At last he came to where the river met the sea and he found people fishing here, too. By now he was weak with hunger. 'Please give me something to eat,' he said. 'I have daylight in my bag and I'll give you some in exchange for fish.'

The people laughed. 'You don't have daylight in your bag!' they said. 'But we'll give you some food anyway,' and they shared their fish with him. When they'd eaten, Raven said, 'Now, I will let out the daylight,' and he ripped open the bag with his beak and *whoosh* the sun flew into the sky. As its rays touched the earth, trees and plants and flowers sprang up, insects and birds flew in the air and tiny creatures scuttled in the soil. But the light of the sun was too strong, its glare too powerful for the poor pale people, and they all fell to their knees. Those that fell to the water turned into water creatures, and those that fell to the earth turned into land animals, but those people who had shared their fish with Raven turned into strong and healthy men and women with a taste for adventure and daring.

Raven was delighted and wanted to show the Old-One-who-lived-at-the-source-of-the-river what he had done to the world. He flew back to the house of the Old-One.

'Come out of your house and see what I have done,' he laughed.

But the Old-One was angry and wanted revenge. 'You stole my bags of treasure,' he thundered. 'And I can see what you have done with them. But, you didn't steal my smallest bag! So now I shall show you what *I* can do!' And the Old-One took a tiny bag out of his pocket. He undid the drawstring and tipped the bag upside down. Drops of water fell out, which turned into heavy rain which turned into a deluge. Torrents of water poured from the tiny drawstring bag and gushed down to the river. The river burst its banks and the water flooded the earth. Terrified people and animals ran to higher ground, but the water kept on rising. Hills and then mountains disappeared beneath the flood.

Raven flew into the sky to escape the rising water, and he looked down on the desolation below. Everything was gone. The people, the animals, the earth itself, all gone under the great flood. Way in the distance was just one piece of land, the top of a high mountain, sticking out above the level of the water. Raven flew to it. There, huddled in fear at the very top, were four children, and a few animals.

Raven picked up the children in his claws, flew up to the very top of the sky, stuck his sharp beak in the roof of the sky, and clung on, sheltering the children underneath his wings until the waters went down. And when the flood had gone, he flew back to earth and set the children gently on the dry ground, where they grew up and became the parents of all the people who ever lived in the world from then on.

What *a story!*

Well, did you spot the two separate parts of the story? The first part was to do with the creation of the sun and moon and stars, and the second part was all about the great flood. Maybe you know of another great flood story. Most of the religions of the world have a flood story in them. You could write about the one you know.

We've listened to three stories this week that are all very different, yet all very similar. They are different in that they are from different parts of the world; they are from different cultures and peoples; they tell of different events; and they have different characters.

But the stories are similar because they are all thousands of years old; they all try to explain the beginnings of the world; they all deal with the sun and the moon and the stars; they all have someone who is very powerful, someone who is a God; and they all have someone who disobeys, or at least who doesn't do as they are told.

Myths are exciting stories. They were told to try and explain things that were impossible to explain, and they can still make us think – even today. Creation stories can still make us wonder.

~

Let's think about the three stories we've heard this week. Think about the one you enjoyed the most, and remember what it was about the story that you liked. Then try to remember something you've enjoyed about the sunshine, or being in moonlight, or seeing the stars. Think what it was that was special or magical. Remember how it felt. Our world is a very special, magical place. We need to make sure we try to understand it so that we can look after it.

Theme 9

Awe and wonder

Something awesome

The other day I overheard two children in our school talking about something-or-other, and one of them said to the other, 'It's awesome!' And that set me thinking! It's a word I often hear you use, but what does it mean?

Yes, it means something that is truly amazing; something that fills you with wonder; something that has you 'gob-smacked' – there's another word I often hear you use! Our world is full of amazing and awe-inspiring things. I'm not talking about man-made things, although they, too, can be awesome; but I mean things in the natural world. Things that make us think 'Wow!' Things that make us so astounded, so awe-struck, we wonder how they could be so amazing.

In today's story, two children went in search of something awesome.

It all started with a poster in the library. It wanted entries for the annual photographic competition. There was to be a first prize of £20 for each section.

The photos were now all in and were neatly arranged on the display boards. The judges were already looking at them, meticulously scrutinising each one, awarding each photograph marks to help them choose the winners.

Jake and Hetty, who were twins, had both entered the junior photography section. The title of this year's competition was 'Something Awesome' and they'd both been really enthusiastic about taking part at the beginning of the summer, when they'd each been given a digital camera for their birthday, but as the summer wore on they had found it more and more difficult to take a photo of 'Something Awesome'. But at last, almost by accident, they'd each found their perfect picture and had entered their photos. It was these photographs that the judges were now looking at so carefully.

The family had gone on holiday to Normandy in France, just before the closing date for the competition, and both Jake and Hetty knew they would *have* to take a photo of 'Something Awesome' during the holiday if they were to enter the competition. They'd thought of everything they considered awesome, from giant waves to pop stars, from enormous buildings to firework displays. And they'd taken dozens of photos with their new cameras, but none of them somehow seemed quite right.

They had photos of the sea; but nothing they considered awesome. They'd been to a local fête where a boy band was playing and had taken several photos, but when they looked at them later they were disappointed. The band certainly didn't look awesome and the photos weren't very good.

One day they'd visited a town with a magnificent cathedral. It had wonderful twin towers soaring into the sky. 'That's pretty awesome,' their dad had said, so Jake took some photos. They turned out OK and Jake thought they might do for the competition.

On the Saturday before their holiday was due to end, the town where they were staying had a festival which finished at midnight with a firework display.

'Can we go, Mum, please,' Hetty said. 'I know it's late but it *is* the holidays, and we might get some pictures for the competition. Can we go, Dad?'

'Any excuse to stay up late!' laughed her parents, but they agreed to go to the festival.

At midnight everyone gathered on the sports field and the fireworks began. Hetty used her camera to capture some of the dazzling fireworks as they exploded high in the air above them, showering them with glittering sparks. The photos turned out quite well, the bright darts of light showing against a black sky.

'There you are,' said her dad. 'That's your competition entry sorted.'

Soon it was the last evening of the holiday and the bags were packed ready for the journey home the next day.

'Let's go and take one last look at the sea,' said the children's dad. So they got in the car and set off towards the coast along the road they'd used many times during the last fortnight. The road was steep and climbed up between the hills to the cliff top that overlooked the beach and the rocks and the sea. Each time they'd been here they'd stopped to enjoy the view; to look at the sea and the cliffs and the tiny pathway that clung to the cliff side and stretched away as far as you could see. Jake knew it had been a smugglers path in days gone by. After a few moments of admiring the view, the children were usually anxious to grab their beach things and scramble down the cliff path to the sands and sea below.

But not that evening.

On that last evening of their holiday as the car rounded the top of the headland and the huge expanse of the bay came into view, they all said, 'Wow!'

The sun was disappearing over the horizon, just a sliver of golden curve was showing above the sea. It reflected, shimmering deep gold in the sea. The enormous sky looked as though someone had taken a huge paintbrush and painted glorious swathes of cream and lemon, pink and violet, indigo purple and mauve, that had all been allowed to run into each other and merge and mingle. The cliffs themselves were coloured red and russet and crimson, and the sea was a deep turquoise with brilliant white frothy waves at the edge of the dark yellow sand.

'Wow!' said Jake, again.

'Isn't that amazing!' said his mum. 'It is beautiful!' Then she added, 'You were looking for 'wow', now you've found it!'

It took the children a minute or two to understand what she meant, then, with a shout of 'Something Awesome!' they both dived out of the car and into the boot for their cameras.

Jake stood on the cliff top and tried to capture the whole of the view in his camera. He tried to get everything in – the sea and the sky, the cliffs and the sheer *amazement* of it all.

Hetty took a similar photo and then noticed something else at her feet. There, on the grass, were dozens of small snails, each one in its brown and white spiral shell, the tiny weight of each one making the blades of grass bend and curve towards the ground.

'Look, Mum!' she said. 'They're just as awesome as all that,' she added, waving at the sunset. She crouched down and took a photo of a snail with the sunset behind it. It looked as though the snail was just about to walk along the curve of the setting sun.

And those two photos, Jake's big view and Hetty's tiny snail, were now causing the judges some concern. They couldn't agree which photo should win first prize.

'The sheer size of that sea view makes it awesome,' said the first judge.

'Yes, but this person has seen beyond the obvious and has noticed that something small can be awesome too,' argued the second.

In the end they decided that they just had to award two first prizes, instead of the one they'd planned.

Later, when they spoke to Jake and Hetty, the judges were surprised to find that the two winning photos had been taken at exactly the same time, on the same day, in the same place.

'But they're so different!' the judges said. 'That's excellent! You've each used your own eyes to see for yourself what was there. And even though you were looking at the same view, you each saw it differently because you are different people.'

They awarded Jake and Hetty their prizes and said, 'Well done! And remember, keep your eyes open!'

What a very good piece of advice. 'Keep your eyes open!' Sometimes we're all so busy getting on with all the things we have to do, that we forget to keep our eyes open and see the awesome things our world has to show us.

Simple things, like a rainbow, or a tree in its autumn colours in the sunshine, or a starlit sky on a frosty winter's evening, or a flower unfolding, or the inside of a shell, or a spider's web with dew on it, or a bird singing – the list is endless – but they can all make us think 'Wow!' The wow-factor of our world is enormous. And all we have to do is keep our eyes open to see it.

~

Dear God, thank you for our beautiful, amazing world. Help us to keep our eyes open to notice the world around us. Help us to use all our senses to appreciate our world. Help us to look after our world and to care for it. Help us to remember that every single thing we do has an effect on our world; help us to do nothing to damage or destroy it. Amen

Lizzie paints dandelions

I wonder how observant you are. I wonder how good you are at noticing things. Some people of course are more observant than others, and different people notice different things; it depends what they're interested in. Most of us, though, are very good at seeing things, but not very good at looking. I wonder if you know what I mean.

For example, you all know what a rainbow looks like! Don't you? But I wonder if you could draw one accurately. Could you make it the right shape, with the right number of colours in the right order? And of course you all know what the inside of an apple looks like, don't you! But could you tell me, exactly, what's in there? And everyone knows what a pine cone is! But do you know what it's for? Why it exists? And could you draw one?

The world is full of amazing things, but we don't always look *at them.*

Lizzie picked up her paintbrush, looked at the view from her open window, and began to paint the glorious profusion of plants in front of her. The garden was a riot of colour and shapes and Lizzie quickly translated this into paint on her canvas.

Lizzie is an artist, and a very good one too. She can paint and draw in extraordinary detail but most of all she likes to take the shapes of real things in front of her and rearrange them to form new patterns. Her finished paintings are semi-abstract; that means you can tell what the paintings are of, and where the ideas came from, but the objects are not painted in a completely realistic way. Lizzie's paintings are not like photographs, they are like colourful patterns inspired by the things in front of her.

Lizzie painted for several hours, and when at last she was satisfied with the work she'd done, she set the canvas aside to dry and stood by the window looking out. She knew it would be the last time that she would paint this particular view, because the old house where she had her studio was about to be pulled down and the area redeveloped. That left Lizzie with a problem. She needed a studio. She needed somewhere to keep all her art materials. She needed space to work. There was no room in her own house for a work-space, so Lizzie had arranged to rent a studio on the edge of an industrial estate. She wasn't looking forward to moving.

The day after the removal men had unloaded all her easels and tables and boxes of equipment into the new studio and Lizzie had sorted out all her stuff, she sat down and prepared a new, clean canvas. She got out her pencils, her brushes, her tubes of paint, and sat in front of the window. She looked out. There in front of her was the most boring and uninspiring view. Immediately opposite her was a row of identical industrial units, each one exactly the same as the last. Each one made of concrete and brick, with a metal roller shutter and a dull grey door.

'Well. I can't paint *those!*' she thought.

Lizzie put down her brushes and went outside. The row of industrial units seemed to go on forever. She walked to the end of them and round the corner. There, an even worse sight met her eyes. There was a derelict factory with a sagging corrugated iron roof, broken window frames and missing doorways that had been boarded up. There was graffiti all over the building.

'Well, I can't paint *that!*' she thought.

She walked to the corner of the old factory, feeling more and more despondent, dejected and depressed. She began to think she had made a huge mistake in renting this unpromising place. She would never find anything to paint here. There was nothing to give her ideas, nothing to inspire her. This place was *awful*.

Lizzie turned the corner of the building to go back to the studio. The concrete here, where the vans and lorries used to turn, was completely broken up and thousands of dandelions had sprung up in the cracks and crevices of the ground. She kicked at a loose piece of concrete and a shower of grit and gravel landed on a clump of dandelions, almost crushing them. Even in this desolate place, Lizzie didn't want to be responsible for destroying something that was managing to live, so she bent down to brush away the debris from the weed.

One of the flower heads had broken off and Lizzie picked it up. She looked at it carefully, and suddenly thought that this was probably the very first time she'd ever *really* looked at a dandelion flower. It was actually quite beautiful, she noticed with surprise. It had an amazingly cheerful colour and its petals were exquisitely arranged with a soft, downy central section she'd never known was there. She turned it over and examined the underside of the flower head. It was perfectly formed. She broke off a bud and looked at the shape hidden beneath the sepals, just waiting for enough sunlight to make it burst open.

Lizzie vaguely remembered a poem she'd read as a child about a dandelion. Something to do with blowing clocks to tell the time. She picked a clock and twirled it in her fingers. It was truly amazing! Why had she never noticed dandelion clocks before? It was a perfect globe of tiny parachutes, each fastened to a little dot and each little dot sitting up close to another little dot on a soft, round cushion.

Lizzie blew the clock, gently. One o'clock. Again. Two o'clock. And again. Three o'clock. She watched the tiny parachutes float off in the air. Each one travelling on the breeze. Each one silently falling to earth. Each one a miniscule seed ready to grow into a new plant as enormous as the ones at her feet. It was breathtakingly astounding. How did it do it? How could such a tiny dot grow into a entire plant? How was the dandelion clock so perfectly made? How did it get like that?

The questions swirled in Lizzie's head. She had no answers to the questions but she did know what she had to do next! She had to draw them, to paint them, to put down all her thoughts in colour and shape onto paper and canvas. She gathered up some of the flowers, leaves and clocks and hurried back to the studio. Even that was an astonishment, as the slightest movement made the dandelion clocks disintegrate and drift away.

Lizzie spent the next few hours drawing the dandelions before they closed their heads and wilted. She spent the next day drawing the dandelion clocks.

And she spent the next few weeks painting patterns and pictures based on dandelions.

The gallery where she sold her paintings said it was some of the best work she'd ever done.

'Whatever inspired you to do dandelions?' asked the gallery owner.

'They are quite simply *the* most amazingly wonderful things,' said Lizzie.

Lizzie discovered something very profound, very deeply important, when she discovered the beauty of the dandelion. She discovered that there are wonderful and beautiful things in our world in places where you would never expect them to be. And she discovered that some things, even though they look simple, are intricately complicated; unexplainable really, in our world.

Have you ever really looked at a dandelion? Or a bird's feather? Or the inside of an orange? Have you ever thought that when you cut open an apple or a kiwi fruit, you are the very first person, ever, to see inside it. Have you ever looked at a snowflake under a microscope? Or seen the pads of your fingers under a magnifying glass? Maybe you should. Those things are incredible and they might surprise you!

~

Let's think for a moment about the very ordinary things around us, the things we take for granted because they are just always there. Things like apples or peaches, beetles or snails; seashells or feathers or snow. Things like pine cones or acorns, roses or daisies; conkers or spiders or skin. Next time we see one of these ordinary, everyday, natural things, let's stop and really look at it. We may discover something amazing. We may find out something about it that we never knew. We may be astonished by how beautiful it is.

Earthrise

Have you ever looked for something, then found something else quite by accident? It happened to me the other day. I was searching in my filing cabinet at home for a letter I needed, and there, in the file, tucked in between some more letters, was a photo I'd spent nearly all last summer looking for! I must have picked it up by mistake when I filed away the letter all those months before. But it was strange that I found it when I wasn't looking for it!

And sometimes, when I'm doing some research, looking something up, I find another piece of interesting information, that I wasn't actually looking for, but which is fascinating and useful. I'm sure that kind of thing has also happened to you. We often discover things when we're looking for something else.

This happened to the American astronauts of the Apollo 8 space mission in 1968. Their job was to find out about the moon. They did that; but whilst they were doing it they surprised themselves by finding out something else as well. They made a wonderful discovery.

The three astronauts in the Apollo 8 spacecraft were the first human beings ever to leave the Earth's orbit, and travel round the moon. This was only the second manned space flight in the Apollo programme. It was 1968 and the race to the moon was on. No one had ever been up close to the moon before. No one had ever seen the far side of the moon before. No one had ever landed on the moon before.

But a moon landing was still a long way off. This mission, the Apollo 8 mission, was for fact-finding and discovery. The mission objective was very clear. The astronauts were to:

- show how the spacecraft behaved in the moon's orbit,
- show how communications and tracking worked in the moon's orbit,
- bring back clear photographs of possible moon landing sites,
- find and photograph places on the moon that had scientific interest.

The astronauts' job was clear: they had to find out about the moon.

Frank Borman, Jim Lovell and Bill Anders entered the spacecraft ready for take-off. All preparations were successfully completed. The countdown began ... five, four, three, two, one, we have lift-off, and the Saturn 5 launch vehicle thrust the Apollo 8 spacecraft into the air.

The first stage was a complete orbit of the Earth, followed by a further thrust to take the spacecraft towards the moon. Then, for the first time ever, astronauts entered the moon's orbit and began to travel completely round it. No one had ever seen the far side of the moon before, because the same side of the moon always faces the Earth. No one knew what lay beyond.

As the spacecraft disappeared round the back of the moon, the three astronauts lost all radio contact with Mission Control at Houston, back on Earth. With the moon now between the spacecraft and Earth, all signals were lost. In Mission Control the whole team stood in silence waiting, watching, wondering when or if the spacecraft would safely reappear. This was being televised across the world, and the whole world waited. Seconds turned into minutes and still there was no signal. Nothing. Everyone waited. Nothing.

Then, faintly at first, the radio crackled into life again and contact was re-established. Success. Apollo 8 had successfully circled the moon. Human beings had seen the far side of the moon.

And as the spacecraft travelled round the moon, the three astronauts wrote down their findings and took photographs, just as their fact-finding mission had instructed them to. But by the end of the second orbit they realised that the moon looked an unfriendly, inhospitable place. It was bleak, grey and lifeless. Bill Anders wrote, 'It looked like a battlefield, pounded by meteorite after meteorite. It didn't look at all friendly.'

Then as Apollo 8 came round from the dark side of the moon for the second time, Bill Anders suddenly said, 'Hey, look at that over there!'

The others looked.

'What is it?' said Frank Borman.

'It's the Earth coming up! Wow, is that pretty!' said Anders, and they all looked in amazement as a beautiful silver-blue disk, laced with white, rose silently above the bleak, grey, desolate surface of the moon. They had all seen a sunrise before, but no one, no human being, had ever before seen an Earthrise, because no human being had ever seen their own planet rise up above the horizon of somewhere in space.

Bill Anders knew that this was an important moment, an important moment in the history of humans, so he grabbed his camera and took a black and white photograph of the Earth, even though he knew that they were there to photograph the *moon*, not the Earth, and that this photo wasn't in the plan of what they had to do.

'It's not scheduled,' said Frank Borman, but Bill realised how important these pictures were going to be.

He turned to Jim Lovell, 'Get me some colour film. Quick!' he said.

But Lovell couldn't easily find the film in the storage cabinet. He scrabbled about, searching for the film.

'Come *on*, hurry up, we don't have much time,' said Anders, impatiently, taking some more black and white photos whilst he waited.

At last Lovell found the colour film and Anders quickly put it in the camera and took the photograph that became one of the most famous photos of the space age. The photograph of a beautiful Earth rising in the blackest space beyond the barren surface of the moon.

Whilst Anders was busy with the camera, Lovell looked again at the Earth. He put his thumb up to the window and hid the Earth completely behind it. He realised that everything he had ever known, his home, his family, his world, was there, hidden behind his thumb. And he realised just how small and fragile the Earth is. He looked at the vastness of space and then again at the beautiful planet beneath his thumb and knew that all the people on this floating island in space must learn to understand each other and get along together. The sight of the Earth, as it had never been seen before, had a huge impact on all three astronauts.

Soon, the Earth had risen out of sight of the spacecraft window and the astronauts went back to their allotted tasks. They made ten orbits of the moon altogether, and marvelled anew each time they saw the Earthrise from the moon's horizon.

After their ten circuits of the moon the Apollo 8 spacecraft headed for home. It returned to the Earth's orbit and made a splash-down in the Pacific Ocean where it was picked up immediately by a ship waiting for it. The world watched and cheered the safe return of the astronauts. They had been in space for almost seven days and brought back masses of information about the moon. The Apollo 8 mission had been a huge success.

But it was Bill Anders who summed it all up by saying later:

'Isn't it ironic? Here we came to study the moon, and yet, it was this gorgeous Earthrise, this colourful, delicate-looking planet coming up that, to me, was the most spectacular view of the whole flight.'*

They had gone into space to discover the moon, but had come home again having discovered the Earth.

Those astronauts, and others who have travelled into space and seen our planet from a long way away, have been able to see how fragile, delicate and beautiful our Earth is. They are very lucky to have been able to do that, because they now understand that we must look after our Earth and the people and living things that exist here.

The rest of us, who haven't been able to travel into space and watch an Earthrise, must rely on photos, like the ones Bill Anders took, to try to understand that we all have a duty to care for our world. It isn't as tough as we think it is. It's fragile, like a Christmas tree ornament, and we must look after it.

~

Thank you God, for our world. Help us to understand that our Earth is just one small planet in a huge universe. Help us to understand how fragile our Earth is, and that we must do nothing to damage it. Help us to understand that all the people on our planet need to work together to look after each other and the world in which we all live. Amen

---

* Bill Anders' photograph 'Earthrise at Christmas' can be found at www.nasa.gov/multimedia/imagegallery/image_feature_102.html.

Alphabetical index of stories

Story source index

Theme index